The FROG

Its Reproduction and Development

The FROG

Its Reproduction and Development

By

ROBERTS RUGH, Ph.D.
Associate Professor of Radiology (Biology),
Department of Radiology, Columbia University

Philadelphia • THE BLAKISTON COMPANY • *Toronto*
1951

PRINTED IN THE UNITED STATES OF AMERICA
AT THE COUNTRY LIFE PRESS, GARDEN CITY, N.Y.

Preface

This book has been written for three reasons. *First,* since T. H. Morgan's "Development of the Frog's Egg" (1897), there has been no book written specifically on this subject. His was a most excellent treatise, still remarkably accurate. *Second,* with the accelerated interest in the experimental approach to the study of embryology, stimulated by Spemann in Germany and Morgan and Harrison in this country, and implemented by a host of their students, there has been accumulated a large volume of information not available in 1897. It is important that the description of normal embryology, aided by this experimental approach, be brought up to date for the frog. *Third,* with the discovery that the frog can be induced to ovulate and provide living embryos at any time of the year, these embryos have become one of the major test organisms in experimental embryology. It is also being used increasingly in the related scientific disciplines such as physiology, cytology, and genetics.

The author disclaims any fundamental originality in this book. All of the previous investigators and authors touching on the normal embryology of the frog, from whose works much information has been gathered, have been listed in the Bibliography. It is they who have done much of the "spade work" for this book and the student is encouraged to refer to these original sources. However, the author has described the normal development of the frog to more than 5,000 students during 19 years of teaching, as a result of which an intimate personal knowledge of all phases of frog embryology has inevitably accrued. Further, the author organized one of the first laboratory courses for experimental embryology in which the major experimental form was the frog egg and embryo. From these two major lines of work a personal interpretation of the development of the frog egg and embryo has developed, built on the broad structural foundation laid by a host of other workers. The author is responsible, however, for any novelty of interpretation.

The author has no intention of claiming any suggestion of finality, in spite of a didactic presentation. The objective presentation of the truth, as far as it can be apprehended at the moment, is the extent of one's responsibility. Accuracy should be the moral and ethical responsibility of every author of a treatise on a scientific subject. To the best of the author's knowledge, the descriptive material of this book is demonstrably accurate.

The author, as a teacher, has found it increasingly important that there be a common language by which information can be imparted to the student. This necessity is met in part by a Glossary of embryological terms, readily accessible to the student and rigidly adhered to by the instructor. For this reason, the book breaks with tradition to include a complete Glossary of some 750 words. A definition will often clarify or crystallize a complicated and detailed description. Therefore it is hoped that the student will increase his functional vocabulary to the extent of the appended Glossary.

The author is also an enthusiastic advocate of the visual elucidation of the oral description. Most illustrations are useful, some are indispensable. Therefore a profusion of illustrations appears in this book, most of which are original and based on direct observation of the egg and embryo. In a few cases excellent illustrations of other workers have been borrowed or slightly modified for inclusion in this text.

The seed for this book was planted early in the author's mind while he was being initiated into the field of embryology by Professor Robert S. McEwen of Oberlin College. During a long period of incubation the plan slowly matured. Experience, gained over the years in teaching and learning from the response of interested students, helped to bring into clearer focus the aims to be sought for in this book as a teaching text. The execution of the task and the finished form presented here could not have been attained at this time but for the invaluable assistance given by the publishers and their staff. Thanks are due to Miss Marie Wilson and to The Blakiston Company—especially to Mr. William B. McNett and Miss Gloria Green of the Art Department who helped with the illustrations; to Mr. Willard Shoener of the Production Department; and most particularly to Miss Irene Claire Moore and Dr. James B. Lackey of the Editorial Staff. Special acknowledgment is also given to the General Biological Supply House of Chicago, whose illustration of the frog is used so effectively on the title page. It remains for the professor and the student of embryology to evaluate the fruits of our common labors.

Embryology is a basic subdivision of biology. From it stem the anatomy, the histology, and the physiology of the adult. To understand it well is to aid in the comprehension of the other biological disciplines.

To know one's self it is not sufficient to study the present-day transiency. Such a study will be enhanced to the degree that it is supported by a knowledge of what preceded the present. To be a Jacques Loeb and thus be qualified to make such a statement as "The most uninteresting thing I know is the normal development of an egg," one has first to know formal, basic, morphological embryology as thoroughly as it is possible to comprehend. It is only then that we can appreciate and intelligently apply the experimental method to the problems of embryology. Possibly, were Loeb alive today, he would be one of the first to admit that we know less about the normal development of the frog than we thought we knew at the time of his statement. Even for the ten-thousandth time, the formation of the tension lines of the first cleavage furrow or the initial involution of the gastrula are still among the most challenging of unsolved mysteries both to the author and to his students.

The adult "organism as a whole" is, in part at least, an expression of its earlier experiences as an embryo. We may even have to admit that the ultimate personality begins its realization at the moment of fertilization. Certainly, to by-pass a study of the development of the most rapid, the most dynamic, the most plastic stage of one's entire physical existence is to miss the sum and substance of life itself. It is the author's firm belief that anyone who completely understands the mechanism of normal embryonic development will, to a comparable degree, understand life at any level. Further, in understanding the embryology of the frog completely, one would come very close to an understanding of the basic principles of development of any form whatsoever.

ROBERTS RUGH

New York City,
June 1950.

Contents

CHAPTER ONE

Introduction

Embryology is a study of **early development** from the fertilized egg to the appearance of a definitive organism. The stage is generally referred to as its **embryonic stage.** It is not so inclusive a term as **ontogeny,** which refers to the entire life history of an organism from the fertilized egg to old age and death. Since either the sperm or the egg (of a zygote) can affect development, the study of embryology might well begin with a study of the normal production and maturation of the germ cells (gametes). It should include fertilization, cleavage, blastula and gastrula formation, histogenesis, organogenesis, and the nervous and humoral integrations of these newly developed organs into a harmoniously functioning organism. When development has proceeded to the stage where the embryo can be recognized as an organism, structurally similar to its parents, it no longer can be regarded as an embryo.

The unfertilized egg is an organism with unexpressed potentialities derived from an ovary containing many essentially similar eggs. Its basic pattern of development is maternally derived and is predetermined in the ovary but its genetic complex is determined at the very instant of fertilization. This predetermination is in no sense structural (i.e., one never has seen a tadpole in a frog's egg) but is nonetheless fixed by both the nuclear and the cytoplasmic influences of the fertilized egg (or zygote). These influences are probably both physical and chemical in nature.

No amount of environmental change can so alter the development of a starfish zygote (i.e., fertilized egg) that it becomes anything but a starfish, or change the potentialities of a fertilized frog egg into anything but a frog. This means that the nucleus and the cytoplasm of the fertilized egg together possess certain potentialities, as well as certain limitations, in development. Within the range of those limitations the potentialities will inevitably become expressed, in any reasonably normal environment.

It is now quite clear that both the nucleus and the cytoplasm are influential in development. The genetic influences are largely nuclear, but cellular differentiation is cytoplasmic. With each of the cleavages there is a synthesis of nuclear material (e.g., desoxyribose nucleic acid) out of the cytoplasmic (ribonucleic acid), and cytoplasmic from the yolk or other extrinsic food sources. Development is not simply growth or increase in mass. It involves a constant synthesis or the building-up of those elements so vital to the normal processes in the development of the individual. Each stage is built upon the successful completion of the preceding stage.

Comparative embryologists have found that there is a somewhat

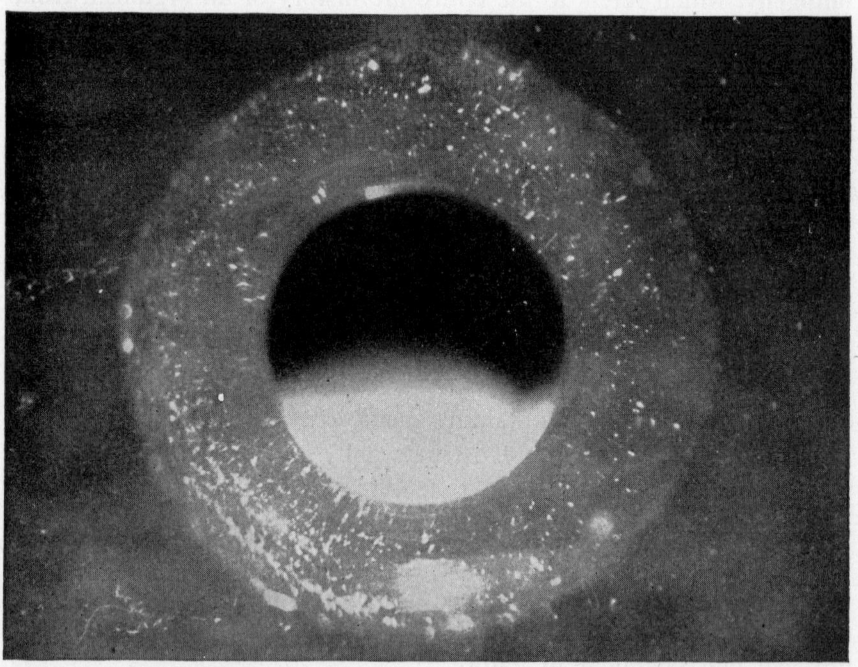

Frog's egg and swollen jelly shortly after fertilization.

similar pattern to the development of all forms. The earlier in development that the comparison is made, the greater the similarity among even widespread species. This may mean that all other possible types of development have failed to survive in a harshly selective environment. Or it may suggest a common ancestry. In any case, all embryos do begin with the fertilized egg. (With the rare exceptions of natural parthenogenesis.) The activated egg immediately manifests certain metabolic changes which may be correlated with the kinetic movements leading toward the completion of maturation or toward the first cleavage. Division results in a shifting of the nucleo-cytoplasmic volume relations from the unbalanced condition of the ovum to the more stable ratio found in the somatic cells. Each division of the egg means more nuclear material, less cytoplasmic material, and more rigid cells. This rigidity, the adhesiveness of cells, and their activity together cause the development of sheets of cells which soon cover (chick) or surround (frog) a cavity, known as the blastocoel. As this sheet of cells expands it becomes necessary for it to fold under (chick), to push inward (frog), or to split into layers (mammal), and thereby form the 2-layered gastrula. In most forms almost immediately the third layer (mesoderm) develops between the two preceding layers, epiblast and endoderm. After the derivation of the mesoderm from the outer layer, the latter is then known as the ectoderm. All of this occurs before the appearance of any discernible organs. There is reason to believe that these sheets of cells have topographical rather than functional significance and that parts of any one of them could be exchanged experimentally with any other at this time without seriously disrupting the normal development of the embryo.

At this point, however, the process of cell division becomes secondary to the process known as differentiation or specialization of cell areas. This is the very beginning of organ formation. Many embryos begin to develop transient (larval) organs which are replaced as the more permanent organs appear and begin to function. Eventually there is produced a highly complex but completely integrated organism which is able to ingest, digest, and assimilate food, and subsist for itself independently of its parent organism. It is then no longer considered an embryo.

This period of ontogeny is the subject matter of embryology. We attempt not to answer the major biological question *"why"* but rather to confine ourselves to a detailed description as to *"how"* an organism is produced from a fertilized egg. It is the purpose of this book to describe *"how"* the frog develops from the fertilized frog's egg, as we understand it. The facts of this book are made available through the accumulated studies of many investigators, in this and other countries.

There are those who are interested in the subject matter of embryology solely because they were once embryos themselves, or because they anticipate becoming partners in the further production of embryos. The closer we can come to the understanding of the mechanism of embryonic development of any single species, the closer will we come to the understanding of the mechanism of life itself. The processes of the embryo are certainly fundamental to all of life. Life exists by virtue of successful embryonic development. There are few things in the living world more absorbing or more challenging to watch than the transformation of a single cell into a complex organism with its many organs of varied functions, all most efficiently integrated.

Embryology is not a new subject. It has a very rich heritage, based upon the solid foundation of pure descriptive morphology. This is followed by the comparison of the variations in development, leading to the recent trend toward the physical and chemical analyses of the developmental processes. In order that we do not lose sight of this heritage, a brief survey is given in the following pages.

The Period of Descriptive Embryology

While organisms must have been reproducing and developing since the beginning of life, knowledge of these processes seems to have begun with Aristotle (384–322 B.C.), who first described the development and reproduction of many kinds of organisms in his "De Generatione Animalium." Since he could not locate the small mammalian egg, he considered its development to be the most advanced of all animals. Below the mammal he placed the shark, whose young develop within the body of the female but are born alive and often with the yolk sac attached. Next, below the sharks, he placed the reptiles and the birds whose eggs are complete in that they are provided with albumen and a shell. The lowest category of development was that of the amphibia and fish, which had what he termed "incomplete" eggs, referring, no doubt, to the method of cleavage. Aristotle believed that development always proceeds from a simple and formless beginning to a complex organization characteristic of the adult. Basing this observation on his study of the hen's egg, he laid the foundation for the modern concept of epigenesis or unfolding development. This concept is opposed to the idea of structural preformation of the embryo within the gamete, or germ cell.

William Harvey (1578–1657) long ago came to the conviction that all animals arise from eggs: "Ex ovo omnis"; and later Virchow (1821–1902) went even further to state that all cells are derived from preëxisting cells: "Omnis cellula e cellula." Flemming stated: "Omne vivum ex nucleo" and later Huxley said, "Omne vivum ex vivo." These concepts, taken for granted today, are basic in biology and emphasize the fact that only through the process of reproduction has the present population of organisms come into existence. Embryonic development is a prerequisite to survival of the species. Therefore, only those organisms that survive their embryonic development and achieve the stage of reproductive ability can carry the baton of protoplasm from the previous to the future generations in the relay race of life with time.

Fabricius (1537–1619) and Harvey were both limited in their studies by the lack of the miscroscope but both of them presented remarkable studies of early chick development. Malpighi (1628–94), using the newly invented microscope, gave us two works in embryology: "De Formatione Pulli in Ovo" and "De Ovo Incubato," which deal largely with the development of the chick from 24 hours to hatching. Beginning at this stage he was misled to believe that all the various parts of the embryo are preformed within the egg (since chick embryos incubated for 24 hours exhibit most of the major organ systems) and that the process of development was one simply of growth and enlargement. This was the theory of "preformationism" which is diametrically opposed to that of epigenesis or unfolding development. This new concept of preformationism found a staunch supporter in Swammerdam (1637–80). In 1675 Leeuwenhoek firmly believed he discovered the human form sitting in a cramped position in the head of the human spermatozoon. This led to the "spermist" school of preformationists.

It was inevitable that, when parthenogenesis was discovered, the spermists would have to retire in favor of the ovists (e.g., Bonnet) since eggs were known to develop into organisms without the aid of spermatozoa. This led to the equally ridiculous concept of the "emboîtement" or "encasement" theory, which suggested that each egg contains, in miniature, all the future generations to be developed therefrom. Each generation was achieved by shedding the outermost layer, like Chinese ivory boxes carved one within another. But preformationism of either school was destined to lose adherents as the microscope became further refined. Caspar Friedrich Wolff (1733–94) attacked the idea of preformationism and supported epigenesis on purely logical grounds, put forth in his "Theoria Generationis." In 1786 he published the most outstanding work in the field of embryology prior to the works of von Baer. It was entitled "De Formatione Intestinorum" and in this treatise Wolff showed that the intestine of the chick was developed de novo (epigenetically) out of unformed materials.

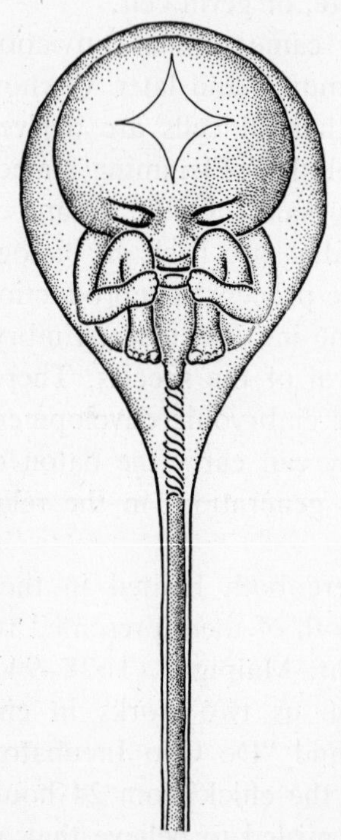

Spermist's conception of the human figure in miniature within the human sperm. (Redrawn after O. Hertwig, from Hartsoeker: 1694.)

The Period of Comparative Embryology

Up to about 1768 embryology was almost exclusively descriptive and morphological. It was inevitable that the second phase in the history of embryology would soon develop, and would be of a comparative nature. This approach was stimulated by Cuvier (1769–1832) and his emphasis on comparative anatomy. In 1824 Prevost and Dumas first saw cleavage or segmentation of an egg in reptiles. In 1828 von Baer published his "Entwicklungsgeschichte der Tier" and thereby became the founder of embryology as a science. He established the germ layer doctrine, proposed a theory of recapitulation, and made embryology truly comparative. From a study of the development of various animals, von Baer arrived at four important conclusions, which are known collectively as the laws of von Baer. They are as follows:

1. "The more general characteristics of any large group of animals appear in the embryo earlier than the more special characteristics."

2. "After the more general characteristics those that are less general arise and so on until the most special characteristics appear."
3. "The embryo of any particular kind of animal grows more unlike the forms of other species instead of passing through them."
4. "The embryo of a higher species may resemble the embryo of a lower species but never the adult form of that species." (This latter statement is the basis of the Biogenetic Law when it is properly interpreted.)

Following von Baer, Kowalevsky (1866) stated that all animals pass through a gastrula stage. Haeckel (1874) proposed a Gastrea Theory which suggested that the permanent gastrula, the adult Coelenterata, might be the form from which all higher diploblastic (gastrula) stages in their life history were derived.

The Period of Cellular Embryology

As the microscope was still further refined, and embryos could be studied in greater detail, it was natural that a further subdivision of the field of embryology would occur. In 1831 Robert Brown discovered the nucleus; in 1838 Schleiden and Schwann founded the cell theory; in 1841 Remak and Kolliker described cell division; in 1851 Newport observed the entrance of the spermatozoon into the frog's egg; and in 1858 Virchow published his "Cellular Pathology." Later, in 1878, Whitman and Mark initiated the study of cell lineage ("Maturation, Fecundation, and Segmentation of Limax") by which the fate of certain early blastomeres of the embryo was traced from their beginning. In 1882 Flemming discovered the longitudinal splitting of chromosomes; and Sutton in 1901 gave us the basis for the modern chromosomal theory of inheritance. The study of the embryo was thus broken down into a study of its constituent cells; then to the nucleus; and finally to the gene. From the morphological, physiological, or genetic aspects, this field of cellular embryology is still very active.

The Period of Experimental Embryology

During the latter part of the nineteenth century, investigators began to alter the environment of embryos, and surgically and mechanically to interfere with blastomeres and other parts of the developing embryo. This new "experimental" approach required a prior knowledge of morphological and comparative embryology. It was hoped that, by altering the physical and chemical conditions relating to the embryo, the normal mechanism of development would be understood better through an analysis of the embryonic adjustments to these alterations. Before the turn of the century, the earlier workers in this field were His, Roux, Weismann, Born, Driesch, and the Hertwigs (Oscar, Richard, and Paula). Then came Morgan, Spemann, and Jacques Loeb. Finally during the last several decades there has developed a host of experimental embryologists, many of whom were inspired by association with the above workers. Reference should be made briefly to Adelmann, Baltzer, Bataillon, Bautzmann, Boell, Brachet, Child, Conklin, Copenhaver, Dalcq, de Beer, Detwiler, Ekman, Fankhauser, Goerttler, Guyenot, Hadorn, Hamburger, Harrison, Herbst, Holtfreter, Just, Korschelt, Lehmann, the Lewises, the Lillies, Mangold, Nicholas, Oppenheimer, Parmenter, Pasteels, Patten, Penners, Rawles, Rotmann, Rudnick, Schleip, Schultz, Spratt, Swingle, Twitty, Vogt, Weiss, Willier, E. B. Wilson, and a host of others.

A further refinement of this approach is in the direction of chemical embryology or a study of the chemistry of the developing embryo and the raw materials from which it is formed. As Needham (1942) says: "Today the interest has been shifted to the analysis of the fundamental morphogenetic stimuli which operate in embryonic life." Such stimuli as these may well be of an ultra-chemical or ultra-physical nature.

Embryology as a division of science has gone through a period of its own development from the purely descriptive phase to the present-day biochemical and biophysical analysis of development. However, each generation must recapitulate this sequence; therefore each student must begin with the foundation of basic, morphological embryology before he can expect to comprehend the possibilities in the superstructure of the experimental approach.

It is the function of this particular book to provide the student with the foundational information relative to one genus, namely the common frog. This will introduce him to the major aspects of embryonic development and at the same time give him a factual foundation upon which he may later make his contribution in one of the fields of embryology. Where it will not confuse, but might clarify the developmental process, reference will be made to specific findings in the field of experimental embryology.

The Embryologist as a Scientist

There are certain characteristics necessary for success and satisfaction in pursuing the study of embryology, or, in fact, any science. Some of these may be inherent, but it is more realistic to assume that they can be developed.

First: One must have the completely open mind characteristic of any true scientist. A student must come to any science without bias, without preconceived or prejudiced concepts. He must be willing to say: "Show me, give me proof, and then I'll believe." Science is a body of knowledge, accumulated through generations by fallible human beings. It is therefore as reliable as human experience but it is subject to change with knowledge gained through further human experience. Basically this body of demonstrated fact can be accepted at its face value as a foundation upon which to build. It is a heritage of generations of trial and error, of observation, experimentation, and verification. But the scientific attitude presumes that there is still much to learn, and some ideas to be revised. The scientist maintains an open mind, eager to be shown and willing to accept demonstrable fact.

Second: The student of embryology must have the ability to visualize dynamic changes in a three-dimensional field. Most embryos are not naturally transparent and it is difficult to observe directly what is

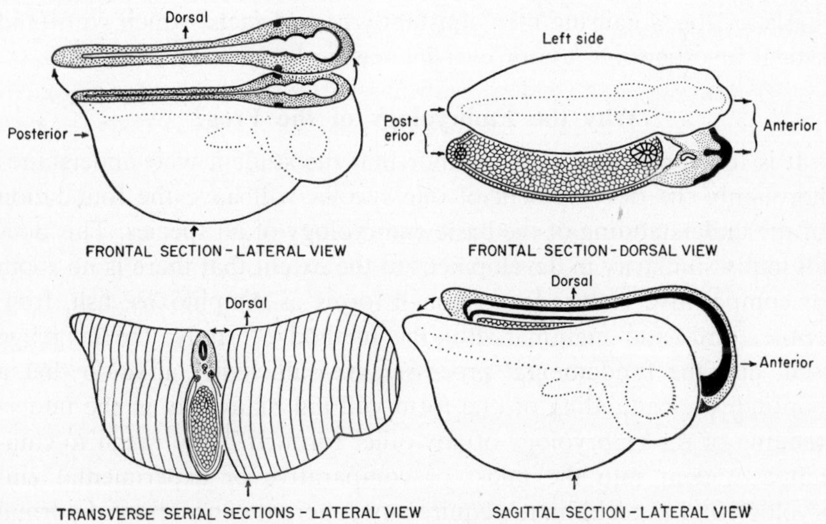

Planes in which the embryo may be cut or sectioned.

transpiring within. It is necessary, therefore, to study such embryos after they have been preserved, sectioned, and stained. Nevertheless, the emphasis in embryology is on the dynamic changes that occur, on derivations, and on the end organs of the developmental processes. One is not interested in a single frame of a moving picture nor is it sufficient to describe all of the structures in a single section of an embryo. The student of embryology is interested in the composite picture presented by a succession of individual frames (sections) which are re-assembled in his mind into a composite, three-dimensional whole. It is necessary, in dynamic embryology, to reconstruct in the mind the inner processes of development which proceed from the single-celled egg to the multicellular organism functioning as a whole. The embryo also must be regarded in the light of its future potentialities. While parts of the embryo are isolated for detailed study, the student must of necessity re-assemble those parts into a constantly changing three-dimensional whole. The embryo is not static in any sense—it is dynamic.

Third: The student of embryology must have an intelligently directed imagination, one based upon a foundation of scientific knowledge. He must be rigidly loyal to demonstrable fact, but his mind must project him beyond those facts. It is through men with intelligent imagination that there have been such remarkable advances in the superstructure of embryology. Coupled with a healthy curiosity, such a characteristic is causing men constantly to add facts, which withstand critical investigation, to our ever-increasing body of knowledge.

Why the Embryology of the Frog?

It is the contention of the author that the student who understands thoroughly the development of one species will have the foundation for the understanding of the basic embryology of all species. This does not imply similarity in development to the extent that there is no room for comparative embryology of such forms as Amphioxus, fish, frog, reptile, bird, and mammal. But the method of study, the language used, and the fundamental processes are sufficiently alike so that a thorough understanding of one form will aid materially in the understanding of the embryology of any other form. It is too much to catapult a student into the midst of comparative or experimental embryology and expect him to acquire any coherent conception of normal development.

The normal embryology of the frog is well understood, and there is no better form through which to introduce the student to the science of embryology. The frog is a representative vertebrate, having both an aquatic and a terrestrial existence during its development. This metamorphosis requires, for instance, several major changes in the respiratory and excretory systems during development. The embryology of the frog illustrates the sequence of developmental events (organogeny) of all higher vertebrates. Finally, the living embryos of the frog are now available at any season of the year and students can observe directly the day-to-day changes that occur from fertilization to metamorphosis.

Some General Concepts in Embryology

Biogenesis

There is no substantiated evidence of spontaneous generation of life, although, as a scientist, one cannot deny its possibility. All life does come from preëxisting life. In embryology we are more specific and state that all organisms come from eggs. This statement is certainly true of all Vertebrates and of the vast majority of animals. However, it cannot be said of the single-celled Protozoa or of some of the lower Invertebrates which reproduce by binary fission, spore formation, or budding.

All protoplasm in existence today is believed to be descended from preëxisting protoplasm and it is therefore related by a continuous line from the original protoplasmic mass, whenever that came into existence. Further, sexual organisms living today are each descendants of a continuous line of ancestors not one of which failed to reach the period of sexual productivity. So, the mere existence of an organism today is testimony of its basic relationship to all protoplasm and to its inherited tendency toward relative longevity. At present one cannot conceive of life originating in any manner but from life itself. All theories are, of necessity, philosophic speculation.

Biogenetic Law—The Law of Recapitulation

The original laws of von Baer are very clearly stated, but Haeckel and others have misinterpreted or elaborated on them so that a confusion about these concepts has arisen in the popular mind. Von Baer clearly emphasized the fundamental similarity of certain early stages of embryos of various forms. He never suggested that embryos of higher forms recapitulated the adult stages of their ancestors; that man as an embryo went through such stages as those of the adult fish, amphibian, reptile, bird, and finally anthropoids and man. The similarities referred to were in the early developmental stages, and most definitely not in the adults.

As one studies comparative embryology it becomes clear that there is a basic similarity in development, and that the brain, nerves, aortic arches, and metameric kidney units (for instance) develop in a somewhat similar manner from the fish to man. Proponents of the theory of evolution have emphasized this as evidence in support of their theory. It is, however, possible that this similarity is due to a highly selective environment which has eliminated those types of development which have digressed from a certain basic pattern. Put another way, the type of development we now know was suited to survive in the environments available. Three primary germ layers may have proved to be more efficient (i.e., to have better survival value) than two or four, and so the gradual transition from pro- through meso- and finally to the meta-nephros may be a necessary corollary of the slow developmental process. Von Baer's laws may simply represent one method of expressing a fundamental law of nature (i.e., survival values) rather than a phylogenetic relationship.

There are many specific instances in development which could be used to refute the Law of Recapitulation as it is often stated, but which would in no way refute von Baer's "Biogenetic Law." One example may be cited: there is no evidence among the lower forms of any anticipation of the development of the amnion and the chorion of the amniotes. The Biogenetic Law was derived from a study of comparative embryology, and possibly it has significance in the understanding of the mechanism of evolution.

Epigenesis vs. Preformationism

The historical sequence from preformationists to spermists and then ovists was very natural. The refinement of optical equipment dispelled these earlier concepts and the pendulum swung to the opposite extreme where embryologists believed that nothing was preformed and that development was entirely epigenetic. As often occurs, the pendulum has swung back to an intermediate position today.

No one has ever seen any preformed structure of the organism in any germ cell. Nevertheless, one can bring together in the same receptacle the fertilized eggs of closely and distantly related forms and yet their individual development is unaffected. A normally fertilized egg of the starfish will always develop into a starfish, a frog's egg into a frog, a guinea pig egg into a guinea pig. The environment of the fertilized egg has never been known to cause the transmutation of species. Further, we cannot see the stripes on a 2-cell mackerel egg, or the green and yellow spots on the 2-cell frog's egg, or the colorful plumage on a peacock blastoderm, or the brown eyes of the human optic vesicle. Nevertheless these intrinsic genetic potentialities are definitely preformed and inevitable in development under normal environmental circumstances. Development is epigenetic to the extent that one cannot see the formed structures within the egg, or the sperm, or zygote. However, the organism is preformed chemically (genetically) to the extent that its specific type of development is inevitable under a given set of circumstances. Our modern interpretation is therefore intermediate between that of preformationism and epigenesis. There is unfolding development within certain preformed limits which must be chemical and/or physical, but not visibly morphological.

Soma and Germ Plasm

It is definite that in some forms there is an early segregation of embryonic cells so that some will give rise to somatic (body) tissues while others will give rise to germ (reproductive) tissues. This was the contention of Weismann and many others about 1900. The germinal cells seem to come from the extra-embryonic regions of many vertebrates and become differentiated at an early stage of development. Whether or not these migrating pre-germ cells are the precursors of the functional gametes has not been determined conclusively. Nevertheless, the germ plasm, once segregated, is immune to damage by the somatoplasm. This has been illustrated many times by men who have incurred injuries and yet who have subsequently produced normal offspring. The germ plasm is therefore functionally isolated, segregated in the adult. Further, x-ray damage to the germ plasm does not show up in the somatoplasm at least until the next generation.

Germ plasm can and does give rise to somatoplasm during normal embryonic development. There is little, if any, evidence that somatoplasm, once formed, can give rise to germ plasm. When the fully formed gonads of higher animals are removed in their entirety, there seems to be no regeneration of germinal tissues from the remaining somatic tissues.

However, modern embryologists are rather reluctant to believe that these two types of protoplasm are as fundamentally segregated from each other as was once believed. Regeneration is a characteristic of lower forms. In these cases it certainly involves a redevelopment of germinal tissue (e.g., Planaria regeneration of a total organism from one-sixth part completely devoid of germinal tissue). The lack of regenerative powers in general among the higher forms may be the intervening factor in the distinction between somatoplasm and germ plasm, and the lack of interchange or regeneration between them.

The Germ Layer Concept

In 1817 Pander first identified the three primary germ layers in the chick embryo, and since then all metazoa above the Coelenterata have been proved to be triploblastic, or tri-dermic. The order of development is always ectoderm, endoderm, and then mesoderm, so that the most advanced forms in the phylogenetic scale are those possessing mesoderm.

We tend to forget that these germ layer distinctions are for human convenience and that the morphogenetic potentialities are relatively unaware of such distinctions. One can exchange presumptive regions of the blastula so that areas normally destined to become mesoderm may remain in a superficial position to function as ectoderm, or become endoderm. The exchanges may be made in any direction in the early stages. The embryo as a whole may develop perfectly normally, with exchanged presumptive germ layer areas.

When we remember that all tissues arise from cells having the same origin (i.e., from the zygote), and that mitosis ensures similar qualitative and quantitative inheritance, then the presumed distinctions of the three primary germ layers seem to dissolve. It is only during the later phases of development (i.e., during differentiation) that the totipotent genetic capabilities of the cells become delimited, and we have the appearance of structurally and functionally different cell and tissue types.

The Normal Sequence of Events in Embryology

Cell Multiplication.

From the single cell (the fertilized egg or zygote) are derived the many millions of cells which comprise the organism. This is done by the process of almost continual mitosis or cell division involving synthesis and multiplication of nuclear materials. This continues throughout the life of the organism but it is at its greatest rate during embryonic development.

Cell Differentiation (Specialization).

After gastrulation the various cell areas, under new morphogenetic influences, continue to produce more cells. However, some of these cells begin to lose some of their potentialities and then to express certain specific characteristics so that they come to be recognized as cells or tissues of certain types. Generally, after this process of differentiation has occurred, there is never any reversion to the primitive or embryonic condition. Differentiation is cytoplasmic and generally irreversible.

Organogeny.

The formative tissues become organized into organ systems which acquire specific functions. The embryo then begins to depend upon these various newly formed organs for certain functions which are increasingly important for the maintenance and integration of the organism as a whole.

Growth.

This phenomenon involves the ability to take in water and food and to increase the total mass through the synthesis of protoplasm. Growth may appear to be quite uniform in the beginning. However, as the organs begin to develop there is a mosaic of growth activity so that various organ systems show peaks of growth activity at different stages in embryonic development. It may be said that embryonic development is completed when differentiation and organogeny have been fully achieved.

CHAPTER TWO

General Introduction to the Embryology of the Leopard Frog, *Rana pipiens*

The embryology of most of the Anura (frogs and toads) is essentially the same. However, since the leopard frog, *Rana pipiens,* is so abundant and is most generally used for embryological, physiological, and morphological studies, the following description will be specifically of this form. Where there are differences in closely related forms that may be used in embryology, those differences will be indicated in the text.

Rana pipiens (Schreiber) has a widespread distribution over entire North America. It hibernates in marshes or pools and seems to prefer the swampy marshlands for breeding in the spring. It may be found in hay fields where there are many insects, but it remains close to a supply of relatively calm water.

When these frogs are sexually mature they measure from 60 to 110 millimeters from snout to anus, the female being about 10 mm. longer than the male of the same stage of maturity. The body is slender and the skin is smooth and slimy, due to a mucous secretion of the integument. The general color is green, except when the animal is freshly captured from hibernation. At this time the chromatophores are contracted by the cold and the frogs have a uniform light brown color. Extending backward from the eyes are a pair of light colored elevations known as the dorsal plicae, between which are two or three rows of irregularly placed dark spots. Each spot has a light (generally yellow) border. On the sides of the body these spots are usually smaller and more numerous, and on the legs they are elongated to appear as bands. Occasionally one may find a dark spot on the tip of each eyelid. Sometimes a light colored line, bordered below by a dark stripe, occurs along the jaw and extends posteriorly below the tympanic membrane and above the forearm. The ventral aspect of the body is always shiny and white.

The period of germ cell formation occupies much of the long in-

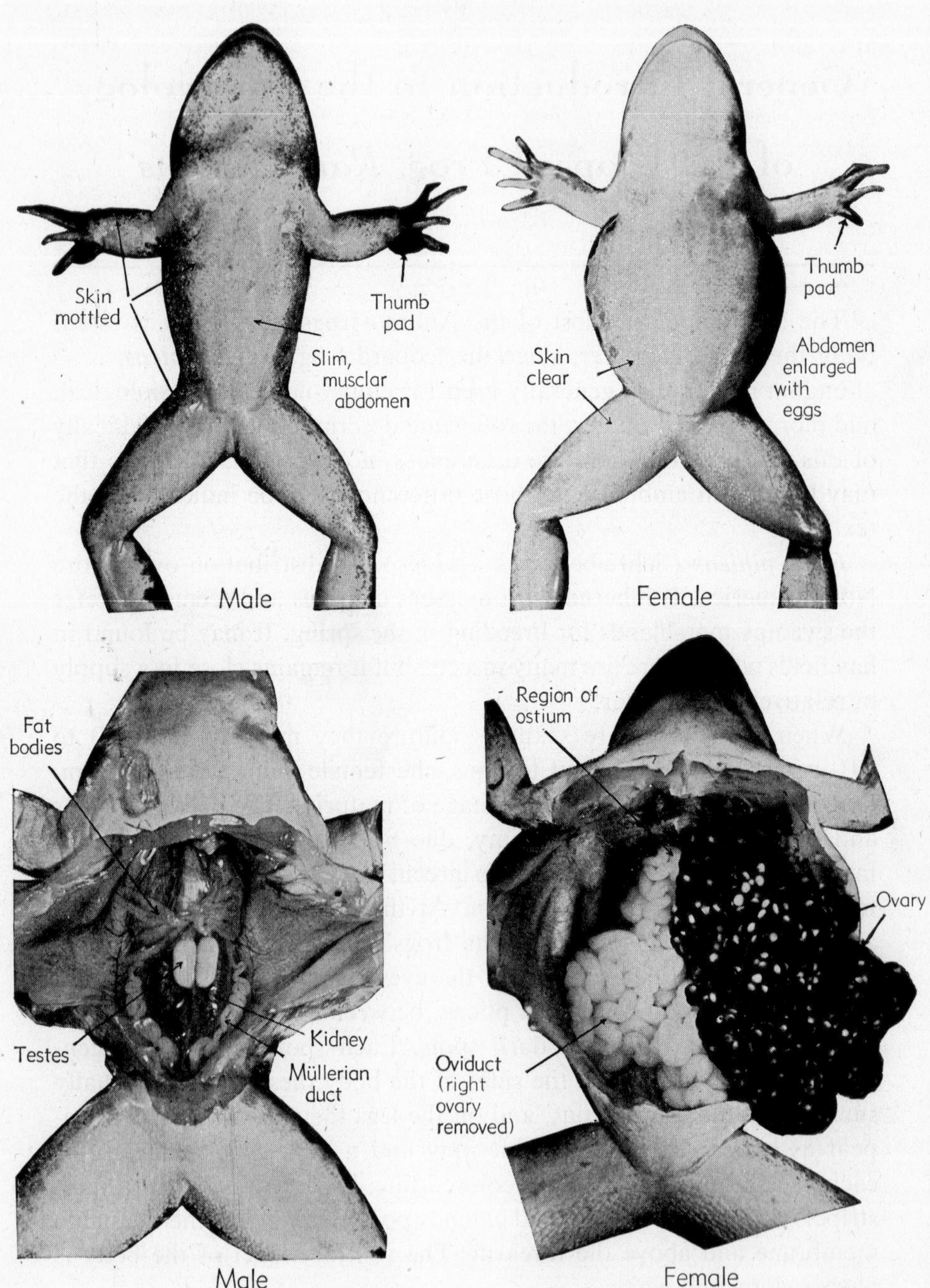

The leopard frog, *Rana pipiens* (photographs by C. Railey).

terval between the annual spring breeding seasons. Breeding occurs normally between the first of April and the latter part of May, depending upon the latitude and upon variations in the temperature. Therefore *Rana pipiens* breeds for about two months, as the temperature rises, from Texas to Canada. In any case, breeding generally occurs before the frogs have had an adequate opportunity to secure food. This means that they must call upon what reserves of fat and glycogen they did not consume during the extended period of hibernation. The interval from egg-laying to metamorphosis of the tadpole is about 75 to 90 days, this phase of development being completed well before the next hibernation period.

Eggs generally are shed early in the morning, and *Rana pipiens* will lay from 2,000 to 3,000 of them. The bullfrog, *Rana catesbiana,* has been known to lay as many as 20,000 eggs. These are laid in heavy vegetation to which their jelly coverings make them adherent. Eggs are found usually in shady places, floating near the surface in rather shallow water.

Fertilization takes place during amplexus, the term for sexual embrace of female by male, as the eggs are laid (oviposition) by the female. The cleavage rate depends upon the temperature of the environment and there may be a lag of from 2½ to 12 hours between

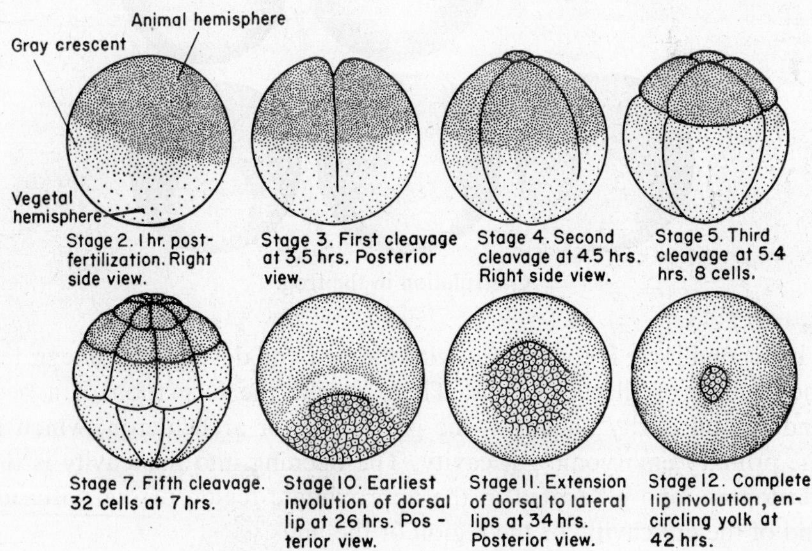

Early development of the frog's egg.

the fertilization of the egg and the appearance of the first cleavage furrow. Often frogs are misled by an early thaw and proceed to shed and fertilize their eggs, and then the pond freezes over. Such eggs usually can withstand a brief (1 to 2 days) freezing without serious effects. Once cleavage has begun, it must proceed (within certain limits of speed) until the egg is divided into progressively smaller and smaller units, first known as blastomeres and later as cells. The first cleavages are quite regular. Since the egg has so much yolk the division of parts of the egg becomes very irregular after about the 32-cell stage. The cleavage planes in the early stages may be altered by unequal pressures applied to any egg within a clump of eggs.

The blastula develops an eccentric cavity because the animal pole cells are so different from the large yolk cells of the vegetal hemisphere. However, the end of the blastula stage is the end of the cleavage stage, although cell division goes on throughout the life of the embryo, the larva, and finally the frog.

The gastrula is an embryo having two primary germ layers, the epiblast (presumptive ectoderm and mesoderm) and the endoderm.

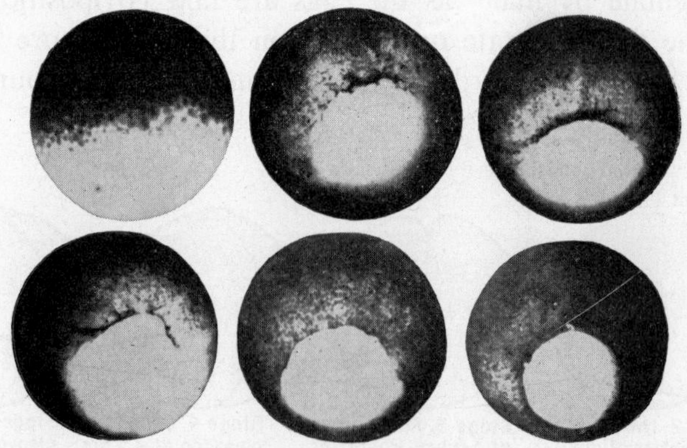

Gastrulation in the frog.

The second layer is continuous with the first and develops by integrated movements of sheets of cells. There results the formation of a new and second cavity known as the gastrocoel, or archenteron, which is the primary embryonic gut cavity. The opening into this cavity is the blastopore, and is located in the approximate region of the posterior end of the gut cavity, or the region of the anus.

The process of gastrulation in the frog is completed by providing also the third germ layer, or the mesoderm, and the notochord, which come from the epiblast. The notochord is the axis around which the vertebral column will be built. The mesoderm will give rise to the bulk of the skeleton and muscle, to the entire circulatory system, and to the epithelium which lines the body cavity.

Shortly after gastrulation the embryo elongates and develops a dorsal thickening known as the medullary plate. This thickened ectoderm

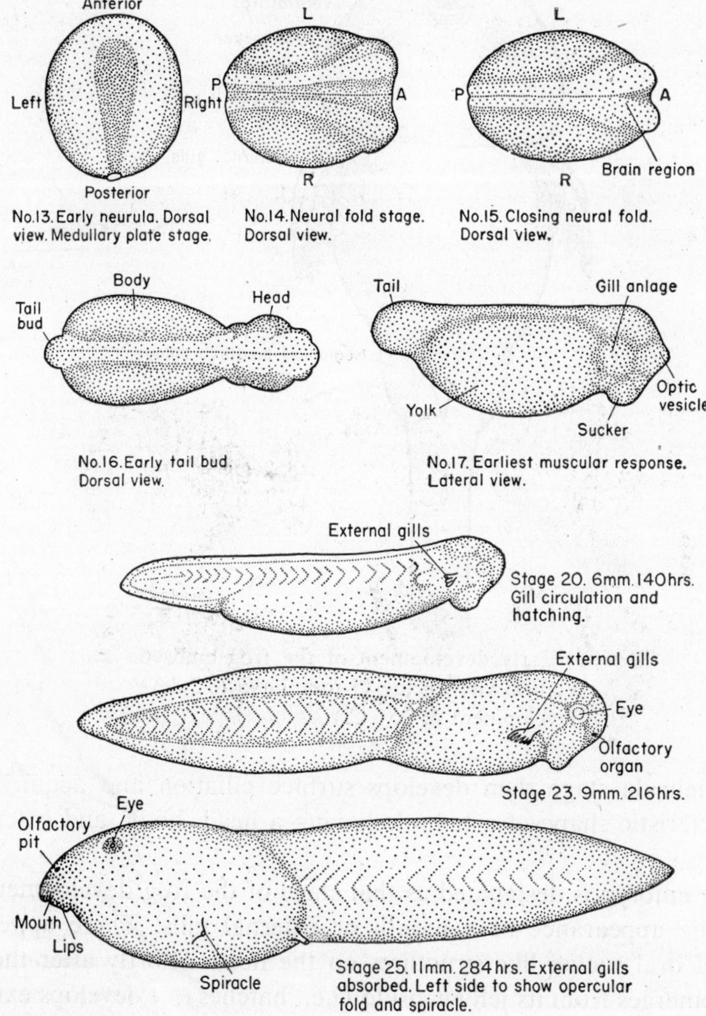

Early development of the frog embryo. (*Top*) Development of the axial central nervous system. (*Bottom*) Development of the external gills and operculum.

will give rise to the entire central nervous system. It closes over dorsally to form the neural and the brain cavities. These continuous cavities are later almost obliterated by the growth and expansion of their walls to form abundant nervous tissue. Extensions of this central nervous system grow out into all parts of the body and all organs as nerves.

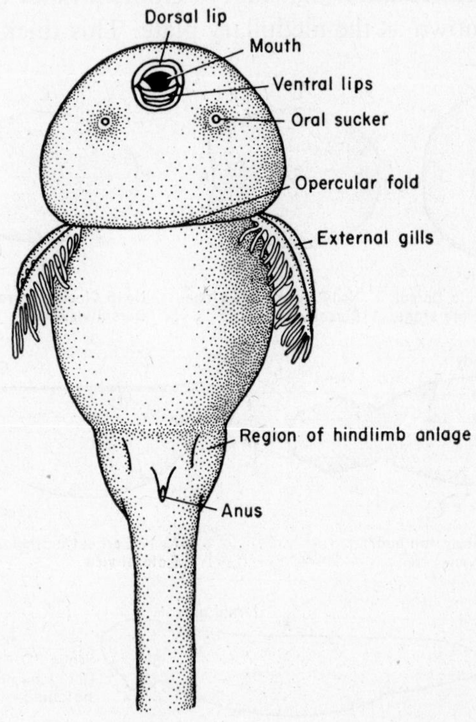

Early development of the frog embryo. Ventral view of the 11 mm. larva (12 days' development at 25° C.).

This neurula stage then develops surface ciliation and acquires the characteristic shape of a tadpole having a head, body, and extending tail.

The embryo is designated as that stage of the frog development before the appearance of a mouth or external gills. There appears a pair of oral sucker-like structures on the head. Shortly after the embryo emerges from its jelly capsule (i.e., hatches), it develops external gills for respiration, and is then known as a larva or tadpole. Embryonic studies include the tadpole because, until metamorphosis is achieved, the organ systems are not all developed to the adult form. The external gills of the tadpole function for a short time and then are replaced by internal gills. The external gills are covered by an operculum or posterior growth of the hyoid arch, with but a small pore or spiracle remaining on the left side of the head. This is the only channel of egress for water from the pharynx and out over the internal gills within the branchial chamber.

From the first day of hatching, when the total water content of the tadpole is about 56 per cent, there is a very rapid rise in the water content until the fifteenth day after hatching, when it reaches the maxi-

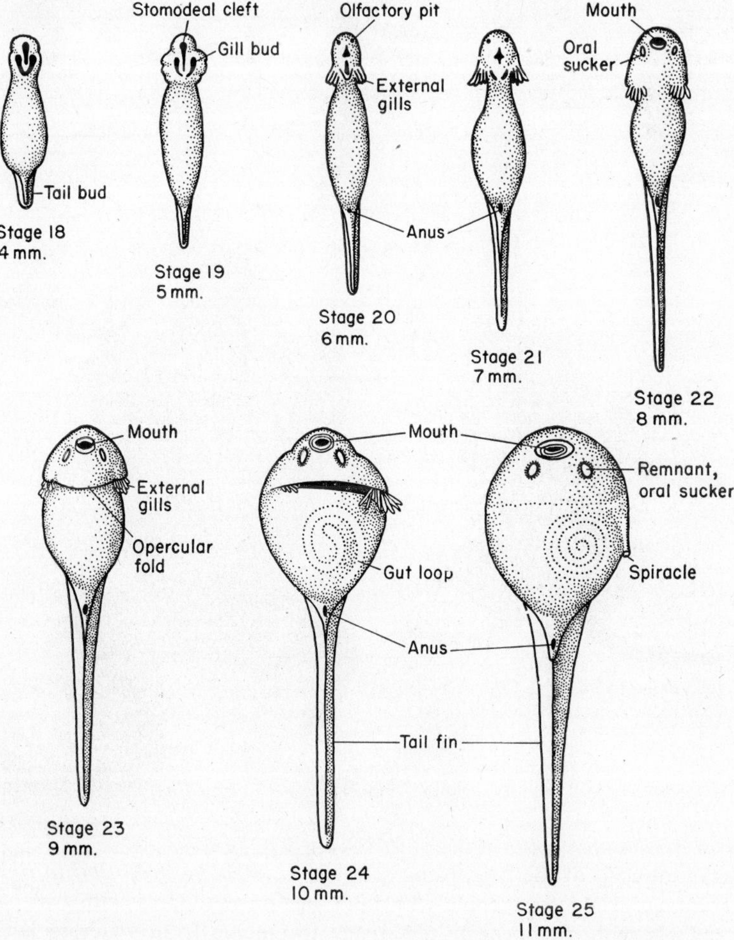

Development and absorption of the external gills of the frog larva.

mum point of 96 per cent water (Davenport, 1899, *Proc. Bost. Soc. Nat. Hist.*) This imbibition accounts for the apparent acceleration of growth of the newly hatched tadpole, but it is not related to an increase in total mass since there is no immediate intake of food. The growth rate is affected by various environmental factors such as space,

Metamorphosis of the frog, *Rana catesbiana.* (*Reading from left to right, top and bottom*): Tadpole; tadpole with hind legs only; tadpole with two pairs of legs; tadpole with disappearing tail, ready to emerge from water to land; immature terrestrial frog; mature frog.

heat, available oxygen, and pressure. The tadpole soon begins voracious feeding on a vegetarian diet.

Shortly after hatching, finger-like external gills develop rapidly on the posterior sides of the head and these constitute the only respiratory organs. Simultaneously with the opening of the mouth a series of visceral clefts (gill slits) develop as perforations in the pharyngeal wall, and their walls become folded to form internal gills. The external gills gradually lose their function in favor of the internal gills. They then become covered over by a posterior growth of tissue known as the operculum. There remains but a single excurrent pore, the spiracle, on the left side at the posterior margin of the operculum. There are but few changes in the respiratory system from this stage until metamorphosis begins at about 2½ months. The internal gills lose their function in favor of lungs at metamorphosis and this allows the aquatic tadpole to become a terrestrial frog. When the tadpole begins to develop its lungs it frequently comes to the surface for air. The forelimbs begin to grow through the operculum, and, about 2½ months after the eggs are fertilized, the hind legs begin to emerge and the tadpole is ready for the critical respiratory and excretory changes that accompany metamorphosis.

Metamorphosis in the leopard frog, *Rana pipiens,* occurs in from 75 to 90 days after the egg is fertilized, generally in the early fall and at a time when the food becomes scarce and the cool weather is impending. Metamorphosis is one of the most critical stages in frog development, involving drastic changes in structure and in function of the various parts of the body. The tadpole ceases to feed; loses its outer skin, horny jaws, and frilled lips; the mouth changes from a small oval suctorial organ to a wide slit and is provided with an enlarged tongue; the eyes become enlarged; the forelimbs emerge; the abdomen shrinks; the intestine shortens and changes histologically while the stomach and liver enlarge; the diet changes from an herbivorous to a carnivorous one; the lungs become the major respiratory organs with the moist skin aiding; the mesonephros assumes greater function; the tail regresses; sex differentiation begins; and the tadpole crawls out of the water as a frog.

We may now summarize the steps in the development of the frog as follows:

1. Fertilization of the egg
2. Formation of the gray crescent due to pigment migration

3. Early cleavage
4. Blastula stage—coeloblastula (see Glossary) with eccentric blastocoel
5. Gastrulation
   Early—crescent-shaped dorsal lip
   Middle—semi-circular blastoporal lip
   Late—circular blastoporal lip
6. Neurulation
   Early—medullary plate
   Middle—neural folds converging
   Late—neural tube formed and ciliation of embryo
7. Tail bud stage—early organogeny
8. Muscular response to tactile stimulation
9. Early heart beat, development of gill buds
10. Hatching and gill circulation
11. Mouth opens and cornea becomes transparent
12. Tail fin circulation established
13. Degeneration of external gills, formation of operculum, development of embryonic teeth
14. Opercular fold over branchial chamber except for spiracle; internal gills
15. Prolonged larval stage with refinement of organs
16. Development of hindlimbs, internal development of forelimbs in opercular cavity
17. Projection of forelimbs through operculum, left side first
18. Absorption of the tail and reduction in size of the gut
19. Metamorphosis complete, emergence from water as miniature, air-breathing frog

The rate of development of the egg and embryo will depend upon the temperature at which they are kept. The approximate schedule of development at two different temperatures is given below.

Stage	*At 18° C.*	*At 25° C.*
Fertilization	0 hrs.	0 hrs.
Gray crescent	1 "	½–1 "
Rotation	1½ "	1 "
Two cells	3½ "	2½ "
Four cells	4½ "	3½ "
Eight cells	5½ "	4½ "
Blastula	18 "	12 "
Gastrula	34 "	20 "
Yolk plug	42 "	32 "
Neural plate	50 "	40 "
Neural folds	62 "	48 "
Ciliary movement	67 "	52 "
Neural tube	72 "	56 "
Tail bud	84 "	66 "

Stage Number	Age-Hours at 18°C		Stage Number	Age-Hours at 18°C		Stage Number	Age-Hours at 18°C	
1	0	UNFERTILIZED	7	7.5	32-CELL	13	50	NEURAL PLATE
2	1	GRAY CRESCENT	8	16	MID-CLEAVAGE	14	62	NEURAL FOLDS
3	3.5	TWO-CELL	9	21	LATE CLEAVAGE	15	67	ROTATION
4	4.5	FOUR-CELL	10	26	DORSAL LIP	16	72	NEURAL TUBE
5	5.7	EIGHT-CELL	11	34	MID-GASTRULA	17	84	TAIL BUD
6	6.5	SIXTEEN-CELL	12	42	LATE GASTRULA			

(From "Stages in the Normal Development of *Rana pipiens,*" by Waldo Shumway. Reprinted from *Anat. Rec.,* **78,** No. 2, October 1940.)

STAGE NUMBER	AGE IN HOURS AT 18° CENTIGRADE	LENGTH IN MILLIMETERS	
18	96	4	MUSCULAR RESPONSE
19	118	5	HEART BEAT
20	140	6	GILL CIRCULATION HATCHING
21	162	7	MOUTH OPEN CORNEA TRANSPARENT
22	192	8	TAIL FIN CIRCULATION

(From "Stages in the Normal Development of *Rana pipiens,*" by Waldo Shumway. Reprinted from *Anat. Rec.*, **78,** No. 2, October 1940.)

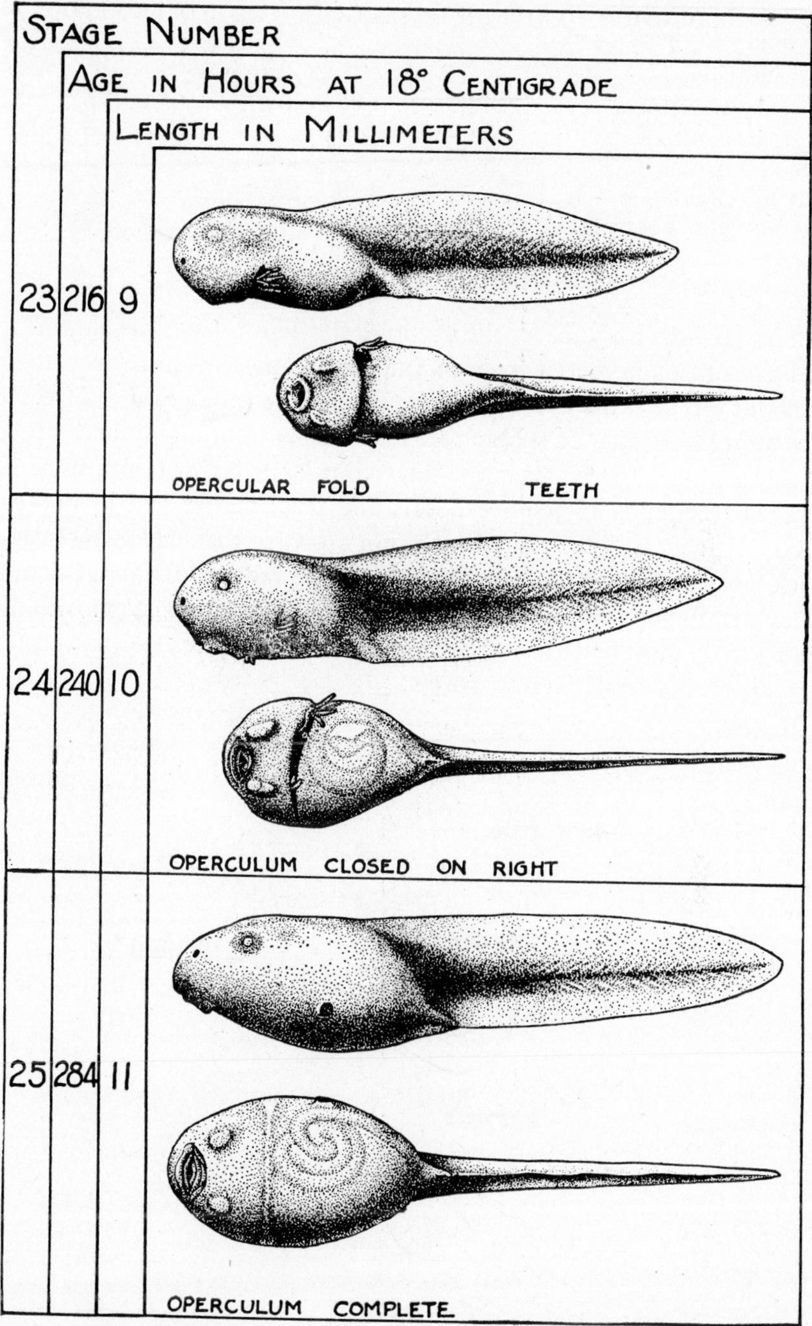

(From "Stages in the Normal Development of *Rana pipiens,*" by Waldo Shumway. Reprinted from *Anat. Rec.,* **78,** No. 2, October 1940.)

Stage	*At 18° C.*		*At 25° C.*	
Muscular movement	96	hrs.	76	hrs.
Heart beat	5	days	4	days
Gill circulation	6	"	5	"
Tail fin circulation	8	"	6½	"
Internal gills, operculum	9	"	7½	"
Operculum complete	12	"	10	"
Metamorphosis	3	mos.	2½	mos.

Those who wish to carry the tadpoles through to later development, and even through metamorphosis into frogs, must begin to feed them at about the time the external gills appear. The food consists of small bits of green lettuce or spinach leaves, washed thoroughly and wilted in warm water. The water in the finger bowls, or larger tanks, must be cleaned frequently to remove débris and fecal matter and to prevent bacterial growth. If the tadpoles are not crowded they will grow faster. After about 10 days the numbers should be reduced to about 5 tadpoles per finger bowl of 50 cc. of water. After metamorphosis, the young frogs must be fed small living worms (Enchytrea) or forced-fed small pieces of fresh liver or worms.

CHAPTER THREE

Reproductive System of the Adult Frog: *Rana pipiens*

The Male

Secondary Sexual Characters

The mature male frog is generally smaller than the female, ranging from 60 to 110 mm. in length from snout to anus. The identifying features which distinguish it from the female are a **darkened thumb pad** which changes thickness and color intensity as the breeding season approaches; a distinct low, guttural **croaking sound** with the accompanying swelling by air of the lateral vocal sacs located between the tympanum and the forearm; a more slender and **streamlined body** than that of the female; and the **absence of coelomic cilia** except in the peritoneal funnels on the ventral face of the kidneys. Males of many species carry additional features such as brilliant colors on the ventral aspects of the legs (*R. sylvatica*), black chin (*B. fowleri*), or the size and color of the tympanic membrane.

Primary Sexual Characters

The Testes.

The testes of the frog are paired and internal organs and are suspended to the dorsally placed kidneys by a double fold of peritoneum known as the **mesorchium.** This mesentery surrounds each testis and is continuous with the peritoneal epithelium which covers the ventral face of each kidney and lines the entire body cavity.

The testes are whitish and ovoid bodies lying ventral to and near the anterior end of each kidney. The **vasa efferentia,** ducts from the testes, pass between the folds of the mesorchium and into the mesial margin of the adjacent kidney. During the breeding season, or after slight compression of the testis of the hibernating frog, these ducts become the more apparent due to the presence in them of whitish masses of spermatozoa in suspension. The ducts are very small in diameter, tough walled, and interbranching. They are lined with closely packed cuboidal cells. Each duct is connected directly with a number (8 to 12) of **Malpighian corpuscles** of the kidneys, by way of the **Bowman's capsules.** These connections are permanent so that many of the anterior **uriniferous tubules** of the frog kidney will contain spermatozoa during the breeding season. The presence of spermatozoa in the kidney also can be achieved artificially by injecting the male frog with the anterior pituitary sex-stimulating hormone. Since these anterior Malpighian corpuscles carry both spermatozoa (during the breeding season) and excretory fluids (at all times), they are truly urogenital ducts having a dual function. This situation does not hold for higher vertebrates.

The spermatozoa are produced in subdivisions of the testes known as **seminiferous tubules.** These are closely packed, oval-shaped sacs, which are separated from each other by thin partitions (septula) of supporting (connective) tissue known as **interstitial tissue.** This tissue presumably has some endocrine function. The thickness of this tissue is much reduced immediately after breeding or pituitary stimulation. The interstitial tissue is continuous with the covering of the testes known as the **tunica albuginea,** and the whole testis is enclosed in the thin **peritoneal epithelium.**

Spermatogenesis.

Shortly after the normal breeding season in the spring for *Rana pipiens,* the **spermatogonium,** which has ceased all mitotic activity, enters upon a period of rest but not inactivity. During this period the nucleus passes through a sequence of complex changes which represent an extended prophase. This is in anticipation of the two maturation divisions that finally produce the haploid spermatid which metamorphoses into a spermatozoon.

The nucleus of the spermatogonium contains chromatin which appears as relatively coarse lumps distributed widely over an achro-

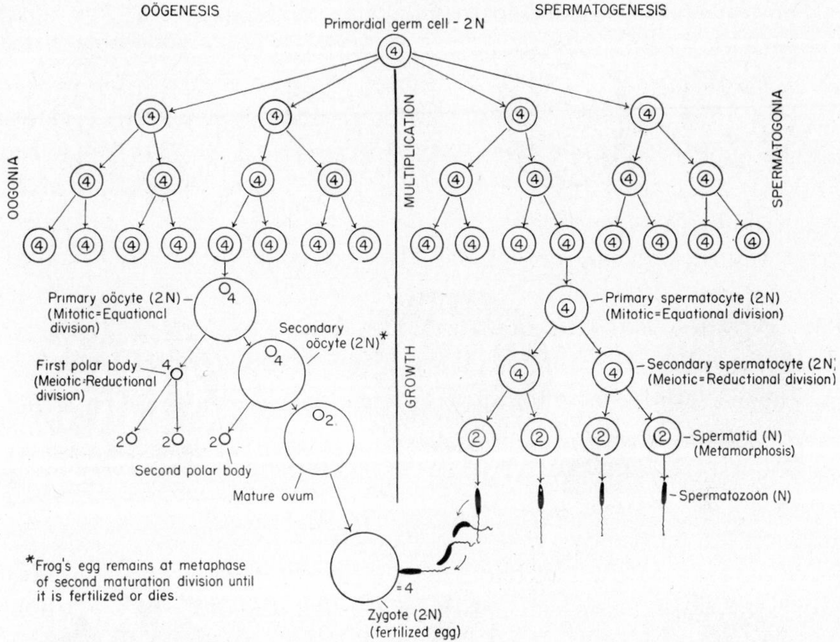

The maturation process. Schematized drawings. The post-reductional division is shown. In many forms the first division is reductional and the second is equational. The end result is the haploid gamete, in either instance.

matic reticulum. Both the cytoplasm and the nucleus grow and the chromatic granules become finely divided and arranged into contiguous rows, bound by an achromatic thread, together known as chromosomes. This is the **leptotene stage** of spermatogenesis. Shortly the chromosomes become arranged in pairs which converge toward that side of the nucleus where the centrosome is found. The opposite ends of the paired chromosomes merge into the general reticulum. This is the **synaptene stage.** The chromatin granules become telescoped together on the filaments so that the aggregated granules, known as chromosomes, appear much shorter and thicker. Pairs of chromosomes become intertwined and the loose terminal ends become coiled and tangled together. This is the **contraction** or **synizesis stage.** Then the members of the various pairs become laterally (parabiotically) fused. While there is no actual reduction in total chromatin, there is a temporary and an apparent (but not real) reduction in the total number of chromosomes to the haploid condition, because of this fusion. There is no actual reduction in the total amount of chromatin

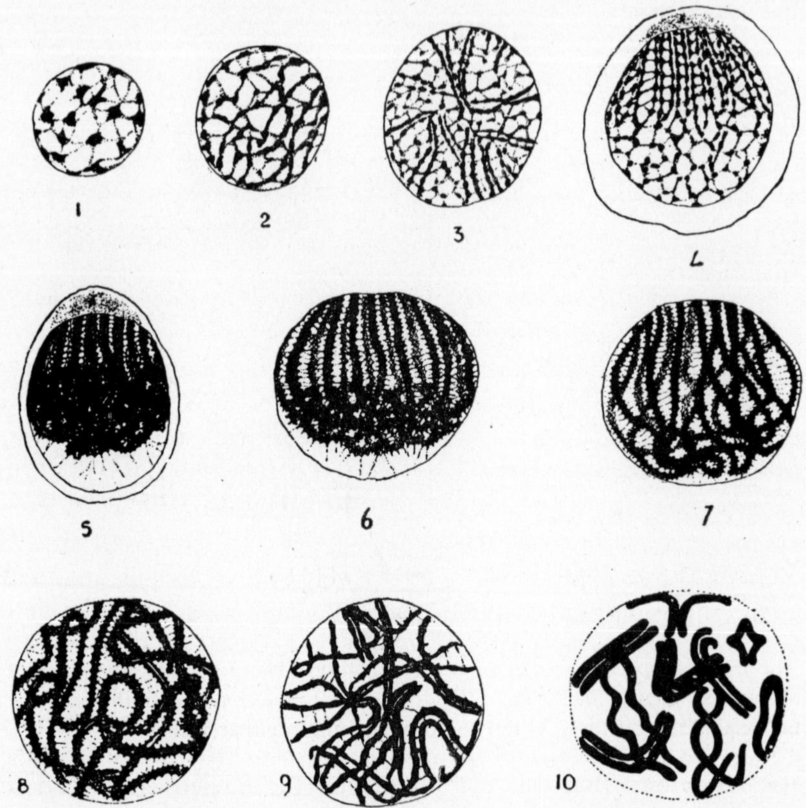

Prophases of the heterotype division in the male Axolotl. (1) Nucleus of spermogonium or young spermocyte. (2) Early leptotene. (3) Transition to synaptene. (4) Synaptene with the double filaments converging toward the centrosome. (5) Contraction figure. (6, 7) Pachytene. (8) Early diplotene. (9) Later diplotene. (10) The heterotypic double chromosomes; the nuclear membrane is disappearing. (Courtesy, Jenkinson: "Vertebrate Embryology," Oxford, The Clarendon Press.)

material, nor is there any permanent reduction at this stage in the number of chromosomes. Their identity is lost only temporarily. This is known as the **pachytene stage.** The members of each pair then separate again. It must be remembered, however, that (a) the separation need not be along the original line of fusion and that (b) an exchange of homologous sections of the chromosomes may occur without any cytological evidence. In any case, the diploid number of chromosomes reappears and this is then known as the **diplotene stage.**

During these changes in the chromatin material of the nucleus, the volume of the nucleus and the cytoplasm are considerably increased, the nuclear membrane breaks down, and the chromosomes assume bizarre shapes and various sizes. They may be paired, curved, or straight; "V" and "C" and reversed "L" shapes, figure 8's, and grouped as tetrads. This is known as the **diakinesis stage.** The chromosomes are then lined up on a spindle in anticipation of the first of the two maturation divisions.

Spermatogenesis in the frog is seasonal and is completed within the testes. The walls of the seminiferous tubules produce spermatogonia which go through mitotic divisions and then the series of nuclear changes (described above) without mitosis. This results in the appearance, toward the lumen of each tubule, of clusters of mature spermatozoa. By the time of hibernation (October) all the spermatozoa that are to become available for the following spring breeding season will have matured. At this time the testis will exhibit only these spermatozoa and relatively few spermatogonia, without the intervening maturation stages. The spermatogonia are found close to the basement membrane of the seminiferous tubule. These then await their turn to undergo the maturation changes necessary for the production of spermatozoa which will be ready for the breeding season a year and a half thereafter. The elongated and filamentous

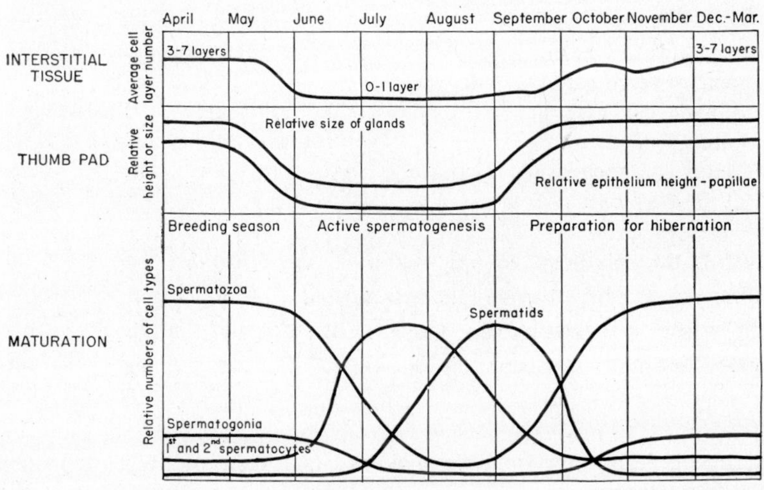

Normal cyclic changes in the primary and secondary sexual characters of the frog, *Rana pipiens*. (From Glass and Rugh, **1944**, *J. Morphol.,* **74**:409.)

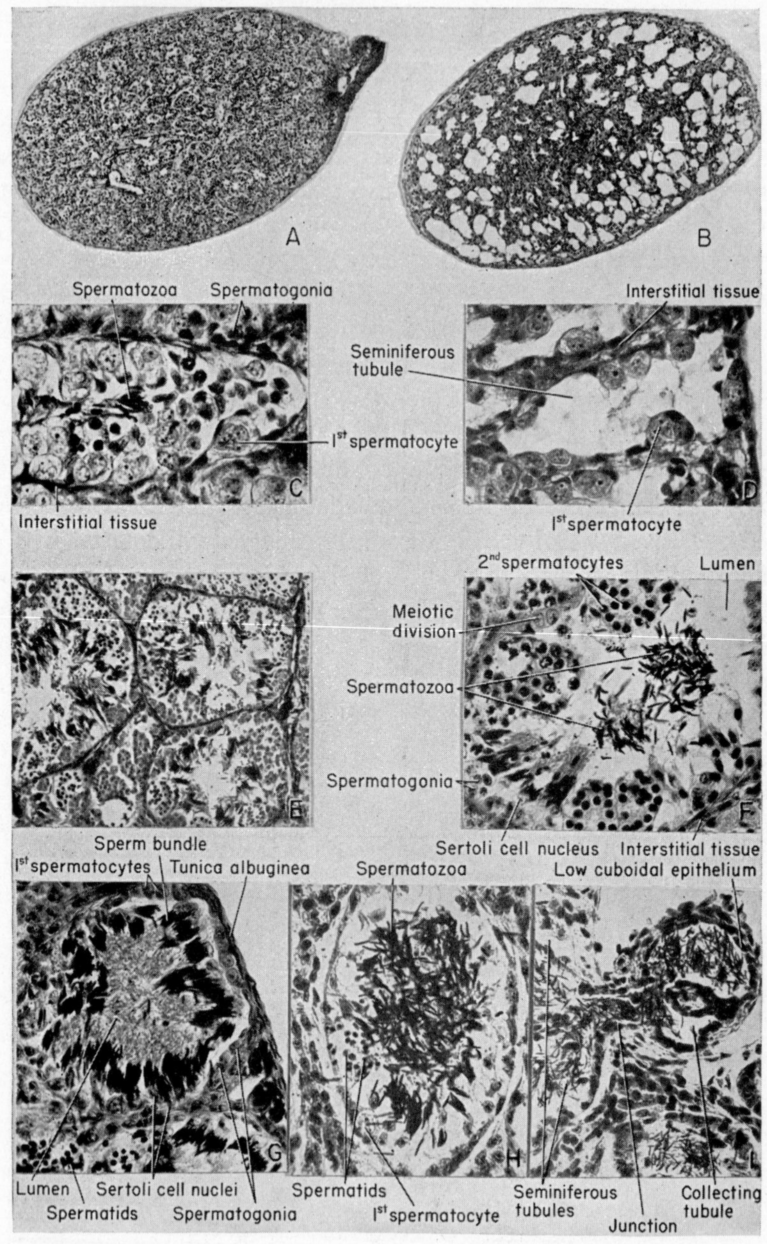

Spermatogenesis in the frog: *Rana pipiens.* (A) Testis of a recently metamorphosed frog. (B) Similar to "A" except that the frog was previously treated with the anterior pituitary hormone to evacuate the seminiferous tubules, leaving only

(*Continued on facing page.*)

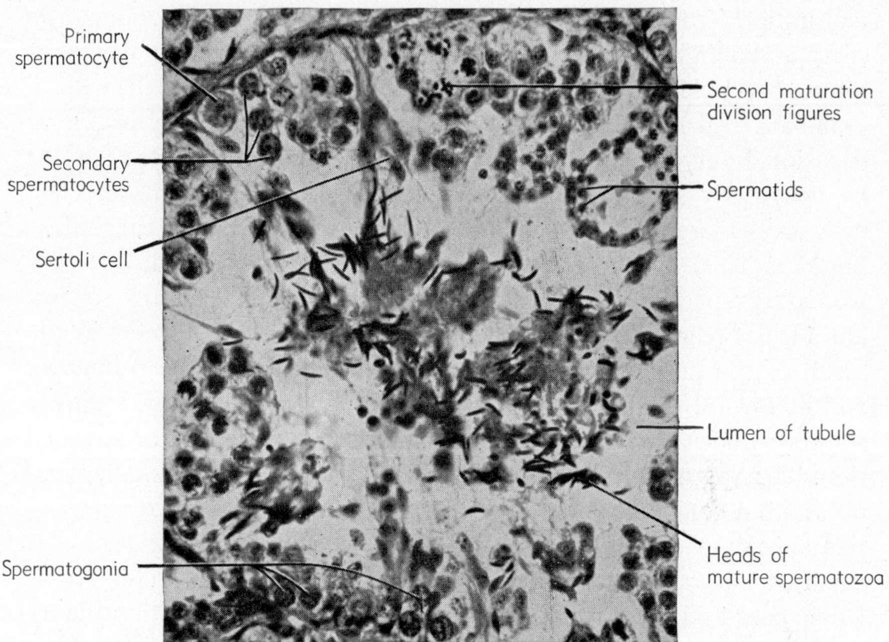

Spermatogenetic stages in the seminiferous tubule of the frog testis.

tails of the clustered mature *spermatozoa* project into the lumen of each seminiferous tubule.

If one studies the July or August testis, which organ is then in its height of spermatogenetic activity, he can find all the stages of

---

(*Continued from opposite page.*)

the interstitial tissue, spermatogonia, and a few primary spermatocytes. The post-breeding condition. (C) High-power magnification of "A." (D) High-power magnification of "B." (E) Testis of an August frog, showing all stages of spermatogenesis. (F) Partially (pituitary) activated testis, similar to "E," showing released spermatozoa within the lumen, and all stages of spermatogenesis around the periphery of the seminiferous tubule. (G) Testis of a hibernating, pre-breeding frog. Note the clusters of mature spermatozoa attached to single Sertoli cells. The lumen is filled with tails, few spermatogonia, and primary spermatocytes around the periphery of the seminiferous tubule. (H) Testis of the male during amplexus, showing spermatozoa liberated into the lumen of the seminiferous tubule. (I) Collecting tubule of the frog testis full of mature spermatozoa, showing their origin from the connecting seminiferous tubules. Collecting tubules are lined with low cuboidal epithelium and are continuous with the vasa efferentia and the Malpighian corpuscles of the kidney.

maturation from the spermatogonium to the spermatozoon. The spermatogonia are always located around the periphery of the seminiferous tubule and are small, closely packed cells, each with a granular, oval nucleus. In between the spermatogonia may be found occasional very large cells, the **primary spermatocytes.** These tend to be irregularly spherical, possessing large and vesicular nuclei. The cells are so large that they may be seen under low power magnification (× 100) of the microscope. Apparently they divide to form secondary spermatocytes almost immediately, for they are so few and far between. The **secondary spermatocytes** (which develop as the result of the first division) are about half the size of the primaries, and lie toward the lumen of the tubule. They generally have a darkly staining nucleus, and the cytoplasm may be tapered toward one side. The **spermatid,** following another division, is even smaller and possesses a condensed nucleus of irregular shape. Clusters of spermatids appear as clusters of granules, the dark nucleus being almost as small as the cross section of a sperm head. The metamorphic stages from spermatid to spermatozoon are difficult to identify with ordinary magnification, and are often confused with the spermatids themselves. During this change the inner of two spermatid centrioles passes into the nucleus while the outer one gives rise to the tail-like flagellum.

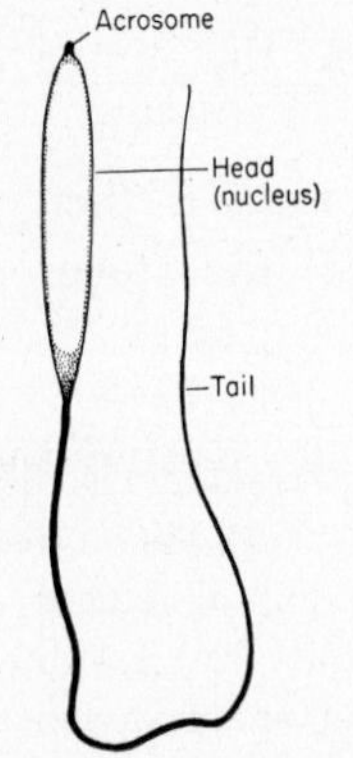

Frog spermatozoon. Total length 0.03 to 0.04 mm.

The mature **spermatozoon** averages about 0.03 mm. in length. It has an elongated, solid-staining head (nucleus) with an anterior acrosome, pointing outwardly toward the periphery of the seminiferous tubule. The short middle piece generally is not visible but the tail appears as a gray filamentous extension into the lumen, about four or more times the length of the sperm head.

In any cross section of the testis, bundles of sperm heads or tails may be cut at right angles or tangentially, giving misleading suggestions of structure. The mature spermatozoon is dependent upon external sources of nutrition so that it joins from 25 to 40 other spermatozoa, all of whose heads may be seen converging into the cytoplasm of a relatively large, columnar-type basal cell known as the **Sertoli cell.** This is functionally a nurse cell, supplying nutriment to the clusters of mature spermatozoa until such

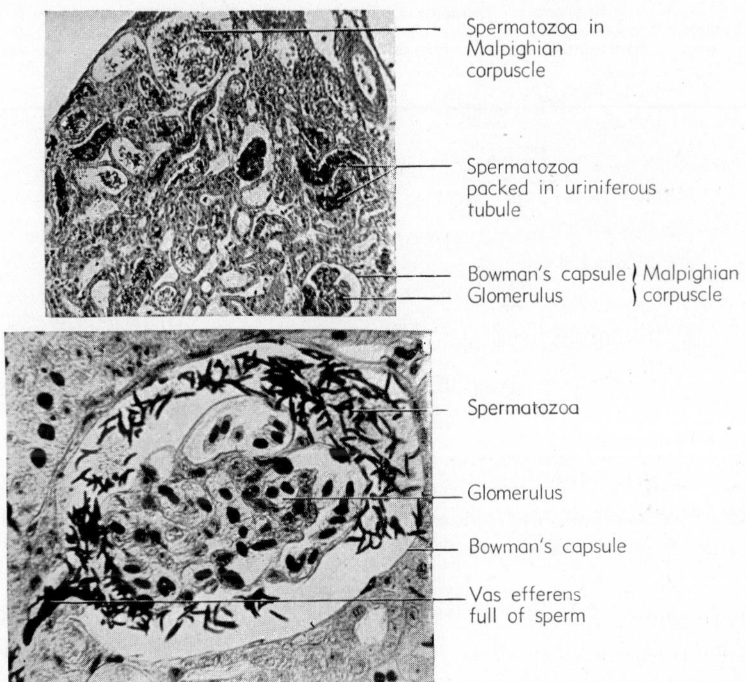

Kidney of the male frog during amplexus showing spermatozoa in the kidney tubules and Malpighian corpuscles, en route to the uro-(mesonephric)-genital (vasa efferentia) duct.

time as they may be liberated through the genital tract to function in fertilization.

In observing a section of the summer testis of the frog under low power magnification, it is readily apparent that each **seminiferous tubule** may contain all the stages of maturation and that each stage is found in a cluster or group within the tubule. Each group of similar cells is derived presumably from a single original **spermatogonium,** by the processes of mitosis and meiosis. This is reminiscent of the condition found in the grasshopper (Rhomaleum) testis. Maturation of the germ cells occurs in groups so that when the **spermatid** stage is reached, the tips of the metamorphosing **spermatozoon** heads are all gathered together into the cytoplasm of the **Sertoli cell.** Spermatozoa may remain thus throughout the entire period of hibernation only to be liberated under the influence of sex-stimulating hormones during the early spring. These spermatozoa are functionally

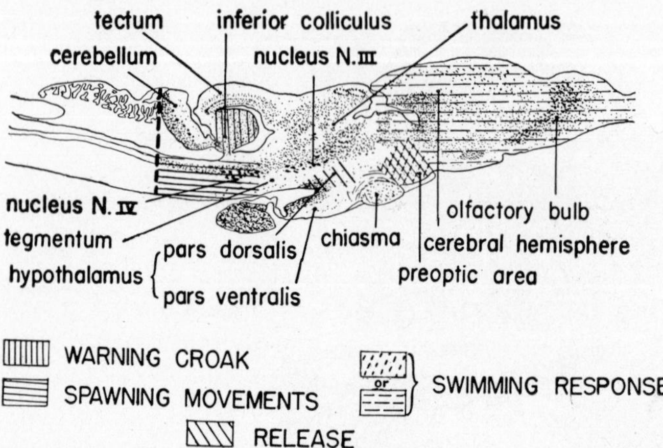

Diagrammatic sagittal section through the brain of *Rana pipiens* indicating the regions of the brain that were found to be of primary importance for the mediation of each of four phases of sexual behavior. (From Aronson, **1945,** *Bull. Am. Mus. Nat. Hist.,* **86:**89.)

mature, as can be demonstrated by dissecting them from the testes and using them to fertilize frogs' eggs artificially at any time from late in August until the normal breeding season in April or May.

Reproductive Behavior

It has been proved definitely that the anterior pituitary hormone causes the release of the mature spermatozoa from the testis. But this hormone also releases other maturation stages. It is therefore probable that there are smooth muscle fibers, either among the interstitial cells or in the tunica albuginea of the testes, which fibers contract to force the spermatozoa from the seminiferous tubules. It would be as difficult to physiologically demonstrate the presence of these fibers in the testis as it is simple to demonstrate them in the contracting cyst wall of the ovary.

Responding to sex stimulation, the spermatozoa become free from their Sertoli cells and are forced from the lumen of the seminiferous tubule into the related **collecting tubule.** These collecting tubules are small and are lined with closely packed cuboidal cells. They join the **vasa efferentia** which leave the testis to pass between the folds of the **mesorchium** and thence into the **Malpighian corpuscles** of the kidney. From this point the spermatozoa pass by way of the excretory ducts, the **uriniferous tubules,** and into the **mesonephric duct** (ureter) which may be found attached to the lateral margin of the kidney. Within the excretory system the spermatozoa are immotile, due to the slightly acid environment. They are carried passively down the ureter to the slight dilation near the cloaca, known as the **seminal vesicle.** Within the vesicle the spermatozoa are stored briefly in clusters until amplexus and oviposition occur. At oviposition the male ejaculates the spermatozoa into the neutral or slightly alkaline water where they are activated and then are able to fertilize the eggs as they emerge from the cloaca of the female.

During the normal breeding season amplexus is achieved as the females reach the ponds where the males are emitting their sex calls. During amplexus there are definite muscular ejaculatory movements on the part of the male frog, coinciding with oviposition on the part of the female. Amplexus may be maintained by the male for many days, even with dead females. As soon as the eggs are laid and the male has shed his sperm, he goes through a brief weaving motion of the body and then releases his grip to swim away. The frogs completely neglect the newly laid eggs.

Accessory Structures

In the male frog the ureter is not directly connected with the **bladder,** as it is in higher vertebrates. It is possible that the bladder in the Anura may be an accessory respiratory and hydrating organ, particularly in the toads, where water may be stored during migrations onto land.

The male frog also has a duct, homologous to the oviduct of the female, known as the "rudimentary oviduct" or **Müllerian duct.** This duct normally has no lumen, and is very much reduced in size so that it may be difficult to locate. There is experimental evidence that this duct may be truly a vestigial oviduct since it responds to ovarian or female sex hormones by enlarging and acquiring a lumen.

At the anterior end of the testes of some Anura (e.g., toads) there may be found an undeveloped ovary known as **Bidder's organ.** This structure is said to respond to the removal of the adjacent testis or to the injection of female sex hormones by enlarging to become structurally like an ovary. Occasionally isolated ova have been found within the seminiferous tubules of an otherwise normal testis, suggesting the similar origin and the fundamental similarity of the testis and the ovary.

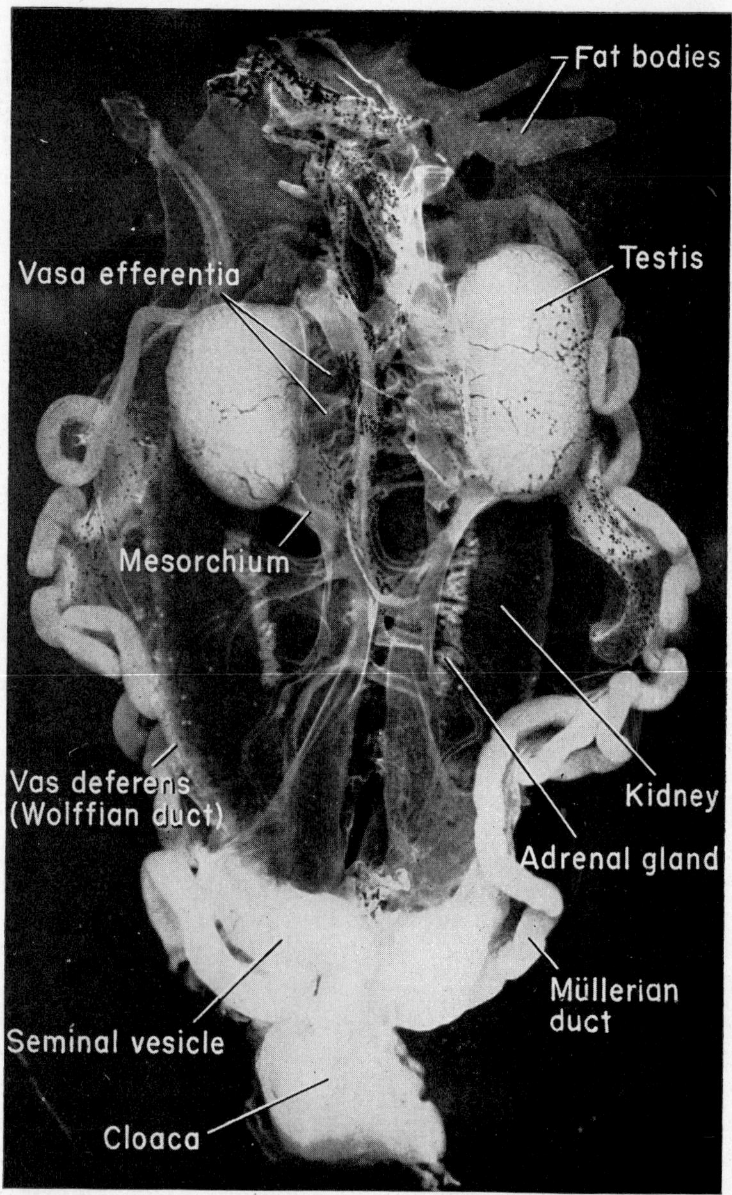

Urogenital system of the male frog. The Müllerian ducts (vestigial oviducts) are seen lateral to the kidneys. They respond to female sex-stimulating hormones. They converge with the Wolffian (mesonephric) duct at the cloaca. Note that the left testis is usually smaller than the right. The vasa efferentia pass between the folds of the mesorchium into the dorsally placed kidneys where they join the uriniferous tubules at the glomeruli.

Finally, attached to the anterior end of the testis of the hibernating frog may be seen finger-like **fat bodies** (corpora adiposa) which represent stored nutrition for the long period of hibernation, and for the pre-breeding season when food is scarce. Under the microscope these fat bodies appear as clusters of vacuolated cells, and are not to be confused with the mesorchium. It is believed that they, as well as the gonads, arise from the genital ridges of the early embryo. The fat bodies tend to be reduced immediately after the breeding season, only to be built up again as the time for hibernation approaches.

The Female

Secondary Sexual Characters

The mature female frog is generally larger than the male of the same age and species, the *Rana pipiens* female measuring from 60 to 110 mm. in length from snout to anus. The sexually mature female has a body length of at least 70 mm. It can be identified by the absence, at any season, of the dark thumb pad; the inability to produce lateral cheek pouches resulting from the croaking reaction; a flabby and distended abdomen; and the presence of peritoneal cilia. These cilia are developed in the female in response to the prior development and secretion of ovarian hormones.

Primary Sexual Characters

The Ovaries.

The **ovaries** of the frog are paired, multi-lobed organs, attached to the dorsal body wall by a double-layered extension of the peritoneum known as the **mesovarium.** This peritoneum continues around the entire ovary as the **theca externa.** Each lobe of the ovary is hollow and its cavity is continuous with the other 7 to 12 lobes. The ovaries of the female are found in the same relative position as the testes of the male but the peritoneum extends from the dorso-mesial wall rather than from the kidneys, as in the male.

The size of the ovary varies with the seasons more than does the size of the testis. From late summer until the spring breeding season the paired ovaries will fill the body cavity and will often distend the body wall. They may contain from 2,000 (*Rana pipiens*) to as many as 20,000 eggs (*Rana catesbiana*), each measuring about 1.75 mm. in diameter (*Rana pipiens*). The mature eggs are highly pigmented on the surface of the animal pole, so that the ovary has a speckled appearance of black pigment and white yolk, representing the animal and the vegetal hemispheres of the eggs.

There is no appreciable change in the size of the ovary during hibernation, nor is there any observable cytological change in the ova. However, if a female is forced to retain her eggs beyond the normal breeding period by isolating her from males or by keeping her in a warm environment and without food, the ova will begin to deteriorate (cytolize) within the ovary. Immediately after the spring breeding season, when the female discharges thousands of **mature ova,** the remaining ovary with its **oögonia** (to be developed for the following year) is so small that it is sometimes difficult to locate. There is no pigment in the tissue of the ovary (in the stroma or in the immature ova), and each growing oöcyte appears as a small white sphere of protoplasm contained within its individual **follicle sac.**

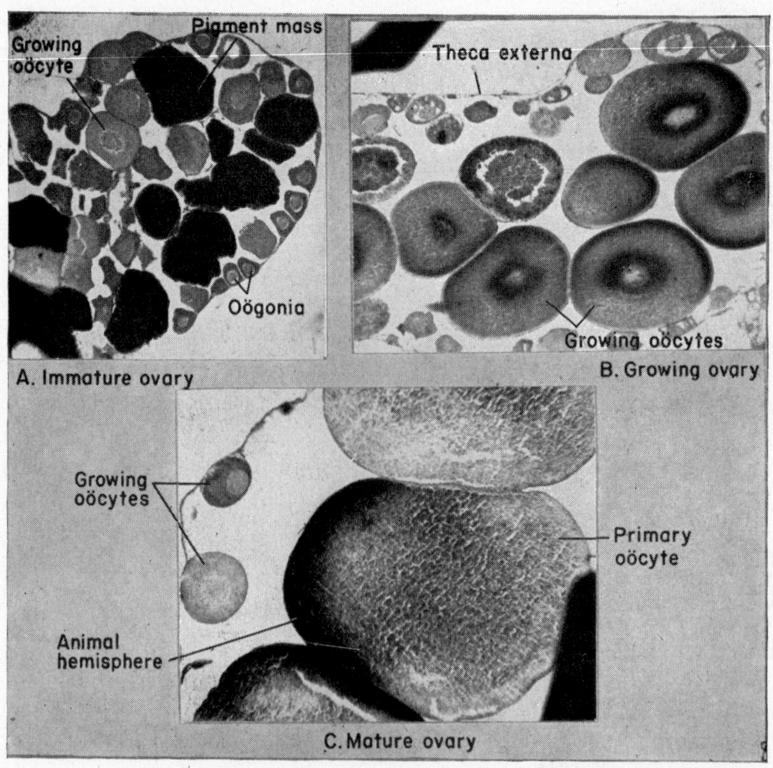

Late development of the frog ovary.

The histology of the ovary shows that within its outer peritoneal covering, the **theca externa,** are suspended thousands of individual sacs, each made up of another membrane, the **theca interna** or cyst wall, which contains smooth muscle fibers. This theca interna is derived from the retro-peritoneal tissue. The smooth muscle fibers can be seen histologically and can be demonstrated physiologically. The theca interna surrounds each egg except for the limited area bulging toward the body cavity, where it is covered by only the theca externa. This is the region which will be ruptured during ovulation to allow the egg to escape its follicle into the **body cavity.** The theca interna, plus the limited covering of the theca externa, and the follicle cells together comprise the **ovarian follicle.** These two membranes make up the rather limited **ovarian stroma** of the frog ovary, and they contain both blood vessels and nerves. Within each follicle are found **follicle cells,** with their oval and granular nuclei, derived originally from oögonia. These follicle cells surround the developing oöcyte and are found in close association with it throughout those processes of maturation which occur within the follicle. Enclosed within the follicle cells, and closely applied to each mature egg, is the non-cellular and transparent **vitelline membrane,** probably derived from both the ovum and the follicle cells. This membrane is developed and applied to the egg during the maturation process so that it is not seen around the earlier or younger oögonia. Since the bulk of the egg is yolk (vitellus), this membrane is appropriately called the vitelline membrane. It is sometimes designated as the primary (of several) egg membranes. After the egg is fertilized this membrane becomes separated from the egg and the space between is then known as the **perivitelline space,** filled with a fluid. The fluid may be derived from the egg which would show compensatory shrinkage. As the oöcyte matures and enlarges, the follicle cells and membranes are so stretched and flattened that they are not easily distinguished. It is therefore best to study these structures in the immature ovary.

The egg will mature in any of a variety of positions within its follicle, the exact position probably depending upon the maximum blood supply. As one examines an ovary the eggs will be seen in all possible positions, some with the **animal hemisphere** and others with the **vegetal hemisphere** toward the theca externa and body cavity. It is believed that the most vascular side of the follicle wall will tend

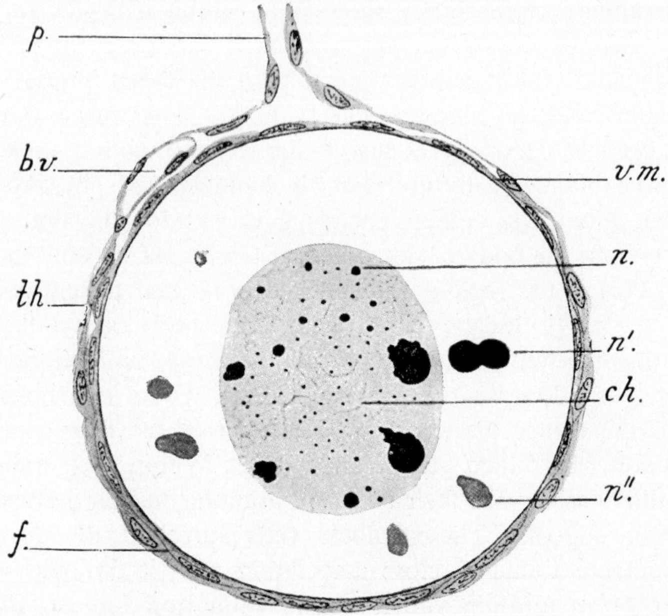

Small ovarian egg of the frog surrounded by its follicle (*f.*) and theca (*th.*), which is continued into the pedicle (*p.*). (*b.v.*) A blood vessel between follicle and theca. (*v.m.*) Vitelline membrane. (*ch.*) Chromatin filaments, now achromatic. (*n.*) Chromatic nucleoli, ejected from the nucleus (*n′.*) and becoming achromatic (*n″.*). (Courtesy, Jenkinson: "Vertebrate Embryology," Oxford, The Clarendon Press.)

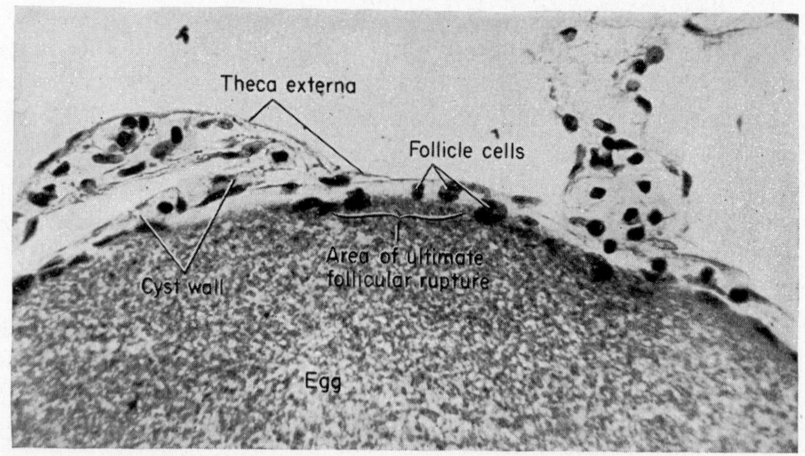

Section of a mature ovarian egg to show the area of ultimate follicular rupture and the surrounding membranes of the egg.

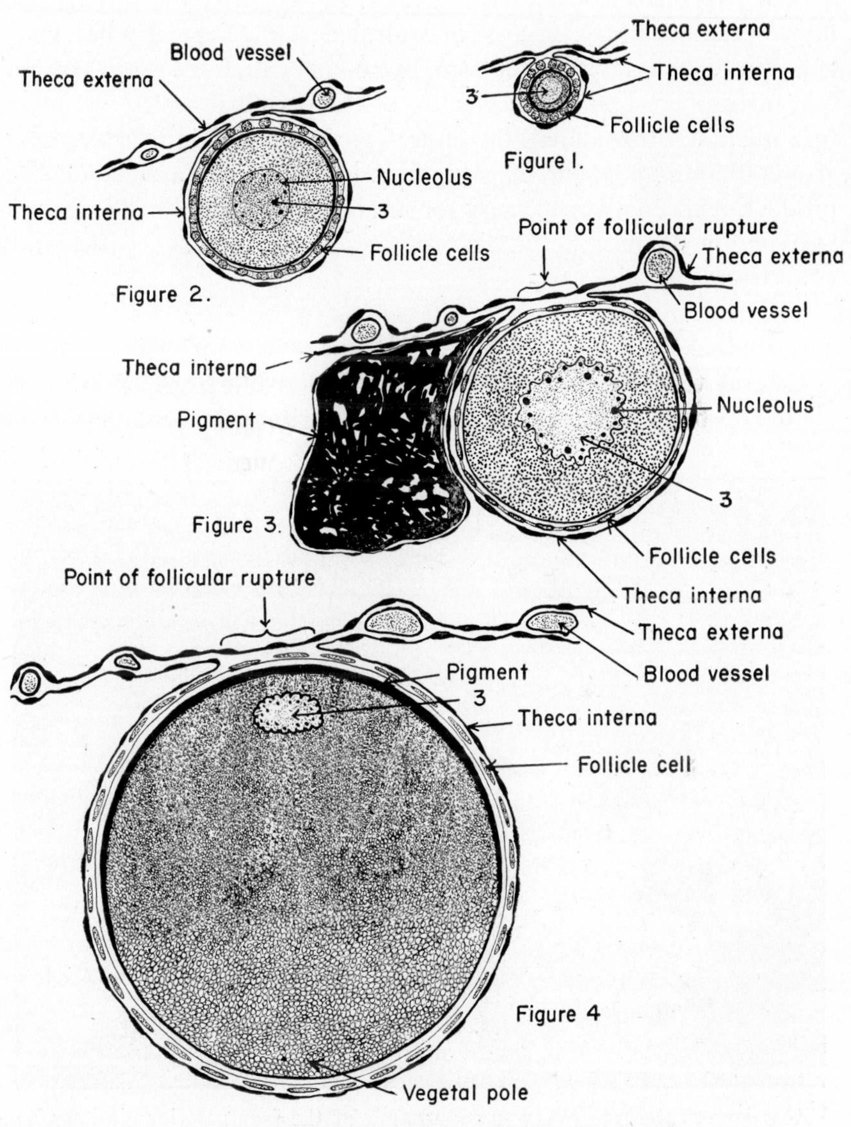
Theca externa
Theca interna
3
Follicle cells
Figure I.
Blood vessel
Theca externa
Nucleolus
Theca interna
3
Follicle cells
Figure 2.
Point of follicular rupture
Theca externa
Blood vessel
Theca interna
Pigment
Nucleolus
3
Figure 3.
Follicle cells
Theca interna
Point of follicular rupture
Theca externa
Blood vessel
Pigment
3
Theca interna
Follicle cell
Figure 4
Vegetal pole

GROWING OÖCYTES OF THE FROG

to produce the animal hemisphere of the egg, and hence give it its fundamental symmetry and polarity.

The frog's egg is essentially a large sac of yolk, the heavier and larger granules of which are concentrated at the **vegetal pole.** There is a thin outer layer of **cytoplasm,** more concentrated toward the animal hemisphere and in the vicinity of the **germinal vesicle** or immature nucleus. Surrounding the entire egg is a non-living surface coat, also containing **pigment.** This pigment is presumably a metabolic by-product. This coat is necessary for retaining the shape of the egg and in aiding in the morphogenetic processes of cleavage and gastrulation (Holtfreter).

The Body Cavity and the Oviducts.

Lateral to each ovary is a much-coiled **oviduct** suspended from the dorsal body wall by a double fold of **peritoneum.** Its anterior end

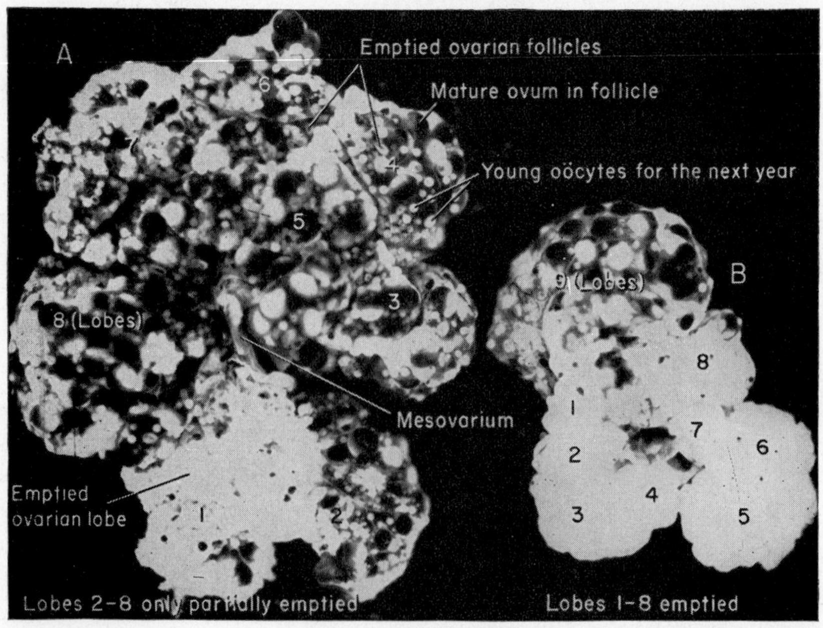

Reactions of the frog ovary to stimulation by the frog anterior pituitary hormone. (A) Ovary of a female receiving inadequate injection of the pituitary hormone, partially emptying the eggs into the body cavity. (B) Ovary of a female receiving almost enough pituitary hormone to empty all of its follicles, one lobe alone retaining some of its eggs. During the breeding season the female's own pituitary gland is sufficient to bring about complete ovulation of all eggs.

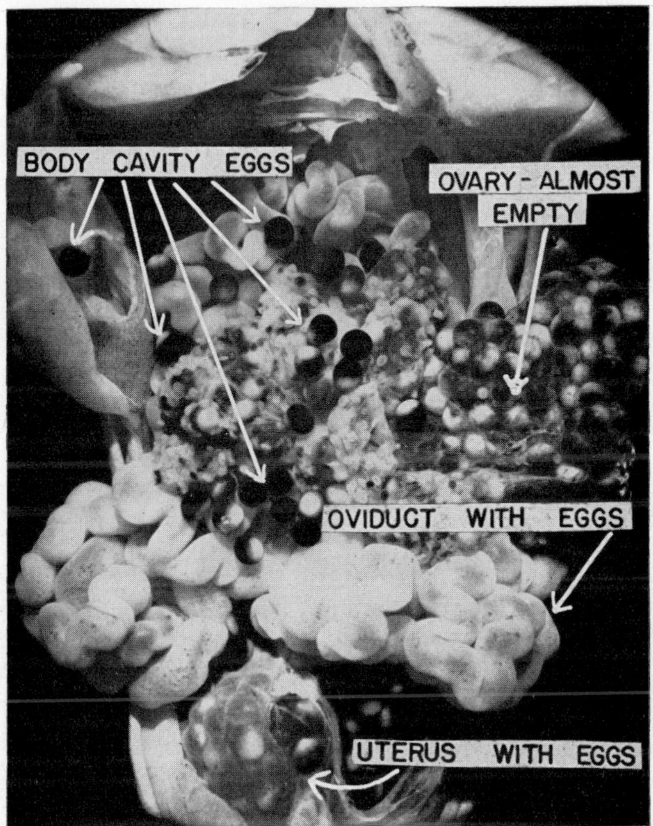

Photograph of *Rana pipiens* female body cavity at the height of ovulation.

is found between the heart and the lateral peritoneum, at the apex of the liver lobe. At this anterior end is a slit-like infundibulum or **ostium tuba** with ciliated and highly elastic walls. The body cavity of the female is almost entirely lined with cilia, each cilium having its effective beat or stroke in the general direction of one of the ostia. These cilia are produced in response to an ovarian hormone and therefore are regarded as secondary sex characters. They are found on the peritoneum covering the entire body cavity, on the liver, and on the pericardial membrane. There are no cilia on the lungs, the intestines, or the surface of the kidneys except in the ciliated peristomial (peritoneal) funnels which lead into the blood sinuses of the kidneys. The abundant supply of cilia of the female means that eggs ovulated from any surface of the ovary will be carried by constant ciliary currents anteriorly toward and into one or another of the ostia. This can be demonstrated easily by opening the body cavity of an actively ovulating frog or by excising a strip of ventral abdominal wall of the adult female, inverting it in amphibian Ringer's solution, and placing on it some of the body cavity eggs. Any object of

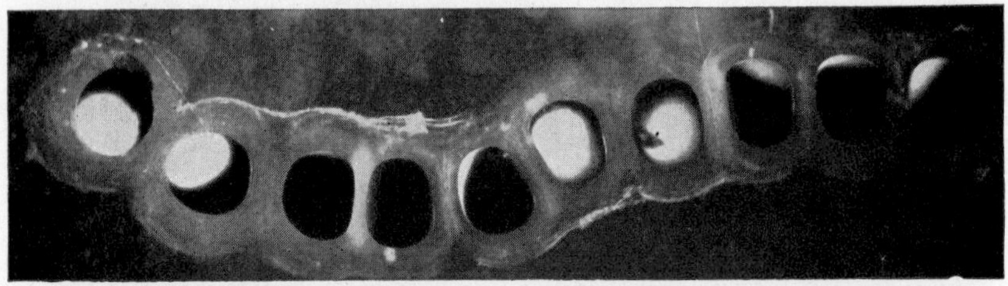

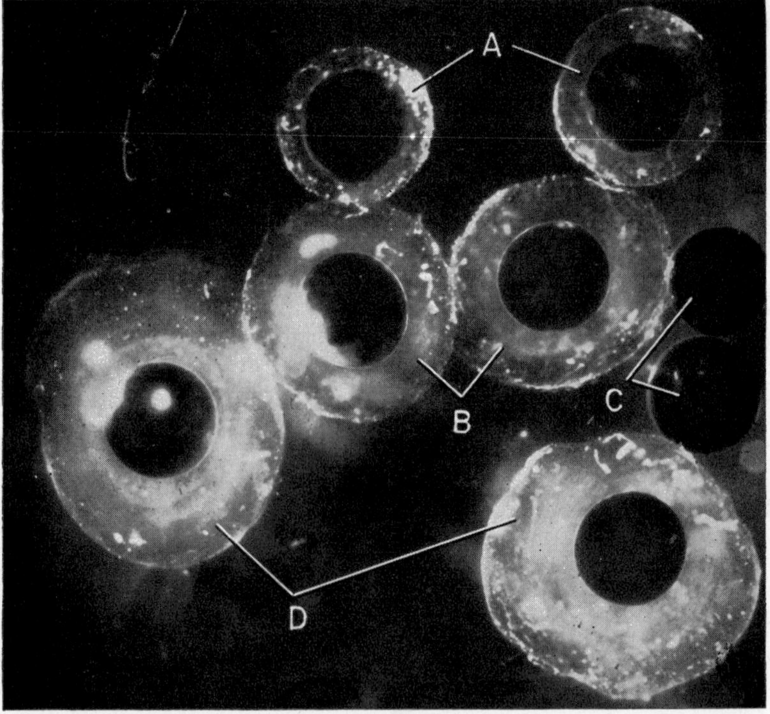

Deposition of jelly on the frog's egg. (*Top*) String of eggs removed from the oviduct to show the deposition of jelly. The jelly is swollen in water. (*Bottom*) Frog's eggs showing varying amounts of jelly, indicating progressive deposition along the oviduct. (A) From upper third of oviduct. (B) From middle of oviduct. (C) From body cavity (no jelly). (D) From uterus.

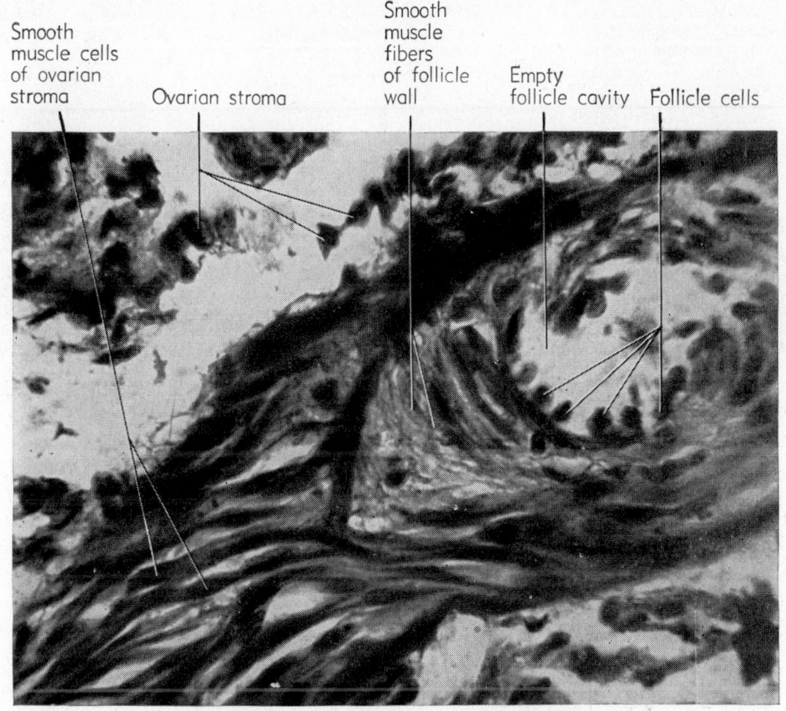

Recently emptied ovarian follicle of the frog.

similar size or weight, such as pellets of paraffin, will be carried along by the ciliary currents in the original direction of the ostium. These cilia function the year around, and will carry to the ostia any objects of approximately the size and weight of frog eggs that may be placed in the body cavity. One might suggest, therefore, that the oviducts may act as accessory excretory ducts, for certainly body cavity fluids must be similarly eliminated.

As the egg leaves the ovary it is nude except for the non-living, transparent, and closely applied **vitelline membrane.** Thus far it has been impossible to fertilize these body cavity eggs and have them develop. When they are placed in a sperm suspension some will show surface markings which resemble very closely the normal cleavage spindles and the cleavage furrows but none have developed as embryos as yet. These body cavity eggs are often quite distorted, due to the fact that the ovulation process involves a rupture of the follicle and forcing out of the egg from a very muscular follicle. The egg is

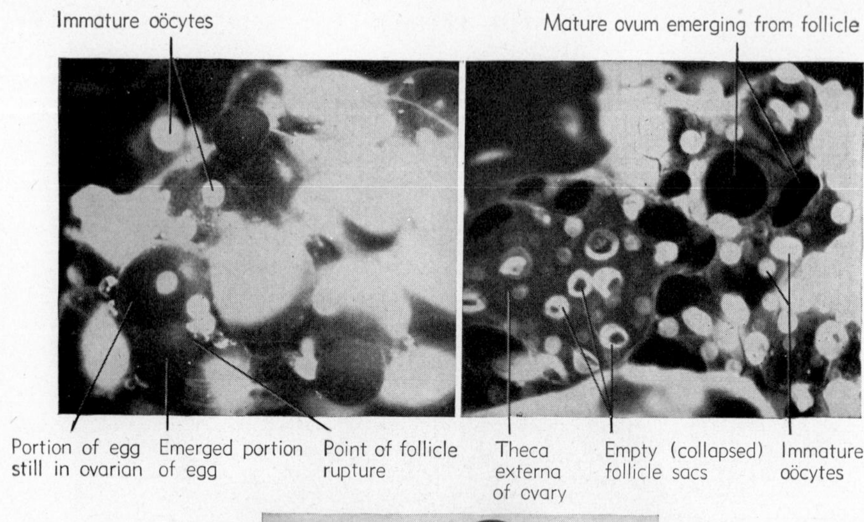

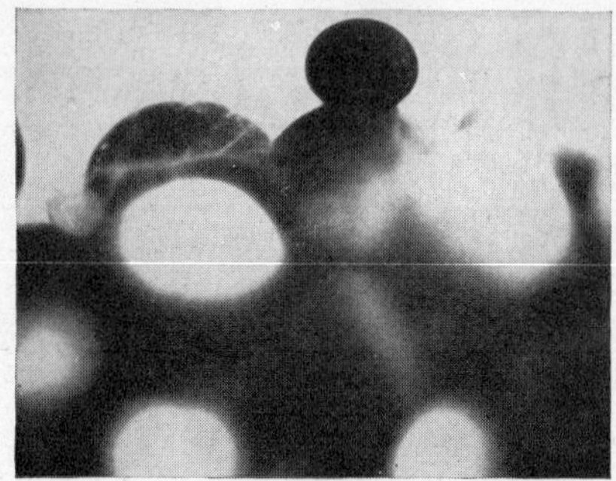

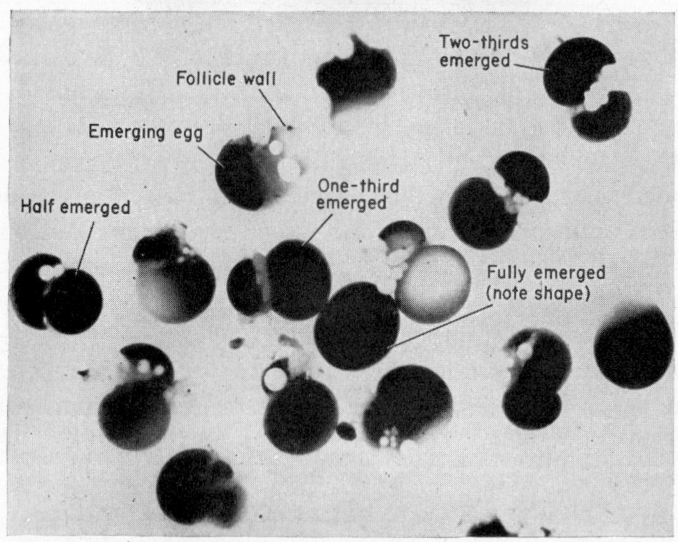

Follicular rupture and ovulation in the frog. (*Top, left*) Three eggs emerging simultaneously from their follicles. (*Top, right*) Eggs in various stages of emer-

(*Continued on facing page.*)

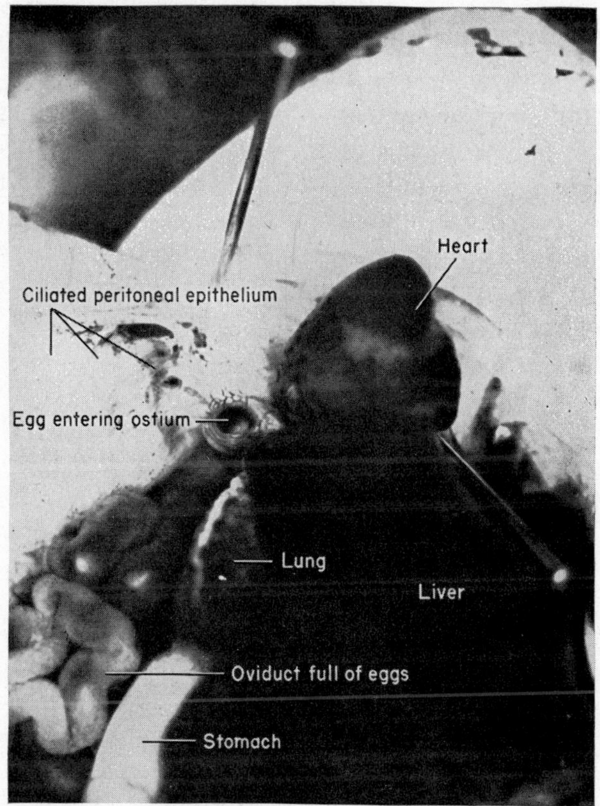

Photograph of the open body cavity of an actively ovulating female frog showing the entrance of an egg into the ostium.

literally squeezed from the follicle, through a small aperture. The process looks like an Amoeba crawling through an inadequate hole. **Ovulation** (rupture and emergence of the egg) takes several minutes at laboratory temperatures, and is not accompanied by hemorrhage. By the time the egg reaches the ostium (within 2 hours), as the result of ciliary propulsion, it is again spherical.

Ciliary currents alone force the egg into the ostium and oviduct. The ostial opening is very elastic and does not respond to the respira-

---

(*Continued from opposite page.*)

gence and adjacent empty follicles. (*Center*) Egg about to drop free into the body cavity, showing degree of constriction by the follicular opening. (*Bottom*) Excised follicles of an ovulating frog continuing the process of emergence of eggs. Note the plasticity of the egg at this time.

tory or heart activity, as some have described. The eggs are simply forced into the ostium, from all angles, stretching its mouth open to accept the egg. As soon as the egg enters the oviduct and begins to acquire an albuminous (mucin-jelly) covering, it becomes fertilizable. One can remove such an egg from the oviduct by pipette or by cutting the oviduct 1 inch or more from the ostium, and can fertilize such an egg in a normal sperm suspension. The physical (or chemical) changes which occur between the time the egg is in the body cavity and the time it is removed from the oviduct, which make it fertilizable, are not yet understood.

As the egg is propelled through the oviduct by ciliary currents, it receives coatings of **albumen** (jelly). The initial coat is thin but of heavy consistency, and is applied closely to the egg. The egg is spiraled down the oviduct by its ciliated lining so that the application of the jelly covering is quite uniform. There are, in all, three distinct layers of jelly, the outermost one being much the greater in thickness but the less viscous. The intermediate layer is of a thin and more fluid consistency. There is hyperactivity of the glandular elements of the oviduct just before the normal breeding season, or after anterior pituitary hormone stimulation, so that the duct is enlarged several times over that of the oviduct of the hibernating female.

The presence of the jelly layers on the oviducal or the uterine egg

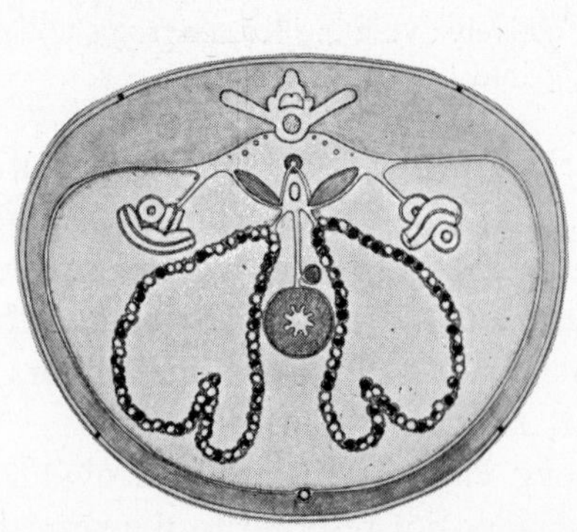

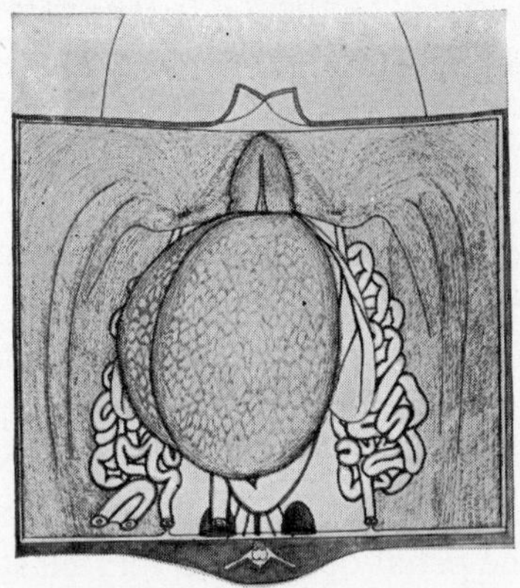

Distribution of coelomic cilia within the body cavity of the female frog. (*Left*) Schematic section through the level of the ovaries. (*Right*) Schematic drawing of the open body cavity. The cilia in the body cavity of the female develop in response to the elaboration of an ovarian hormone, and function in propelling the eggs to the two ostia.

is not readily apparent because it requires water before it reaches its maximum thickness. Eggs sectioned within the oviduct show the jelly as a transparent coating just outside the vitelline membrane. As soon as the egg reaches the water, however, imbibition swells the jelly until its thickness becomes greater than the diameter of the egg.

The function of the jelly is to protect the egg against injury, against ingestion by larger organisms, and from fungus and other infections. Equally important, however, is the evidence that this jelly helps the egg to retain its metabolically derived heat so that the jelly can be said to act as an insulator against heat loss. Bernard and Batuschek (1891) showed that the greater the wave length of light the less heat passed through the jelly around the frog's egg, in comparison with an equivalent amount of water and under similar conditions.

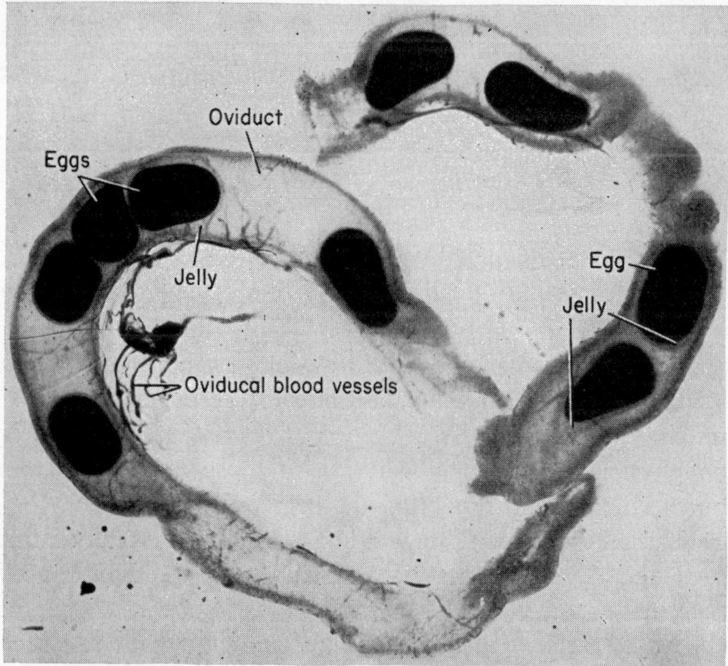

Passage of eggs through the oviduct. The eggs of the frog are greatly distorted as they pass down the oviduct toward the uterus. They accumulate albumen around them, but, since they spiral down the duct, the albumen jelly is evenly deposited and the eggs become spherical as the jelly swells when the eggs pass from the uterus into the water.

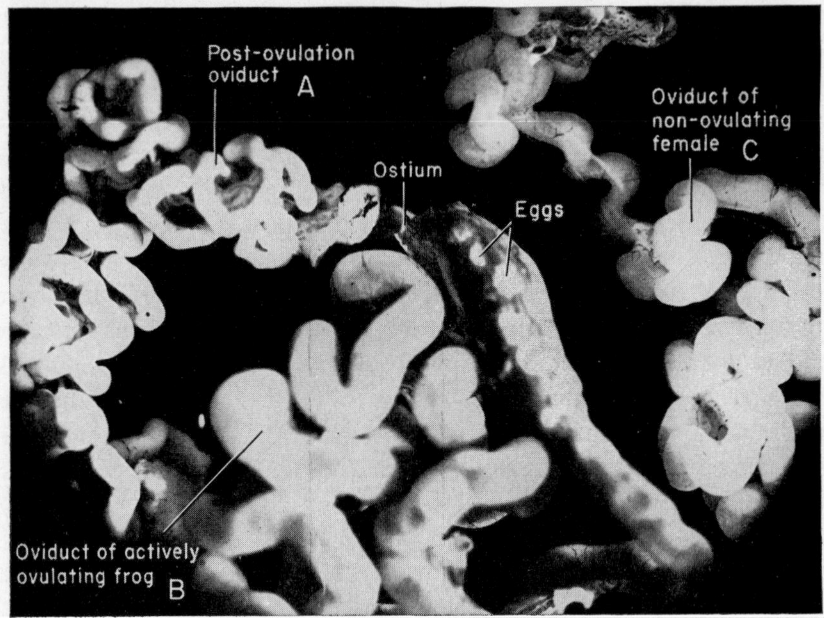

Oviducts of the frog under various states of sexual activity. (A) Post-ovulation condition, collapsed and dehydrated. (B) Actively ovulating condition, oviduct full of eggs, edematous. (C) Oviduct of non-ovulating, hibernating female.

Originally, and erroneously, the jelly was thought to act as a lens which would concentrate the heat rays of the sun onto the egg, but since the jelly is largely water, which is a non-conductor of heat rays, this theory is untenable. One can demonstrate that the temperature of the egg is higher than the temperature of the immediate environment, even in a totally darkened environment. So, the jelly has certain physical functions in addition to those as yet undetermined functions which aid in rendering the egg fertilizable.

The egg takes about 2 to 4 hours, at ordinary temperatures, to reach the highly elastic **uterus,** at the posterior end of the oviduct and adjacent to the **cloaca.** Each uterus has a separate opening into the **cloaca,** and the ovulated eggs are retained within this sac until, during amplexus (sexual embrace by the male), they are expelled into the water and are fertilized by the male. Generally the eggs are not retained within the uterus for more than a day or so. There may be quite a few hours between the time of appearance of the first and the last eggs in the uteri.

Oögenesis—Maturation of the Egg.

The **maturation** process can best be described as it begins, immediately after the normal breeding season in the spring. At this time the ovary has been freed of its several thousand mature eggs and contains only **oögonia** with no pigment and little, if any, yolk. Even at this early stage each cluster of oögonia represents a future ovarian unit, consisting of many **follicle cells** and one **ovum.** There has been no way to determine which oögonium is to be selected for maturation into an ovum and which will give rise to the numerous follicle cells that act as nurse cells for the growing ovum. It is clear, however, that both follicle cells and the ovum come from original oögonia. All ova develop from oögonia which divide repeatedly. These pre-maturation germ cells divide by mitosis many times and then come to rest, during which process there is growth of some of them without nuclear division. These become ova while those that fail to grow become follicle cells. However, there are pre-prophase changes of the nucleus of the prospective ovum comparable to the pre-prophase changes in spermatogenesis. The majority of oögonia, therefore, never mature into ova, but become follicle cells.

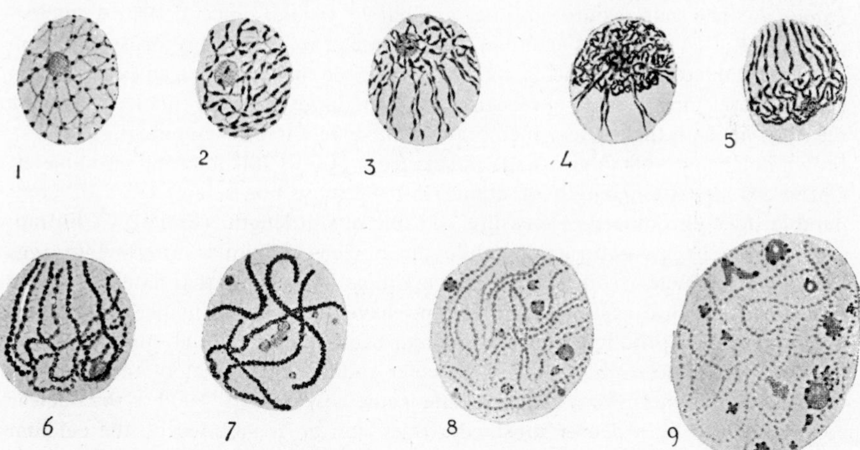

Prophases of the heterotypic division in the female (ovary of tadpole). (1) Nucleus of oögonium. (2) Leptotene. (3) Synaptene. (4, 5) Contraction figures. (6) Pachytene. (7) Later pachytene, multiplication of nucleoli. (8, 9) Diplotene: the chromatin filaments are becoming achromatic; granules of chromatin are being deposited on the nucleoli. (Courtesy, Jenkinson: "Vertebrate Embryology," Oxford, The Clarendon Press.)

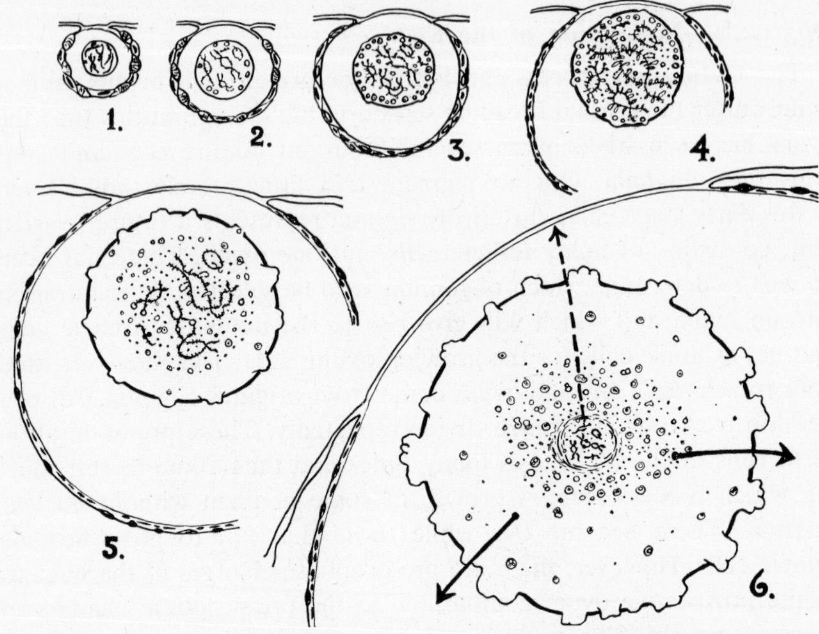

Normal nuclear growth cycle of the ovum of *Rana pipiens*. (*Stage 1*) Smallest follicle in which the chromosomes within the germinal vesicle can be seen. (*Stage 2*) The paired chromosomes are barely visible, embedded in a nucleoplasmic gel. Egg diameters less than 200 microns. (*Stage 3*) Eggs measuring from 200 to 500 microns in diameter, more detail visible through the transparent theca cells. Lateral loop production begins. Zone of large irregular nucleoli may be seen just beneath the nuclear membrane. (*Stage 4*) First development of yellow-brown color and yolk. Eggs range in size from 500 to 700 microns in diameter. Chromosomes attain length of about 450 microns. For salamanders of comparable stage chromosomes measure 700 microns in length. (*Stage 5*) Chromosome frame begins contraction while the nucleus continues to grow in eggs ranging in diameter from 750 to 850 microns. This is approximately half the ultimate size. Chromosomes shorten and have fewer and smaller loops. The major nucleolar production continues and sacs appear on the surface of the nuclear membrane. (*Stage 6*) Egg diameter about 1.8 millimeters and germinal vesicle is of maximum size. Chromosome frame now about 1/1000 of the nuclear volume, coated by a denser substance which can be coagulated by the calcium ion. Chromosomes have shortened to 40 microns or less and have lost all large and small hyaline bodies called loop fragments.

Heavy arrows indicate the mixing of nuclear material in the cytoplasm after the breakdown of the germinal vesicle. The *dotted arrow* indicates migration of the central chromosomal mass toward the animal pole to become the maturation spindle for the first polar body. (From W. R. Duryee, **1950,** *Ann. N. Y. Acad. Sci.,* **50,** Art. 8.)

The process of maturation involves contributions from the nucleus and the cytoplasm. **First,** chromatin nucleoli aid in the synthesis of yolk, and **second,** the breakdown of the germinal vesicle allows an intermingling of the nuclear and the cytoplasmic components. Only a small portion of the germinal vesicle is involved in the maturation

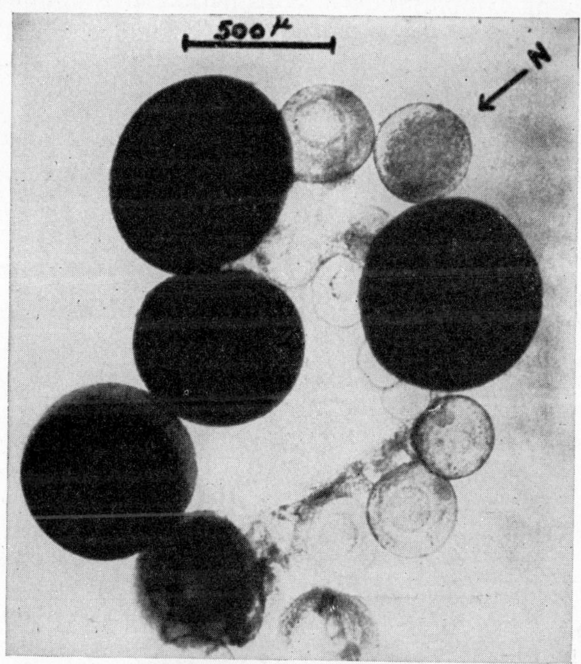

Ovarial wall of *Rana temporaria.* Note young transparent eggs (*stages 1 and 2*) and larger opaque eggs (*stage 3*). The arrow points to an isolated nucleus from another egg (*stage 3*), which has floated into the field. (Courtesy, W. R. Duryee, **1950,** *Ann. N. Y. Acad. Sci.,* **50,** Art. 8.)

spindle so that it may be at this time that the nucleus exerts its initial influence on the cytoplasm. All cytoplasmic differentiations must be initiated at a time when the hereditary influences of the nucleus are so intermingled with it.

Growth Period to Primary Oöcyte Stage. Growth is achieved largely by the accumulation of **yolk.** As soon as growth begins the cell no longer divides by mitosis and is known as an *oöcyte* rather than an oögonium. The growth process is aided by the **centrosome,** which is found to one side of the **nucleus,** and around which gather the granules or **yolk platelets.** The **chromatin** filaments become achromatic and the **nucleoli** increase in number, by fragmentation, and become more chromatic. Many of the nucleoli, which are concentrations of nucleo-protein, pass through the nuclear membrane into the surrounding cytoplasm during this period. It is not clear whether this occurs through further fragmentation of the nucleoli into particles of microscopic or sub-microscopic size, and then their ejection through the nuclear membrane. It may occur by the loss of identity (and chromatic properties) by possible chemical change and subsequent diffusion of the liquid form through the membrane to be

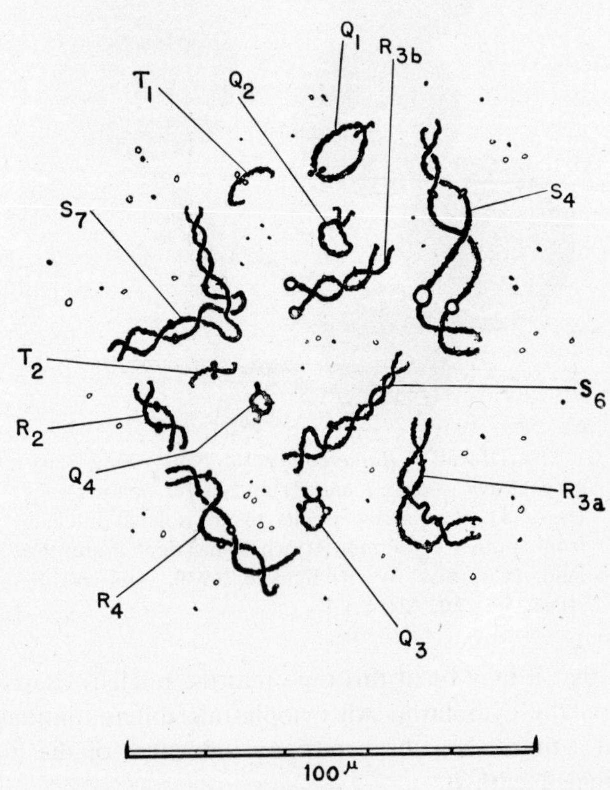

The entire set of chromosomes of *Rana temporaria.* The 13 pairs of chromosomes in this species are remarkably like those of other species of *Rana.* They are seen in stage 6. (Q) Four ring-shaped pairs. (R) Four medium-sized pairs. (S) Three longest (super) pairs. (T) Two short T-shaped pairs. (Courtesy, W. R. Duryee, **1950,** *Ann. N. Y. Acad. Sci.,* **50,** Art. 8.)

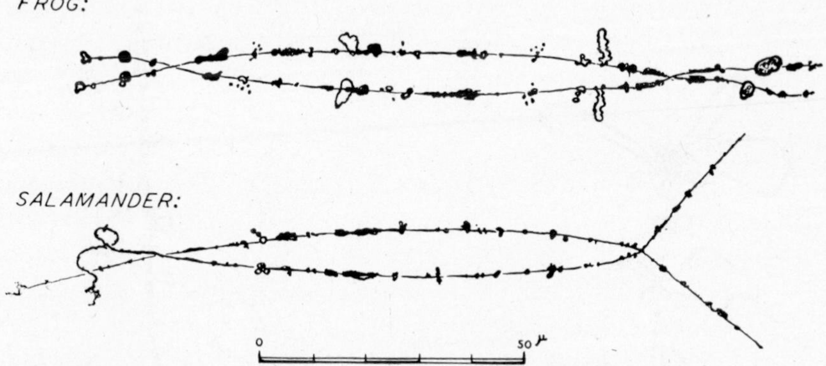

Similarity of frog and of salamander chromosome structure. Stage 4 chromosomes. There is apparently a single chromonema along which compound granules and chromomeres of varying shapes and sizes are firmly embedded or attached. These chromosomes were treated with O.2 M $NaHCO_3$ to remove the lateral loops and reveal the chromonemata. Chromosome granules are attached to the paired chromonemata at homologous loci. Some matric coating is present. Mild acidification following carbonate treatment has removed most of the lateral loops. (Courtesy, W. R. Duryee, **1950,** *Ann. N. Y. Acad. Sci.,* **50,** Art. 8.)

resynthesized on the cytoplasmic side of the membrane. During the growth of the oöcyte, further nucleoli appear within the nucleus, only to fragment and later to pass out into the cytoplasm. The presence of chromatic nucleoli in the cytoplasm is closely associated with the accumulation (deposition) of yolk.

The granules within the cytoplasm (extruded fragments of nucleoli) function as centers of yolk accumulation and have therefore been named **"yolk nuclei."** This is an unfortunate name, for the structure is a nucleus only in the sense that it is a center of aggregation. It is not a true cell nucleus. The centrosome and other granular centers lose their identity and the yolk granules then become scattered throughout the cytoplasm.

The source of all yolk for the growing ova is originally the digested food of the female. This nutrition is carried to the ovary by way of the blood system and conveyed to the nurse or follicle cells and thence to the oöcyte. The yolk is at first aggregated around yolk nuclei, then concentrated to one side of the nucleus. Finally it assumes a ring shape around the nucleus between an inner and an outer zone of cytoplasm. Subsequently the nucleus is pushed to one side by the ever-increasing mass of yolk so that eventually there is an axial

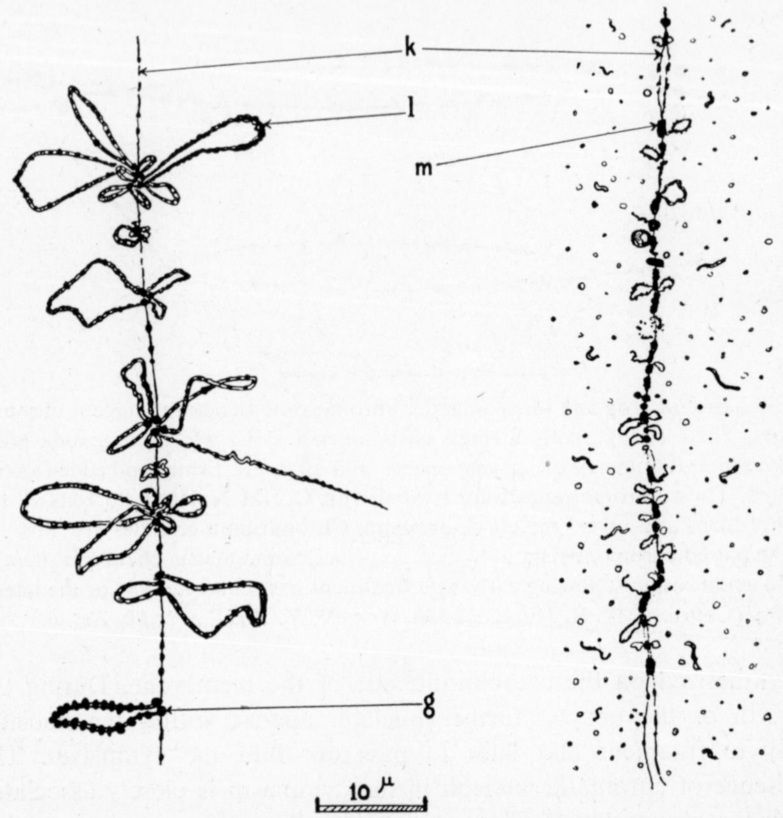

Lateral loops of the amphibian chromosome. The lateral loops originate from chromosomal granules and the lateral branches are not homogeneous in structure, but are made up of smaller particles embedded in a hyaline cylinder. These lateral loops occur in separable clusters of 1 to 9 loops along a single chromonema. These loops reach their greatest development at stage 4, when the chromosome frame is most expanded. They average 9.5 microns in length but may reach 24 microns. They are not resorbed back into the chromosome and the number of loops per chromosome decreases with time, although the number of chromomeres per chromosome remains constant. (Courtesy, W. R. Duryee, **1950,** *Ann. N. Y. Acad. Sci.,* **50,** Art. 8.)

gradient of concentration of oval **yolk platelets** from one side of the egg to the other. The smaller platelets are found in the vicinity of the nucleus, in the animal hemisphere. The larger platelets are located toward the vegetal hemisphere. There is an increase averaging from 200 to 700 per cent in the total lipoid substance, neutral fat, total fatty acids, total cholesterol, ester cholesterol, free cholesterol,

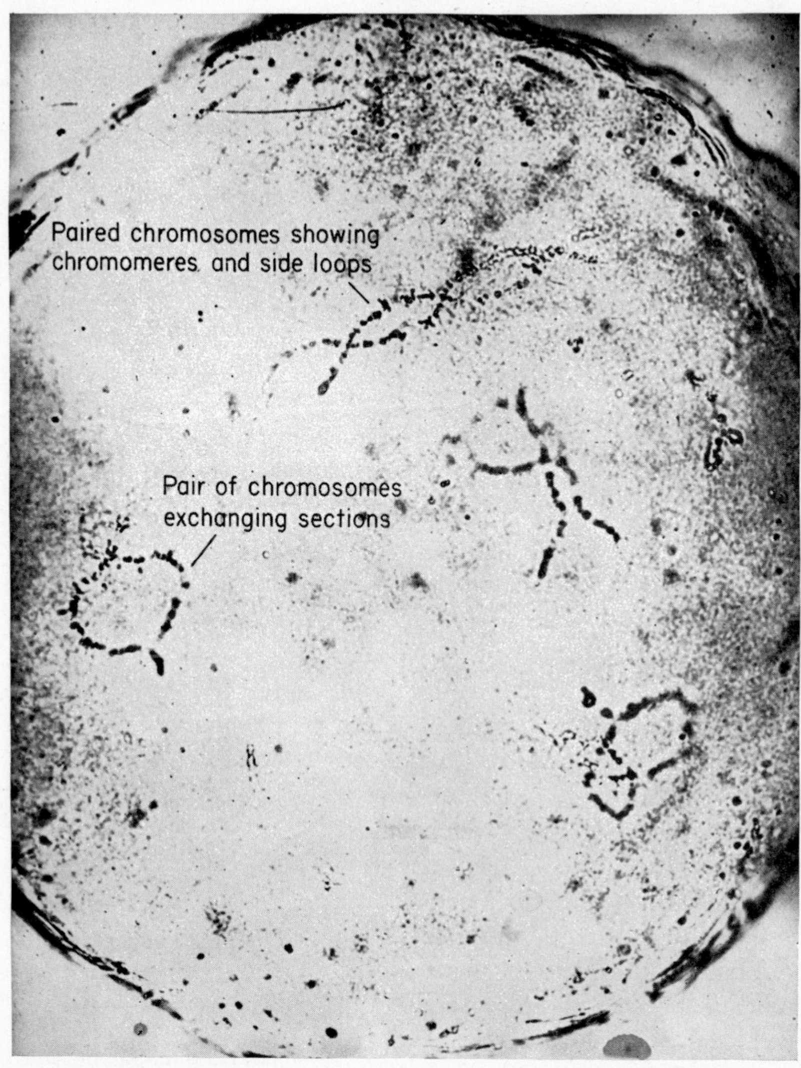

Chromosomes in the amphibian nucleus. Stage 5 of the growing oöcyte showing the isolated nucleus and its paired chromosomes with chromomeres and side loops. (Courtesy, W. R. Duryee, Laboratory of Terrestrial Magnetism, Washington, D. C.)

and phospholipin content of the ovaries of *Rana pipiens* occurring during the production and growth of ova (Boyd, 1938). The primary oöcyte may show a slight flattening of the surface directly above the region of the nucleus.

These growth changes and the unequal distribution of pigment, yolk, and cytoplasm are the first indications of **polarity** or a gradient system within the egg. When the polarity is well established, the cytoplasm, the superficial **melanin** or black pigment, and the nucleus are all at the animal hemisphere (pole). The light colored yolk is more concentrated toward the vegetal pole. The egg is then regarded as a **telolecithal egg.** During this phase of egg maturation there is a drain on the metabolism of the frog which requires an excess of food intake because the materials for egg growth must be synthesized from nutritional elements received from the vascular system of the female. For *Rana pipiens* this period of most active feeding comes during the summer when the natural foods, insects, worms, etc., are the most abundant.

During the growth of the oöcyte in general there are important changes occurring within the nucleus (germinal vesicle) of the egg. Thirteen pairs of **chromosomes** may be seen in synizesis (contraction), converging toward the centrosome at the "yolk nucleus" stage. A little later the nuclear membrane develops sac-like bulges, the **nucleoli** are scattered, and there is a colloidal chromosome core which almost fills the entire nucleus. The chromosomes themselves are small and almost invisible. When the **primary oöcyte** is about half its ultimate size, there appear definite sacs on the nuclear surface. The fragmented nucleoli are located at the periphery of the lobulated nuclear membrane, and the chromosome frames have become relatively large. The chromosomes, by this time, have reached their maximum length and possess large lateral loops. Finally, in the fully grown nucleus of the primary oöcyte the nuclear sacs are very prominent, and the nucleoli appear in clusters in the center of the

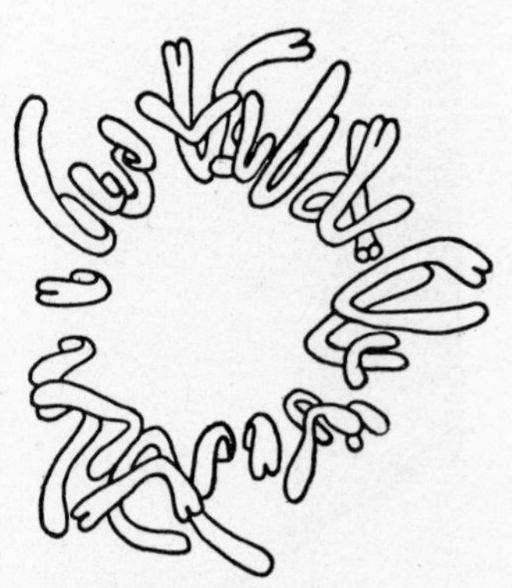

Diploid metaphase chromosomes from the tail fin of a 15-day-old *Rana pipiens* tadpole. (Courtesy, K. R. Porter, **1939,** *Biol. Bull.,* **77:**233.)

egg, surrounding the **chromosome frame.** This frame is a gel structure which gives rise to the **first maturation spindle,** containing 13 pairs of slightly contracted chromosomes.

These structural features can be observed in the living germinal vesicle if it is removed from the oöcyte and placed in isotonic and balanced salt medium, omitting the calcium ion. A minute amount of NaH_2PO_4 is added to shift the pH toward the acid side, which makes the chromosomes the more visible. Or, the chromosomes may be

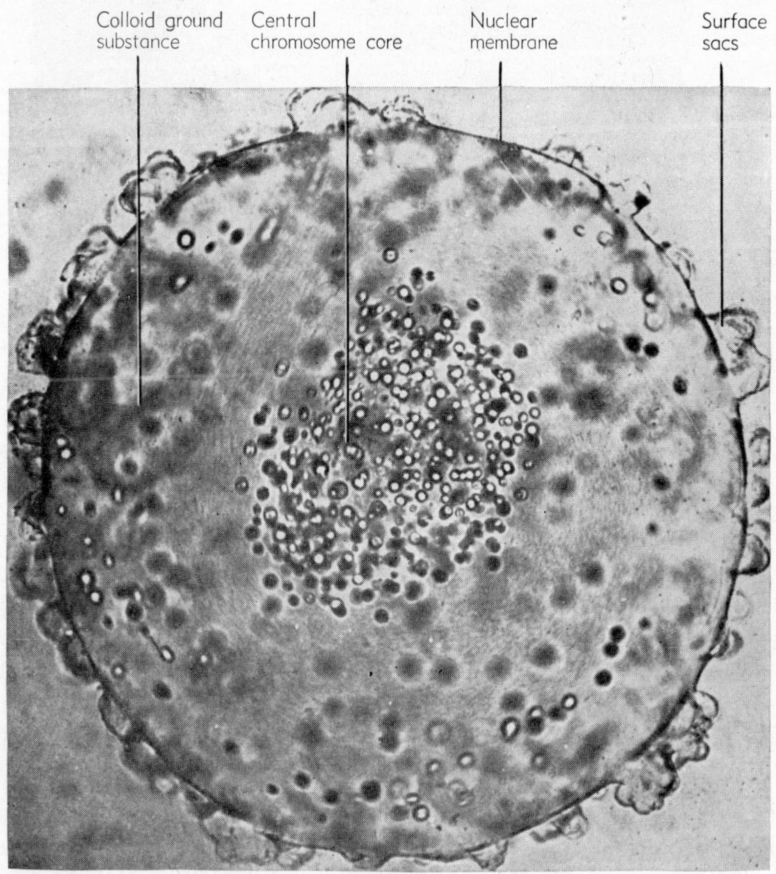

Isolated germinal vesicle (nucleus) of *Rana pipiens.* Nucleus isolated in calcium-free Ringer's solution, from stage 6, showing sac-like organelles which protrude from the nuclear membrane. The cloud of central nucleoli surrounds and obscures the chromosome frame. (Courtesy, W. R. Duryee, **1950,** *Ann. N. Y. Acad. Sci.,* **50,** Art. 8.)

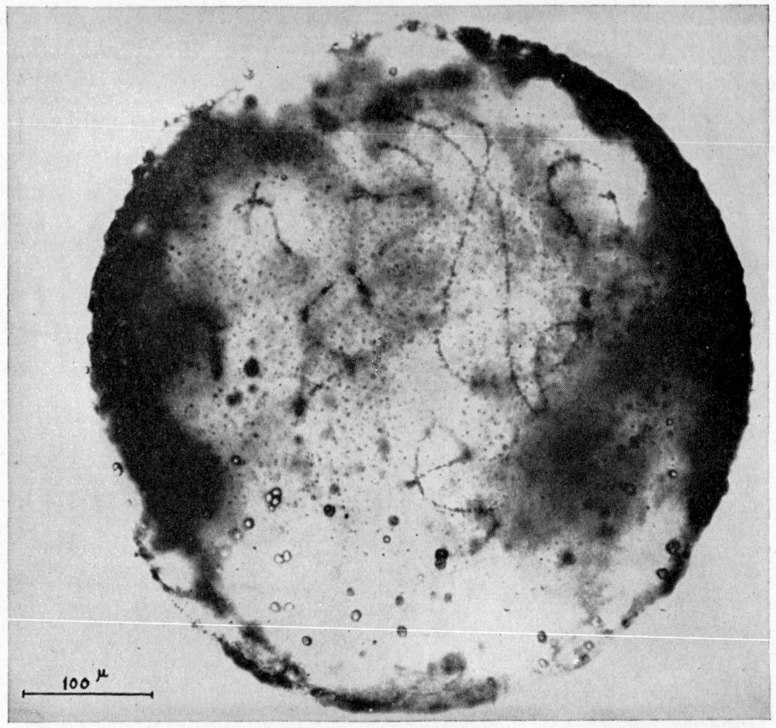

Stage 5 germinal vesicle of *Rana catesbiana.* Shows chromosome pairs with but few lateral loops and peripheral nucleoli outside of the chromosome frame. (Courtesy, W. R. Duryee, **1950,** *Ann. N. Y. Acad. Sci.,* **50,** Art. 8.)

stained with crystal violet in a calcium-free medium. Amphibian cells are among the largest in the animal kingdom and the frog's egg nucleus is large enough to see with the naked eye. It can be removed with considerable ease and examined beneath the binocular microscope.

Before the time of hibernation the eggs that are to be ovulated for the next spring are in the fully grown primary oöcyte stage, having their full complement of yolk, cytoplasm, and pigment. Externally more than one-half of the egg appears densely black, due to surface pigment granules, while the rest is creamy white. The nucleus is prepared for the maturation divisions. Such an egg measures about 1.75 mm. in diameter. The surface layer of the amphibian egg is formed before fertilization and it is definitely not hyaline, as it is in some Invertebrate eggs. It contains many small yolk grains and irregular accumulations of spherical, black pigment granules. With each cleavage, subsequent to fertilization, this superficial coat is divided between the blastomeres, being an integral part of the living cell. There is no clear-cut demarcation between this surface coat and the inner cytoplasm and yolk. It is believed that these growth changes of the egg are under the influence of the basophilic cells of the anterior pituitary gland, which cells are greater in number at this time than at any other.

During the growth period the vitelline membrane appears on the surface of the oöcyte as a thin, transparent, non-living, and closely adherent membrane. It is formed presumably by a secretion from the egg itself, aided by the surrounding follicle cells. It appears to be similar in all respects to the membrane of the same name found around the eggs of all vertebrates.

OVULATION AND MATURATION. **Ovulation,** or the liberation of the egg from the ovary, is brought about by a sex-stimulating hormone from the anterior pituitary gland. Just before and during the normal spring breeding period there is a temporary increase in the relative number of acidophilic cells in the anterior pituitary. It is believed that this is not coincidental but a causal factor in sex behavior in the frog. However, until such time as extracts of specific cell types can be made, this will be difficult to prove conclusively. Attempts on the part of the male to achieve amplexus are resisted by the female not sexually stimulated. However, such a female can be made to accept the male by injecting the female with whole anterior pituitary glands from other frogs. It is very probable that environmental factors such as light, temperature, and food may act through the endocrine system to prepare the frogs for breeding when they reach the swampy marshes in the early spring, after protracted hibernation. It must be pointed out, however, that there are frogs in essentially the same environments which breed in July (*Rana clamitans*) and August (*Rana catesbiana*), so that the causal factors appear to be either complex or possibly different for different species. The pituitaries of the hibernating frogs do contain the sex-stimulating factor, but apparently to a lesser degree than the glands of frogs approaching the breeding season. The injection of 6 glands from adult female frogs will cause an adult female of *Rana pipiens* to ovulate as early as the last week in August, some 8 months before the normal breeding period. One or two such glands will accomplish the same results if used early in

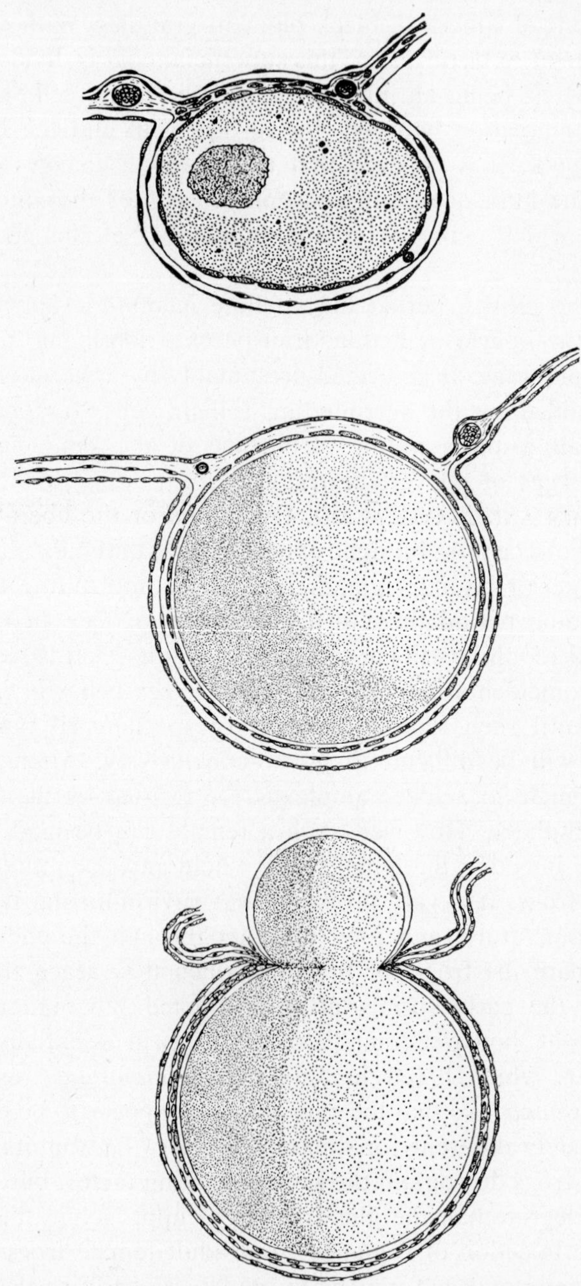

Production of ova and the process of ovulation. (*Top*) Section through a primary oöcyte of *Rana pipiens* showing the absence of the vitelline membrane,

(*Continued on facing page.*)

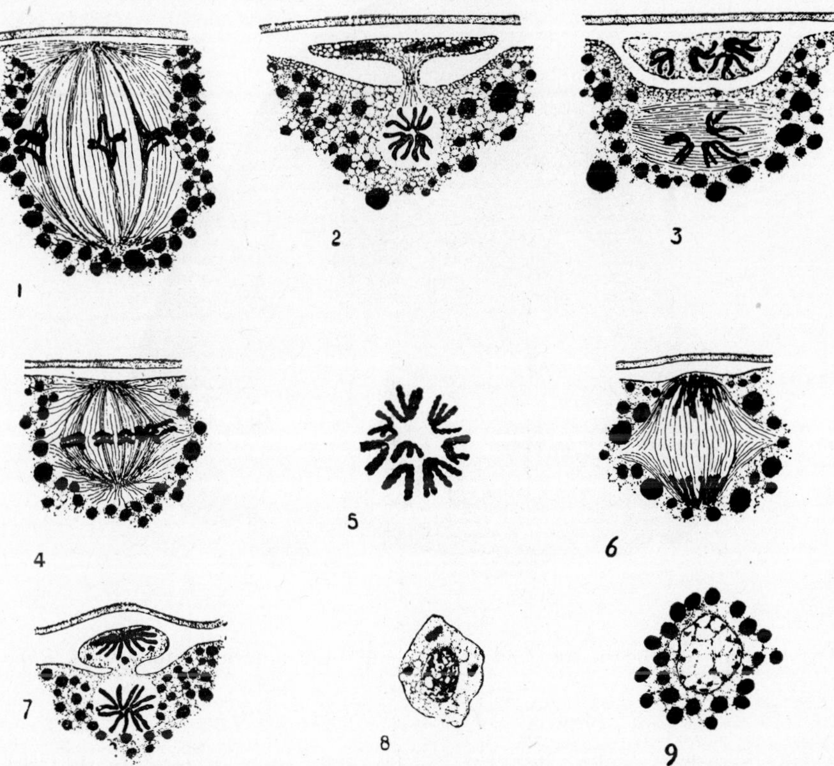

The maturation divisions in the female (Axolotl). (1) First polar spindle with heterotypic chromosomes. (2) Extrusion of first polar body. (3) Appearance of second polar spindle. Longitudinal division of chromosomes in egg and in first polar body. (4) Second polar spindle radial. Homoeotypic chromosomes on equator (metaphase). (5) Polar view of the same. (6) Anaphase. (7) Extrusion of second polar body. (8) Second polar body with resting nucleus. (9) Female pronucleus in resting condition, closely surrounded by yolk granules. (Courtesy, Jenkinson: "Vertebrate Embryology," Oxford, The Clarendon Press.)

(*Continued from opposite page.*)

the presence of the follicle and cyst wall, and the predetermined area of ultimate follicular rupture. (*Center*) Mature ovum with axial gradient of pigment and yolk. The vitelline membrane is now present, and the cyst wall of smooth muscle cells is stretched. (*Bottom*) Ovarian egg partially emerged from its follicle during ovulation. Note degree of constriction, contraction of cyst wall, and fully developed vitelline membrane around the entire egg.

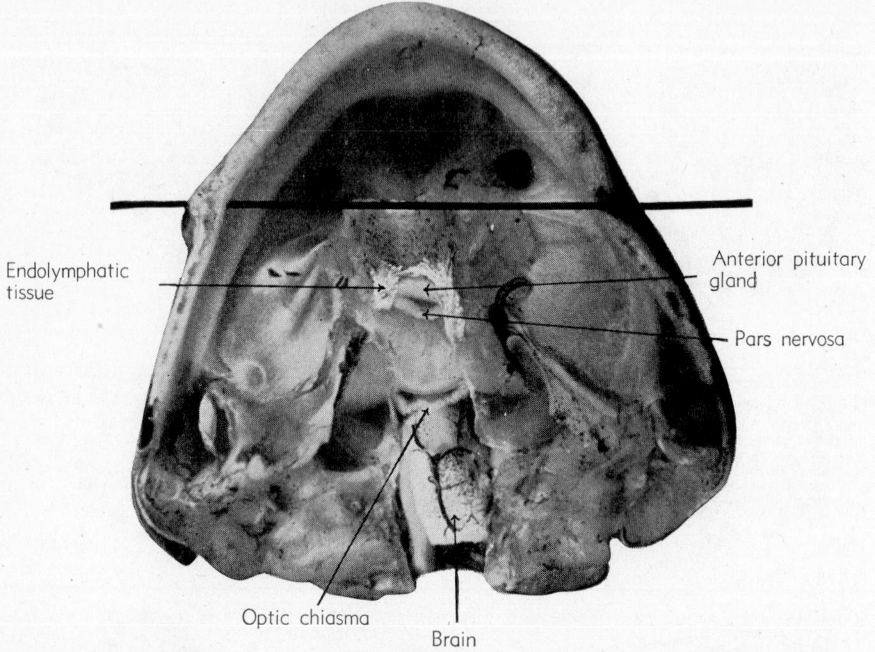

The position of the master endocrine gland—the anterior pituitary of *Rana pipiens.*

April. Another explanation for this may be offered, namely that the ovary itself may become more sensitive to such stimulation as the breeding season approaches.

The ovulation process itself consists of the rupture and the emergence of eggs from their individual follicles. The surface of the egg, separated from the body cavity by only the non-vascular **theca externa,** is first ruptured and then the egg slowly emerges through the small opening. Since the egg is known to contain a peptic-like enzyme, it is believed that the pituitary hormone may activate this enzyme to digest away the tight and non-vascular covering. Then by stimulation of the smooth muscle fibers of the cyst wall (**theca interna**) the process of emergence is completed. The relation of the pituitary to smooth muscle activity has long been established clinically.

It is true that the ovarian stroma shows undulating contractions at all seasons, irrespective of sex activity. An egg will emerge at any time from a surgically ruptured follicle. If an ovulating female is etherized and the body cavity is opened, the ovary may be removed and placed in amphibian Ringer's solution and the ovulation process may be observed directly. This will go on for several hours after all connections with the nerve and blood supply are cut off. From the initial rupture of the theca externa until the egg drops free into the body cavity there is a lapse of from 4 to 10 minutes at ordinary laboratory temperatures.

The **first maturation division** occurs at the time of ovulation. The heterotypic chromosomes (i.e., of bizarre shapes) are placed on the spindle of the amphiaster whose axis is at right angles to the egg surface. Movement of the chromosomes is identical with that found in ordinary mitosis. The outermost group of telophase chromosomes are pinched off, with a small amount of cytoplasm and no yolk, to comprise the **first polar body.** The innermost telophasic group of chromosomes remain within a clear (i.e., yolk-free) area of the egg as the nuclear mass of the secondary oöcyte. These changes occur as the egg leaves the ovary and before it reaches the oviduct. Possibly the same forces which bring about follicular rupture also influence this maturation process.

The **second maturation division** begins without any intermediate rest period for the chromosomes, at about the time the egg enters the oviduct. There may be a variation in time up to 2 hours for eggs to reach the ostium, depending upon the region of the body cavity into which they are liberated. Thus the stage of maturation of different eggs within the oviduct may vary considerably. There is a longitudinal division of the chromosomes of the egg which are lined up in metaphase on the **second maturation spindle,** the axis of which is at right angles to the egg surface. Since the spindle is primarily protoplasmic, and is made up in part of fibers (which may be contractile), the space occupied by the spindle will be free of yolk. Since it is peripherally placed, and represents a slight inner movement after the elimination of the first polar body, the surface layer of the egg is slightly de-pigmented just above the spindle region. This situation is exaggerated in aged eggs, a relatively large de-pigmented area of the cortex appearing toward the center of the animal hemisphere.

Maturation is not completed until or unless the egg is activated by sperm or stimulated by parthenogenetic means. However, every egg reaching the uterus is in metaphase of the second maturation division, awaiting the stimulus of activation to complete the elimination of the **second polar body.**

CHAPTER FOUR

Fertilization of the Frog's Egg

Completion of Maturation of the Egg
Penetration and Copulation Paths of the Spermatozoon
Symmetry of the Egg, Zygote, and Future Embryo

"The unfertilized egg dies in a comparatively short time, while the act of fertilization saves the life of the egg and allows it to give rise, theoretically at least, to an unlimited series of generations. . . . Fertilization makes the egg immortal." (J. Loeb, 1913.)

Fertilization generally is regarded as a two-fold process, involving **first** the **activation** of the egg. This can be accomplished by the sperm or by a variety of parthenogenetic agents. **Second,** there is the mixing of hereditary (nuclear and chromosomal) potentialities, a process known as **amphimixis.** Insemination means simply the exposure of the eggs to spermatozoa. The most accepted evidence for activation is an elevation of the **vitelline membrane** away from the egg and its transformation into what is then called a **fertilization membrane.** The vitelline membrane can be lifted from the ovarian eggs of the frog in distilled water or calcium-free Ringer's solution at pH 7.5 to 10.2. This purely physical change seems to be the result of progressive cytolysis or coagulation of the egg cortex, and the membrane itself has the consistency of thin cellophane. There are, of course, physiological changes in the egg accompanying fertilization which are so dynamic that even the microscopic surface pigment granules become violently active. The ultimate proof of successful fertilization is, of course, the diploid condition of the chromosomes of the zygote.

As the frog's egg is shed into the water, the male (in amplectic embrace) simultaneously and by active expulsion movements sheds clouds of spermatozoa over the eggs. Fertilization in Anura is therefore external. The jelly, deposited on each egg as it passed through the oviduct, swells almost immediately thereafter, partially protecting the egg against multiple sperm entrance. The swollen jelly appears to be arranged in three layers, being twice the thickness of the egg diam-

Amplexus in the toad: *Bufo fowleri*. Pectoral grip.

eter. Polyspermy, or multiple sperm invasion of the egg, occurs naturally in some telolecithal eggs such as those of the bird. It is also common in urodele eggs, but not so with the Anura (e.g., the frog). More effective than the jelly in limiting fertilization to one sperm is the negative chemical and/or physical reaction of the egg toward any extra spermatozoa after one of them has made contact with the egg surface. Simultaneously with sperm activation there appears an immune reaction of the egg to the invasion of any accessory spermatozoon, even of the same species. In any case, one and only one spermatozoon nucleus normally fuses with the egg nucleus. Any accessory spermatozoa which are successful in invading the egg attempt to divide independently of the egg nucleus and then degenerate. Extensive polyspermy, which may occur in aged eggs, interferes drastically with the cleavage mechanism and the eggs reach an early cytolysis and death.

The effective frog spermatozoon always enters the egg in the **animal hemisphere.** This does not deny the possibility of sperm entrance in the metabolically more sluggish vegetal hemisphere. The sperm nucleus which conjugates with the egg nucleus is one that

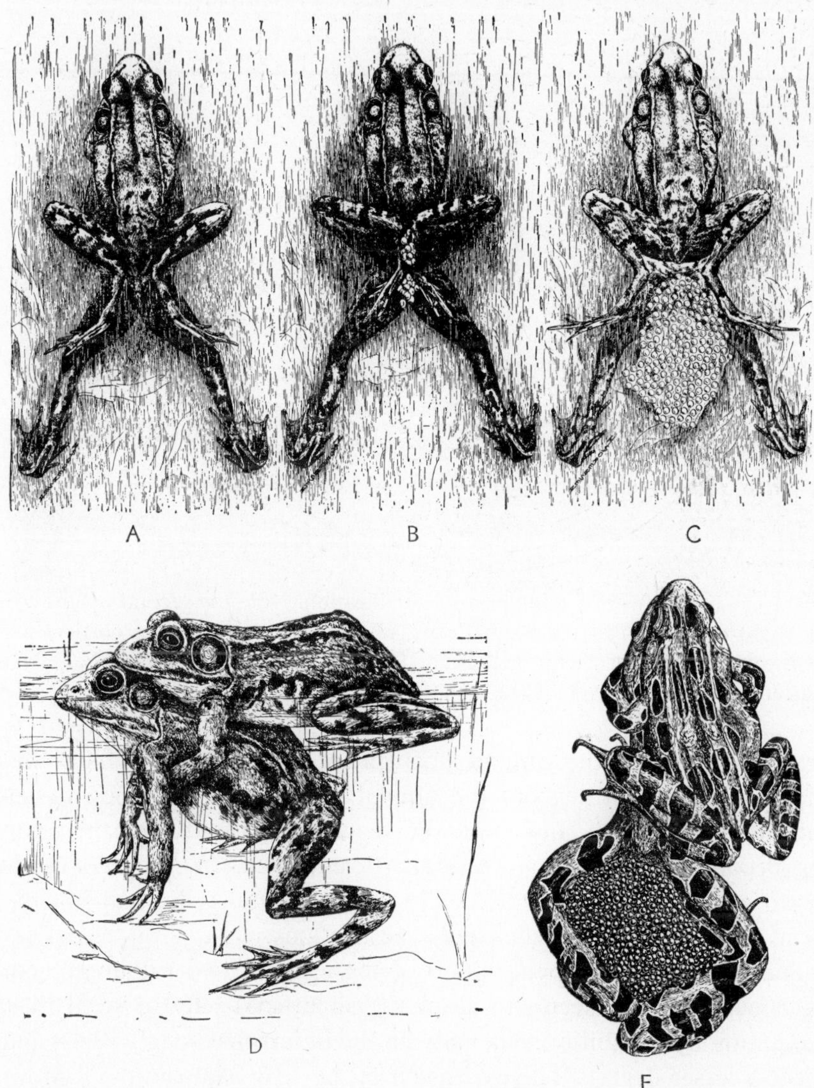

Oviposition and fertilization in *Rana.* (A) Egg-laying posture of *Rana clamitans,* just prior to the onset of oviposition: dorsal view. (B) Upstroke of the male and the appearance of the first batch of eggs. (C) Downstroke of the male and the formation of the surface film: dorsal view. (D) Typical amplexus in *Rana clamitans:* lateral view. (E) Pre-release motions of paired *Rana pipiens.* (Courtesy, Dr. L. R. Aronson, American Museum of Natural History.)

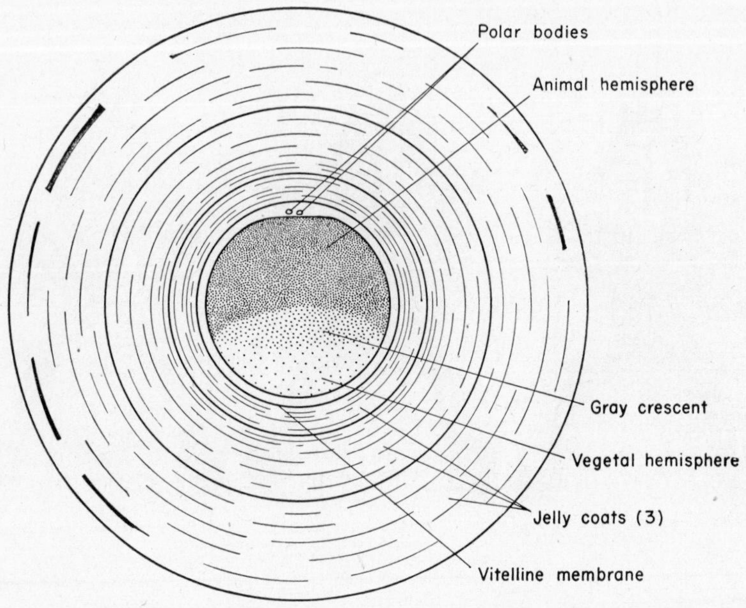

The egg of the frog 35 minutes after fertilization. Note the second polar body, the slight depression at the animal pole, and the recession of the cortical pigment toward the sperm entrance point, forming the gray crescent. The jelly is thicker than the diameter of the egg.

enters by way of the animal hemisphere. The factors which limit effective sperm entrance to the animal hemisphere may be physical and/or chemical. In any case, the reaction is rapid and the entire egg becomes resistant to excess sperm entrance. In Amphioxus the sperm entrance is characteristically in the vegetal pole, and in other forms there may be no such polar restrictions.

Sperm contact and penetration of the egg has two rather immediate effects. **First,** it seems to allow the superficial **jelly** to swell to its maximum, by imbibition. The jelly on the unfertilized egg will expand, but to a lesser degree. The expansion of the jelly is at quite a uniform rate and can be observed under low power magnification against a dark background. Within 5 minutes there has been about 30 per cent swelling, in 15 minutes about 75 per cent swelling, and thereafter the imbibition is slower. Eventually the thickness of the three jelly layers is several times the diameter of the egg. **Second,** another effect of sperm penetration is that there is an almost immediate loss of **water** from the egg so that a space appears between the egg surface and the enveloping vitelline membrane now known as the **fertilization membrane.** This is known as the **perivitelline space,** filled with a fluid, within which the egg is free to rotate. Since the mature egg has a definite yolk-cytoplasmic gradient, it slowly rotates within the gravitational field (inside the fertilization membrane) until the black pigmented animal hemisphere is uppermost and the heavier yolk-laden vegetal hemisphere is lowermost. When eggs are artificially inseminated with frog sperm in the laboratory, this rotation will be complete within an hour after insemination and the egg mass will present a uniform black appearance from above, provided there is adequate water coverage.

Completion of Maturation of the Egg

At the time of insemination the frog's egg nucleus is in the metaphase of the second maturation division, and the egg is provided with a vitelline membrane and a covering of unswollen jelly. The activation of the egg by the spermatozoon brings on a resumption of the maturation process so that the suspended mitosis is completed, and the **second polar body** is given off into the perivitelline space.

Occasionally at the time of insemination eggs will show a minute polar body pit or fovea, a surface marking indicating the point of previous emergence of the first polar body. The first polar body can be found generally as a translucent bead, floating freely within the perivitelline space in the general vicinity of the animal hemisphere. Within 7 to 10 minutes (at ordinary laboratory temperatures) a distinct pit will appear in the animal hemisphere, and this marks the position of the activated amphiaster. Apparently sperm activation causes the whole amphiaster to recede slightly into the egg, or such slight movement might be the result of cortical changes following activation, since the amphiaster is of quite different consistency from the balance of the egg. In any case, there appears a small pit measuring about 16 microns in diameter and often near the first polar body. Within another 15 to 20 minutes (a total of 25 to 30 minutes from insemination) the pit seems to disappear but only because there is seen emerging from it the second, and also translucent, polar body. Within about 1 minute this second body (nucleus) has emerged and its diameter measures about 26 microns, indicating that it was squeezed through an orifice somewhat smaller than its own diameter. There remains no evidence of any pit and, even though the egg nucleus is just below the surface, there is no superficial evidence of its presence. The egg nucleus now recedes into the egg, re-forms, and moves slightly in the direction of the approaching sperm nucleus. The path of the egg nucleus is not marked by any pigment as is the path of the invading spermatozoon.

Penetration and Copulation Paths of the Spermatozoon

The sperm head generally makes a direct perpendicular contact with the egg cortex, through the unswollen jelly and the vitelline membrane. Usually the entire spermatozoon enters the egg, taking several

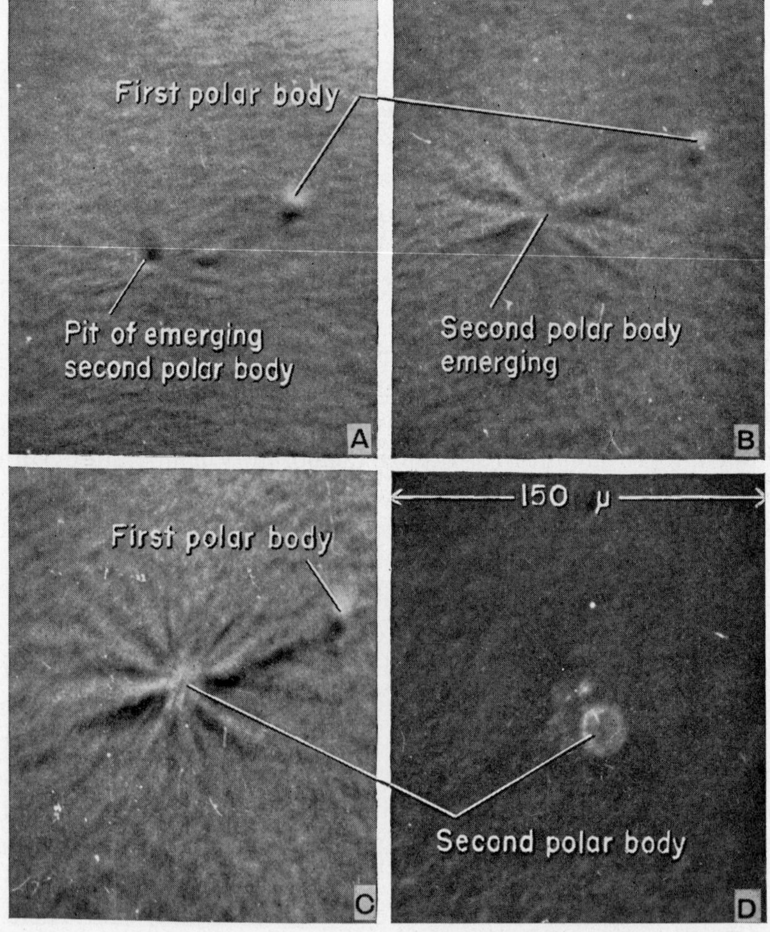

Polar body emergence: *Rana pipiens*. Note tension lines in the cortical layer caused by the 26-micron polar body emerging through a 16-micron opening.

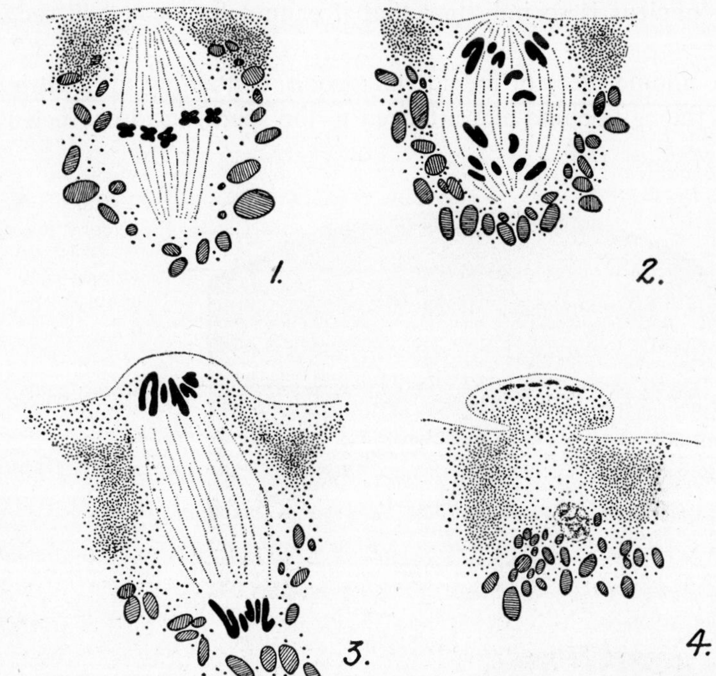

The four stages in polar body emergence in *Rana pipiens.* (*1*) Division spindle as in egg at time of insemination. (*2*) Anaphase of maturation division. Stage at which spindle can be seen from exterior of the egg as a black dot. Egg fixed 35 minutes after insemination. (*3*) Early telophase. Egg fixed 50 minutes after insemination. (*4*) Polar body just forming. Egg fixed 56 minutes after insemination. (Courtesy, K. R. Porter, **1939,** *Biol. Bull.,* **77**:233.)

minutes for the complete invasion of the cortex. The tail piece may be broken off, but the head and middle piece continue through the egg substance in the general direction determined by the direction of penetration, usually along the egg radius. This is therefore known as the **penetration path.** Almost immediately, however, the sperm head enlarges and loses its identity and is difficult to find by any known cytological method.

In the process of invading the egg, the spermatozoon takes along with it some of the pigment granules of the surface (cortical) layer so that a cone-shaped **penetration path** can be seen in sections cut in a parallel plane. This path is rather straight, indicating a certain amount of directional force on the part of the penetrating spermatozoon. The pigment path is the only evidence of the sperm movement, since the sperm nucleus is so indistinct that it cannot be located in sectioned eggs.

The middle piece of the spermatozoon, containing the **centrosome,** enters the egg behind and attached to the sperm head or nucleus. As

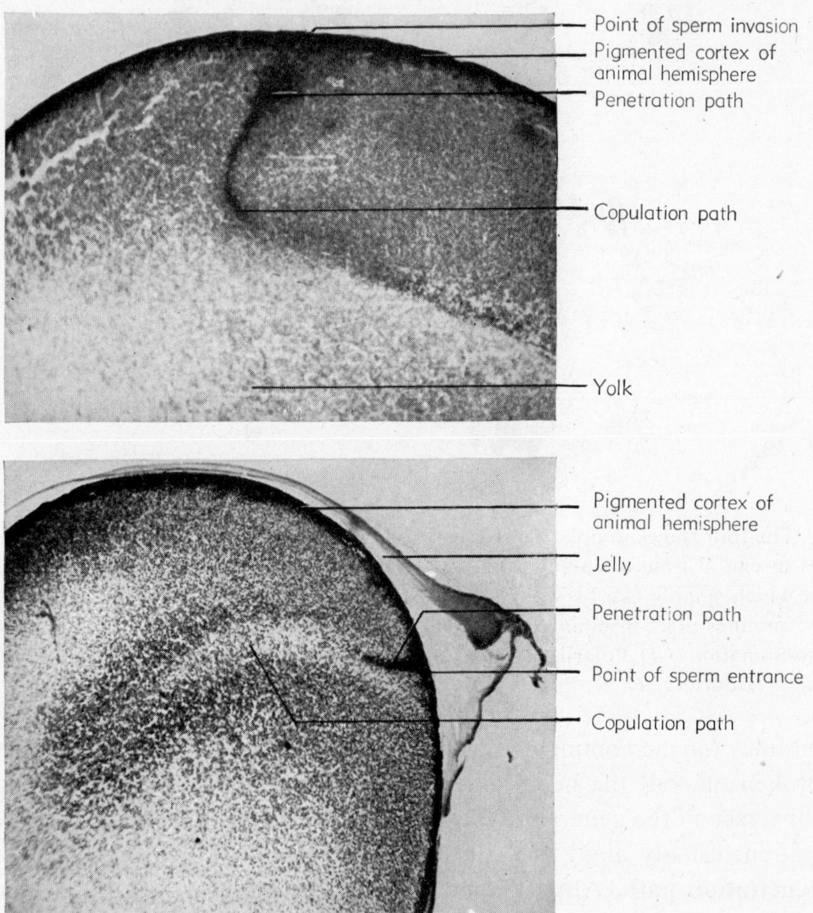

Invasion of the frog's egg by a spermatozoon. (*Top*) The first step in fertilization, the second (*bottom*) being syngamy or the fusion of the sperm and egg nuclei.

this sperm head (nucleus) swells and loses its identity and establishes the penetration path, the associated centrosome divides. The resulting centrosomes establish an axis at right angles to the direction of sperm progression. Frequently, however, the sperm penetration path will not

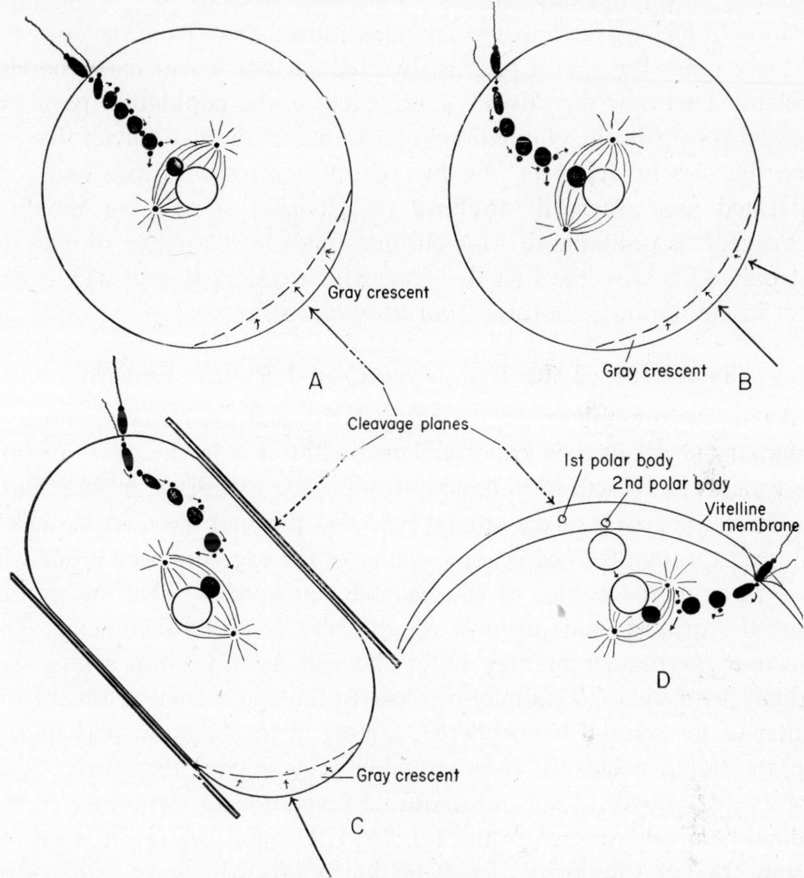

Fertilization of the frog's egg. (A) Sperm penetration and copulation paths in the same direction, forming a straight line, in which case the first cleavage bisects the gray crescent. (B) Sperm copulation path veers away from the penetration path, causing the first cleavage furrow to deviate from bisecting the gray crescent. (C) Under compression, the egg protoplasm is re-oriented, and the cleavage spindle comes to lie in the plane of the longest protoplasmic axis, regardless of sperm activity. (D) Profile view showing slight movement of the egg nucleus toward the sperm nucleus, after the egg nucleus has given off its second polar body.

These diagrams are simplified by omitting the changes attending nuclear dissolution, prior to syngamy, so that the nuclear paths in syngamy can be emphasized. Only in "A" does the first cleavage coincide with the embryonic axis and bisect the gray crescent. (*Solid arrows*) Penetration path, gray crescent, embryonic axis, (*broken arrows*) cleavage plane, which occurs at right angles to the mitotic spindle. Egg nucleus is clear, sperm nucleus is solid.

lead the sperm nucleus directly to the egg nucleus, or to the final position of the egg nucleus (which itself moves away from the cortex). In these cases the sperm path is diverted so that it will meet the egg nucleus. This new direction is designated as the **copulation path** because it results in the copulation (or fusion) of the two nuclei. By the time the two nuclei meet, the two sperm centrosomes are then well separated and are ready to form the division spindle for the first cleavage. It is probable that the chromosomes from the two sources do not pair off before the first division, which occurs within 2½ hours after insemination at normal laboratory temperatures.

Symmetry of the Egg, Zygote, and Future Embryo

As has been emphasized, the egg polarity and the radial (rotatory) symmetry about its axis are established while it is in the ovary during the process of growth or yolk acquisition. One can draw an imaginary line from the center of the animal pole and through the nucleus which will pass through the geometrical center of the egg, and such a line will pass through the center of the vegetal hemisphere. This line represents the primary axis around which there is radial symmetry. The effective spermatozoon may enter the egg at any point within the animal hemisphere. This may be close to the egg nucleus (toward the center of the animal hemisphere), almost at the equator, or between these extreme positions. It is probably very seldom that penetration occurs just above the second maturation spindle, in the center of the animal hemisphere (i.e., in the egg axis). For this reason, it is safe to assume that the majority of penetration points will be at some other region of the animal hemisphere. This means that a third point is established (i.e., by sperm penetration), the other two being any two points on the linear axis of the egg. These three points will establish a plane, the **penetration path plane,** which is of major importance in establishing embryonic planes. The egg therefore loses its rotatory symmetry at the moment of sperm penetration.

The significance of the sperm entrance point is brought out when it is realized that it immediately establishes the antero-posterior axis or **bilateral symmetry** of the future embryo. That side of the animal hemisphere which is toward the sperm entrance will be toward the anterior, the opposite will be toward the posterior, of the future embryo. This antero-posterior plane (formerly the sperm penetration path plane) separates the future embryo into right and left halves.

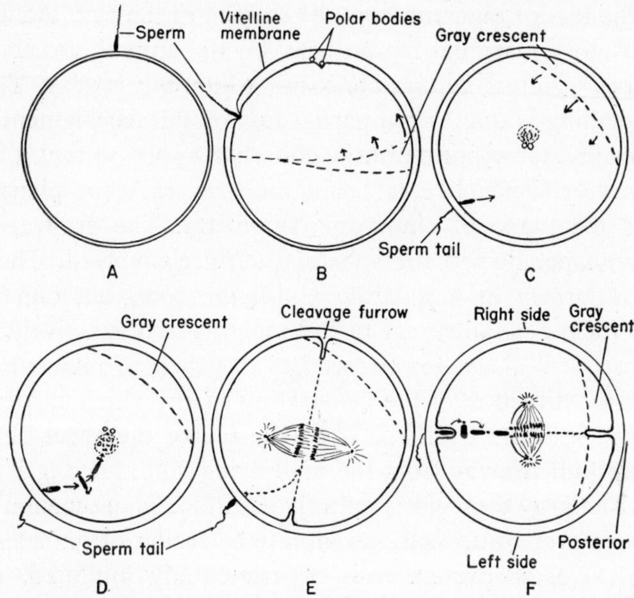

Surface changes of the frog's egg at the time of fertilization. (A) Sperm contact, entrance generally in the animal hemisphere. (B) Second polar body emerges, the sperm penetrates the cortex, and the surface pigment recedes toward the sperm entrance point forming the gray crescent. Lateral view. (C) Dorsal view showing the sperm penetration path, centrally located polar bodies and egg nucleus, and (*arrows*) pigment recession to form the gray crescent. (D) Rotation of the sperm head and middle piece 180° as it veers from the penetration path to the copulation path, in line with the egg nucleus. (E) First division spindle forming at right angles to the copulation path. Since the copulation and penetration paths are not in the same plane, the cleavage furrow does not cut through the middle of the gray crescent. (F) When the penetration and copulation paths are continuous and in essentially a straight line, the first cleavage furrow will bisect the gray crescent.

Immediately upon invasion by the spermatozoon the egg substance becomes more labile and there is a streaming of the protoplasm toward the animal pole and of the yolk (deutoplasm) toward the vegetal pole. Polarity is therefore accentuated. The movement of the egg contents is reflected in the very violent activity of the microscopic pigment granules on the surface. These granules appear motionless in the unfertilized or the dead egg. These facts have been established by cytological and experimental investigations, and observed in high magnification motion pictures. However, since the sperm penetration involves the loss of pigment from the surface of the egg, there appears a compensatory marginal region between the animal and the vegetal hemispheres which is neither black nor white, but is gray. This intermediate shading is due to the partial loss of surface pigment and the consequent greater exposure of the underlying yolk, so that it is known as the **gray crescent.** It establishes the gray crescent plane, and is known as the plane of embryonic symmetry. The gray area has a crescentic shape, due to the spherical surface involved. The surface pigment is largely in a separate non-living coat, but one which is necessary for the maintenance of cell integrity and is actively involved in the subsequent cleavage process. But this sheet of pigment is pulled slightly in the direction of the penetrating sperm which carries part of the pigment into the egg. The opposite side of the sheet of pigment is therefore pulled away from the underlying yolk, leaving it partially exposed. The gray crescent is entirely a surface phenomenon and has nothing whatever to do with syngamy (the fusion of gametes). Even if the sperm aster formation is experimentally inhibited, the gray crescent will form, it being a response to sperm penetration. The region of the gray crescent will become the posterior side, and the opposite (region of sperm entrance) will become the anterior side of the future embryo. If we now take any two points on the egg axis, and the center of the gray crescent as a third point, this plane represents the **median sagittal plane** of the future embryo. It must be pointed out that the gray crescent is not always readily apparent, and yet such eggs will develop normally.

It is presumed that the closer to the equator that the sperm makes

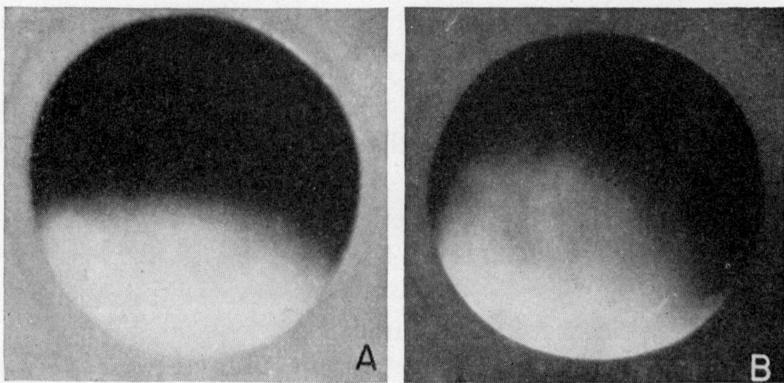

Formation of the gray crescent. (A) Egg of *Rana pipiens* at the moment of insemination. (B) Same egg 20 minutes later showing the formed gray crescent.

its entrance into the egg, the more extensive will be the opposite gray crescent. And the nearer it is to the animal pole the less apparent will the gray crescent be. This gray crescent appears in about one hour after insemination. It may develop earlier and be more extensive in aged eggs. While it will move somewhat, by the process of epiboly (e.g., downgrowth of surface materials), it will ultimately be found in the region of the blastopore and the anus. This is the region of origin of most of the mesoderm. It can be seen readily with the naked eye or under low magnification, but it is difficult to detect in the sectioned egg because the pigmented layer is relatively very thin. These descriptions of egg polarity and rotatory symmetry, and of the secondarily imposed bilateral symmetry, are of fundamental importance in understanding the development of the normal embryo. However, factors of unequal pressure on the egg in any clutch of eggs may so alter the position of the nucleus and the distribution of yolk and/or cytoplasm that the bilateral symmetry of the fertilized egg and the early cleavage planes may not be so causally related. Even so, normal embryos will develop.

CHAPTER FIVE

Cleavage

Determination of Planes
Cleavage Laws
Steps in the Cleavage Process

Determination of Planes.

The plane of the **first cleavage** is determined in a very different manner. The cytoplasm within which the cleavage is initiated is somewhat flattened beneath the pigmented cortex of the animal hemisphere. The egg nucleus lies within this cytoplasm, and, as the sperm nucleus approaches it, preceded by its divided centrosome, an **amphiaster** is set up to divide the chromatic material of the two syngamic nuclei. The cleavage plane therefore is determined by the direction of approach of the sperm nucleus, or rather, the copulation path. It can be assumed that in the undisturbed egg the cytoplasm also has a slight axial distribution, paralleling that of the yolk, with its maximum in the opposite direction to the yolk. The cleavage furrow will form at right angles to the amphiaster, and this coincides exactly with the sperm copulation path. One may conclude, therefore, that under undisturbed conditions the first cleavage furrow includes (or is determined by) the copulation path.

It should be made clear at this point, however, that the cleavage plane need not necessarily represent the median longitudinal axis (sagittal plane) of the embryo, cutting it into right and left halves. Should this happen it would mean that the penetration and the copulation paths were in exactly the same plane and the first cleavage would represent a median sagittal plane of the future embryo. Further, the mere pressure from other eggs in the same clutch can so alter the distribution of cytoplasm that the cleavage spindle may be shifted from its expected position. The median plane of the bilaterally symmetrical embryo may, but does not necessarily, coincide with the plane of egg symmetry.

To summarize, the penetration point combined with any two points on the egg axis establishes a plane which represents the median sagittal plane of the future embryo. The copulation (syngamic) path of the sperm nucleus to the egg nucleus determines the first cleavage plane. Should the penetration and copulation paths be in a direct line to the egg nucleus, the first cleavage would bisect the future embryo (and the gray crescent) into right and left halves. There is a natural tendency for the coinciding of the gravitational plane, the sperm entrance point, the sperm penetration path, the median plane of the egg, the median plane of the embryo, and the plane of the first cleavage. But this is not essential to the production of a normal embryo.

Cleavage Laws.

There are four major cleavage laws, known by the names of those who first emphasized their importance.

1. PFLÜGER'S LAW. The spindle elongates in the direction of least resistance.

2. BALFOUR'S LAW. The rate of cleavage tends to be governed by the inverse ratio of the amount of yolk present, in holoblastic cleavage. The yolk tends to impede division of both the nucleus and the cytoplasm.

3. SACH'S LAW. Cells tend to divide into equal parts and each new plane of division tends to bisect the previous plane at right angles.

4. HERTWIG'S LAW. The nucleus and its spindle generally are found in the center of the active protoplasm and the axis of any division spindle lies in the longest axis of the protoplasmic mass. Divisions tend to cut the protoplasmic masses at right angles to their axes.

Steps in the Cleavage Process.

The frog's egg is **telolecithal,** meaning that there is a large amount of yolk concentrated at one pole, opposite to the concentration of cytoplasm and the location of the nucleus. The cleavages are **holoblastic** (i.e., total), and, after the second cleavage, they are unequal. They eventually cut through the entire egg from the surface inward. About 2½ hours after the egg is fertilized there appears a very short inverted fold near the center of the pigmented and slightly depressed animal hemisphere cortex. This depression is extended in both directions and in the pigmented surface coat there appear lines radiating outwardly from the deepening **first cleavage furrow.** It appears as though some internal force is drawing this cortical region (surface) of the egg toward its center, and the apparent tension lines may be the result of these inner pulling forces. The facts that the radiating "tension" lines are not always developed, that they vary in different eggs, and that they can be chemically obliterated without interfering with the cleavage indicate that they are not the forces involved in cleavage but that they result from such forces. As the furrow is deepened and becomes fully formed, these lines disappear, and the surface of the egg

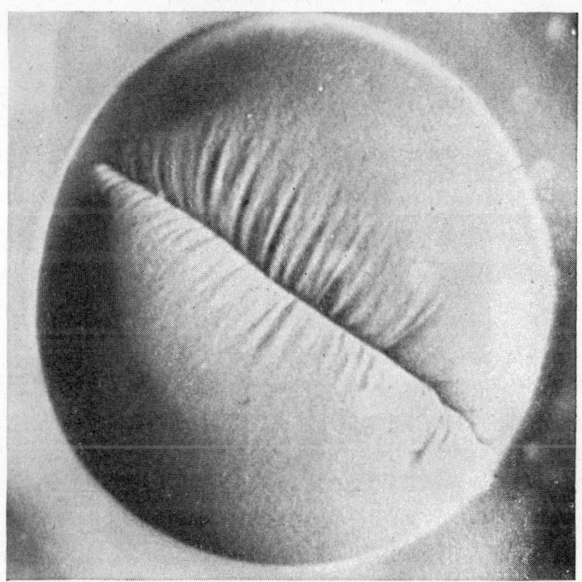

The first cleavage. Tension lines in the cortex during furrowing.

again becomes smooth. Similar though less pronounced lines generally are seen in association with the second and subsequent cleavages.

The furrow is at first very shallow (superficial), extending from the center of the animal hemisphere around the egg toward the vegetal hemisphere. Its greatest depth is where it is first seen, in the animal hemisphere. Within about 3 hours after fertilization the entire egg is ringed by a vertical furrow. This is always slightly deeper at the animal than at the vegetal hemisphere, and is clearly marked by the concentration of surface pigment. Such grading of the furrow may be due to the mechanical factor of the more resistant yolk at the vegetal pole. In most, but not in all, cases the first cleavage cuts through the gray crescent. After the first cleavage and up to the late blastula stage, each cell of the embryo is known as a **blastomere.**

Before the first cleavage furrow has completely encircled the egg, a **second furrow** begins at the center of the animal hemisphere and at right angles to the first furrow. This cleavage is also vertical and will progress down and around the egg to become deeper and deeper, but always deepest at the animal hemisphere. This second cleavage first begins to appear at about 3½ hours after fertilization, or 1 hour after the completion of the first cleavage. Again the so-called tension lines appear, and, since the lines of the first furrow have by this time flattened out, the presence of these new lines plus the relative shallowness of the furrow will help in its identification as the second furrow. As in the case of the first, this second furrow progresses superficially around the egg until the two ends meet at the vegetal pole. In the meantime the first cleavage furrow has cut more deeply into the egg so that in transverse (horizontal) sections of such an egg one can identify the two cleavage furrows easily by their relative depth.

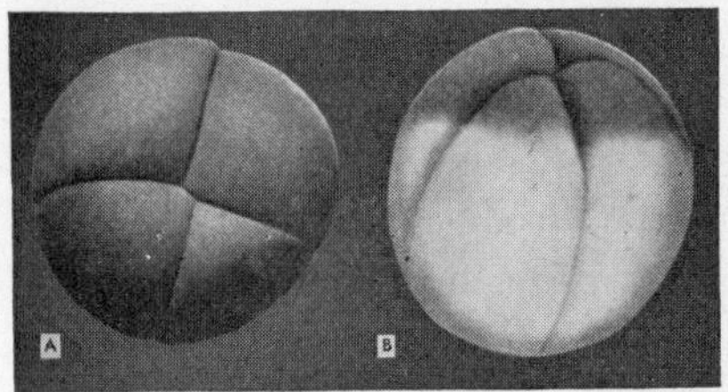

The 4-cell stage. (A) Animal pole view, to show second cleavage at right angles to the first. (B) Lateral view of the 4-cell stage showing incomplete encirclement of the vegetal hemisphere of the second cleavage furrow.

We can picture the egg at this stage as a core of yolk, concentrated more toward the vegetal pole, and with the cytoplasm, nuclei, and deepest portions of the cleavage furrows located at the pigmented animal hemisphere. However, all of the animal hemisphere structures will spread progressively toward the vegetal pole. With each division of the cytoplasm, cells are formed which contain yolk. By the time the third cleavage makes its appearance, the first cleavage has all but cut the entire egg mass into two equal parts. Each of these first two blastomeres (and the subsequent four blastomeres) is identical with all of the others with respect to the cytoplasm, pigment, and yolk gradients. In the 4-cell stage they are not qualitatively identical, for only two of the four cells contain any of the gray crescent material.

Often in closely packed eggs these first two cleavages may appear not quite in the center of the animal hemisphere, or may be not at right angles to each other. This would be the exception, however, and generally is due to the physical compression of the closely packed eggs whereby (as pointed out by Sachs and Hertwig) the cytoplasmic axis is shifted. The description given here applies to the isolated and unrestricted egg and should be considered as the more nearly normal. However, it must be pointed out that this minor compression and shifting of cleavage planes does not affect the normal development of the embryo, provided the distortion is not too great.

The **third cleavage** begins about 30 minutes after the second is completed, or 4 hours after fertilization. The cleavage rate is accelerated with each division, possibly because the resulting blastomeres are progressively smaller. The third cleavage plane is horizontal (latitudinal) and at right angles to both the first and the second cleavages. It is slightly above the level of the equator, about 60° to 70° from the center of the animal hemisphere. This shifting of the cleavage plane toward the animal hemisphere from the equator of the otherwise equatorial cleavage is due, no doubt, to the presence of more cytoplasm in that region and to relatively less yolk. Yolk is generally resistant to cleavage forces. When the cleavages are completed, the uppermost and smaller cells are sometimes designated as **micromeres** (smaller blastomeres) and the lowermost and larger cells are then designated as **macromeres** (larger blastomeres). This **third cleavage furrow** is seen as a horizontal groove varying from 20° to 30° above the equatorial line, toward the animal hemisphere. It provides four clear-cut blastomeres in the animal hemisphere, each equally pigmented. Since the second cleavage may not have been completed at the vegetal pole, there is a brief transitional period in which from some aspects there appear to be the surface markings of 6 rather than 8 cells.

The **fourth cleavage** is usually double and occurs about 20 minutes after the third. It tends to be vertical, but is seldom meridional. The furrows begin near the center of the animal pole and progress vegetally, dividing each of the original four blastomeres of the animal hemisphere. Instead of intersecting at the center of the animal hemisphere the fourth cleavage furrows may run into the first or the second cleavage furrows. This cleavage shows the first digression from a regu-

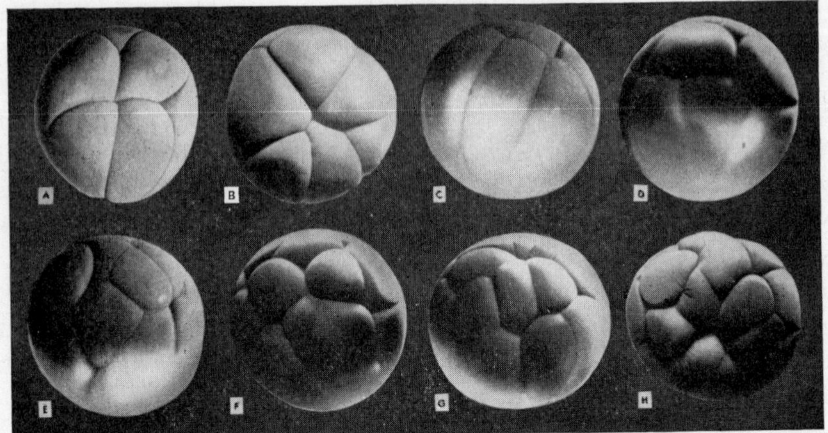

The third, fourth, and fifth cleavages from the animal pole and lateral views.

lar pattern in the undisturbed egg, and may appear even as a well-defined furrow before the third (horizontal) cleavage has reached its maximum depth. The cleavage rate is accelerated with each of the early divisions, and, since the blastomeres are of unequal size and have varying amounts of cytoplasm and yolk, synchronous cleavage is lost and there is an obvious overlapping of the divisions. The uppermost cells (micromeres) divide the most rapidly so that for a period there may be a 12-cell stage, made up of 8 upper and 4 lower blastomeres. Perfect symmetry in cleavage and in the blastomeres from this point on is a rarity, and yet the embryo will develop perfectly normally.

The **fifth cleavage** (also double), which should provide a 32-cell embryo, is more apt to be out of line, and the symmetry and regularity of the earlier cleavages is lost. The gradient of cleavage rate from the rapidly dividing animal hemisphere blastomeres to the slowly dividing vegetal hemisphere cells now becomes more apparent. These new furrows tend to be horizontal (latitudinal), as was the third cleavage. One cuts the animal hemisphere blastomeres and the other the vegetal hemisphere blastomeres horizontally, so that tiers of blastomeres are formed. The smallest cells, which contain the most pigment, are now found at the animal pole, and the largest blastomeres with no pigment and the most yolk are at the vegetal pole. There is evident, however, some movement of the surface (cortical) pigment in the direction of the vegetal pole accompanying each division of the blastomeres. This process is known as epiboly, to be described later in this book.

CHAPTER SIX

Blastulation

Internally the 8-cell stage of the frog shows the beginning of a cavity where the well-formed animal hemisphere cells have completed their 6-sided cell membrane. Once a blastomere is formed it tends to acquire a certain degree of rigidity and will maintain its spherical cell boundaries independently of its neighbors. Cortical and vitelline membrane pressure may flatten cells slightly against each other. When segmentation of the egg occurs, dividing it into smaller and smaller cellular units, there naturally follows the appearance of an internal cavity known as the segmentation cavity or **blastocoel.** The aggregate becomes about 20 per cent larger than the total volume of the cells. The earlier cleavages (described above) tend to be perpendicular to the egg surface. However, after the 32-cell stage there appear division planes more or less parallel to the egg surface, cutting off surface protoplasm from inner protoplasm and yolk. With increased cell rigidity, following each division, these surface cells push against each other until they are lifted up and away from the underlying cells. A crude simile would be to hold four or more marbles tightly together in the hand, and no matter how much pressure is exerted there will always be a space in the center of the group of marbles (i.e., cells). In the frog's egg the formation of complete cells is rather slow, and the blastocoel is small and not readily apparent until about the 32-cell stage.

The blastocoel is therefore a cavity, and this stage of development is known as the blastula, overlapping the stages of cleavage. The cavity is enlarged with each of the early cleavages and it is filled with an albuminous fluid, arising from the surrounding cells. Even though the frog's egg is telolecithal, cleavage has been described as **holoblastic** (opposed to meroblastic) and the presence of this cavity distinguishes it as a **coeloblastula** (as opposed to stereoblastula which has no cavity). Since the horizontal cleavages appear toward the animal hemisphere, this newly forming blastocoelic cavity will appear in an eccentric position above the level of the equator, and slightly toward

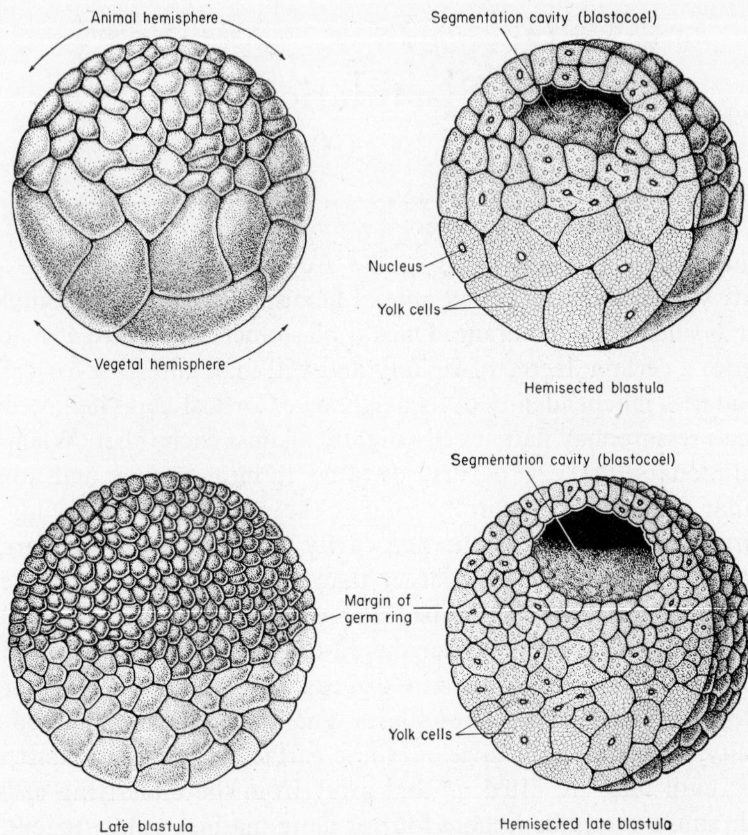

Blastulation in the frog. (Redrawn and modified after Huettner.)

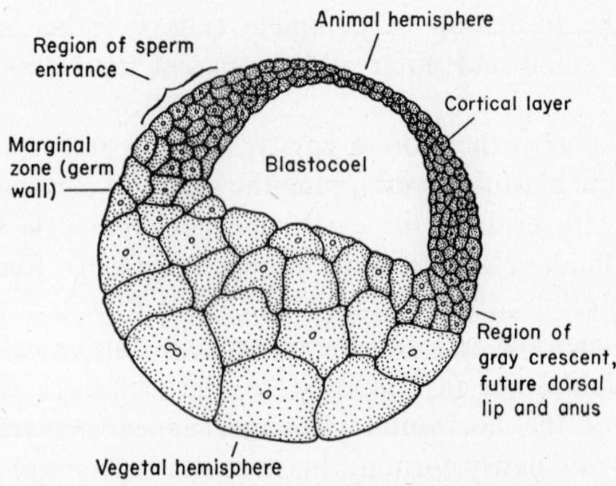

Frog blastula: sagittal section.

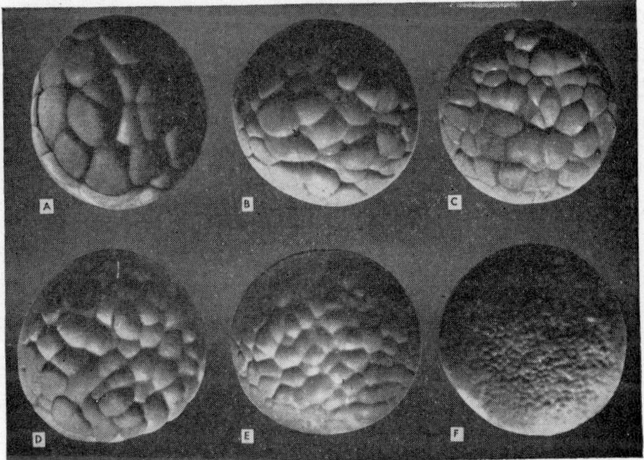

Progressive stages in blastulation.

the gray crescent side of the cleaving egg. It will remain in this position, beneath the animal hemisphere, until it is later displaced by the development of other cavities. The size of the blastocoel increases with the formation of smaller and smaller surrounding cells. The late blastula of the frog, by virtue of this blastocoel, has a volume displacement about 20 per cent greater than that of the fertilized egg.

Following the 32-cell stage the egg loses all semblance of rhythmic or synchronized cleavage and there is developed a **gradient of cleavage** with the most active region being at the animal pole and the least active being at the vegetal pole. In addition to this there are some characteristic changes in the blastula of the frog embryo. **First,** the smaller pigmented animal pole cells tend to spread their activity in a downward direction toward the vegetal pole, by a sort of contagion, so that there is an actual migration of pigment-covered cells toward the vegetal pole. This, and the horizontal cleavages, result in increasing the cell layers but thinning of the roof of the blastocoel. **Second,** the horizontal cleavages in the very small animal pole cells give the blastula a double or multi-layered roof. The single outer layer of cells contains most of the superficial pigment and is now recognized as the epidermal layer which will give rise to epithelium, either of the integument or lining the nervous system. The inner tiers of cells of the blastular roof are less pigmented and are known collectively as the nervous layer because they will give rise largely to the neuroblasts of the nervous system.

Either on the surface of the whole blastula or in sections of the blastula, one can determine the margins of the downward-moving pigmented coat and active animal hemisphere cells and the consequent slight thickening of the equatorial band. This margin is known as the **marginal zone, marginal belt,** or **germ ring.** Such a marginal region of activity, where yolk is most actively being transformed into cytoplasm, is found in Amphioxus and chick, and probably in all vertebrate embryos. It will have much to do with the subsequent formation of the lips of the future blastopore.

The marginal zone is approximately equatorial in the blastula stage, except for the slight reduction in pigmented cells at the side where the original gray crescent was located. Opposite to this gray crescent region the wall of the blastula appears to contain relatively more layers of cells and is therefore somewhat thicker. These changes occur in anticipation of the next process in embryonic development, namely gastrulation.

There have been numerous attempts to explain blastocoel formation and the movements anticipating gastrulation. These have been based largely on purely physical phenomena. An attempt has been made recently to summarize these concepts, as follows (Holtfreter, 1947: *Jour. Morph.,* **80**:42):

> If present in large numbers, the cells at the periphery of the body tend to establish a semipermeable layer, while the cells of the interior become separated from each other by secretion fluid. Thus the aggregation may be transformed into the configuration of a blastula or, if the amount of internal fluid increases further, into an epithelial vesicle. The occurrence of cylindrical stretchings and of migrations of the peripheral cells into the interior of the vesicle has been interpreted as possibly being caused by a surface tension lowering action of the inner fluid. Even in the absence of a gradient of surface tension, however, isolated embryonic cells tend to elongate and to migrate in one direction, with their original proximal pole leading the way, and possibly invagination movements may be partly due to this inherent dynamic tendency of the individual cell. Other factors influencing shape and movements of the cells in aggregate, or in a normal embryo, appear to be cell-specific differences of adhesiveness arising in the course of differentiation and making for a sorting out, grouping and aggregation of the various cell types into tissues and organs. With the appearance of fibrous and skeletal structures, of local differences in mechanical stress and hydrostatic pressure, of differential growth and a variety of metabolic processes, so many new factors are introduced that the principle of interfacial tension loses more and more of its original primacy as a morphogenetic agent.

CHAPTER SEVEN

Gastrulation

Gastrulation is that dynamic process in early development which invariably results in the transformation of a single-layered blastula stage to a didermic or 2-layered embryo. It involves, but is independent of, mitosis. The process varies considerably among the Vertebrates, but to a lesser extent when the process is compared in closely related species. The two layers to be distinguished are the ectoderm and the endoderm. In many forms (e.g., the frog) the third germ layer, or mesoderm, is formed almost simultaneously with the endoderm.

Significance of the Germ Layers

The distinction of **germ layers,** such as the **ectoderm, mesoderm,** and **endoderm,** is purely a matter of human convenience and is of no real concern to the embryo. The mere fact that the endoderm and the mesoderm are both derived originally from the **ectoblast** (outermost layer of the blastula) suggests their fundamental similarity. By means of experimental procedures it is possible to demonstrate that these presumptive germ layers are interchangeable and that regions ordinarily destined to become, for example, brain (ectoderm), may be transplanted to another region of the blastula where they will become muscle (mesoderm) or possibly thyroid (endoderm). The germ layer distinctions are based upon their position in the developing organism, and their fate. The ultimate tissues of the adult are often classified, again as a matter of human convenience, on the basis of groups which are derived from one or another of these three primary germ layers.

The germ layers, which are first distinguishable with gastrulation, therefore are definable by their fate in embryonic development. However, this fate is an arbitrary distinction since the fate of any group of cells can be altered by transplantation. The importance, then, of this distinction is one of position, and the ectoderm is always the outermost layer of cells, the endoderm the innermost, and the mesoderm the intermediate layer of cells present when gastrulation has been completed.

In recapitulation, a histologist could define the ectoderm as that group of embryonic cells which, under normal conditions of development, give rise to the epidermis and the epidermal structures, to the entire nervous system and sense organs, to the stomodeum, and to the proctodeum. The endoderm would be defined as that group of embryonic cells which normally give rise to the lining epithelium of the entire alimentary tract and all of its outgrowths, such as the thyroid, lungs, liver, pancreas, etc. The mesoderm would be defined as that group of cells which normally give rise to the skeleton and connective tissues, muscles, blood and vascular systems, to the coelomic epithelium and its derivatives, and to most of the urogenital system. The notochord in the frog is derived simultaneously with the mesoderm, and probably from the dorsal lip epiblast.

It is important, therefore, for the student to avoid ascribing any peculiar powers to the germ layers as such. They have their particular fate in development not by virtue of any peculiarly endowed power but rather by their position in the developing embryo as a whole.

Origin of Fate Maps

Gastrulation is a critical stage in the development of any embryo. This is due in part to the fact that the positional relationship of the various cells of the late blastula and early gastrula begins to take on special significance. This has been demonstrated by many experimental embryologists, among whom are His, Born, Bütschli, Rhumbler, Spek, Vogt, Dalcq, Pasteels, Vintemberger, Holtfreter, Nicholas, and Schechtman. They have used various experimental devices, such as injury or excision of cell areas, or staining local areas with vital dyes and following their subsequent movement. By such methods the so-called "fate maps" of various blastulae have been worked out.

A fate map is simply a topographical surface mapping of the blastula with respect to the ultimate fate of the various areas. When one traces a cell group on the surface of a blastula which has been vitally stained with Nile blue sulfate, for instance, and finds that these cells move from the marginal zone (between the animal and the vegetal hemispheres) over the dorsal lip of the early blastopore and into the embryo,

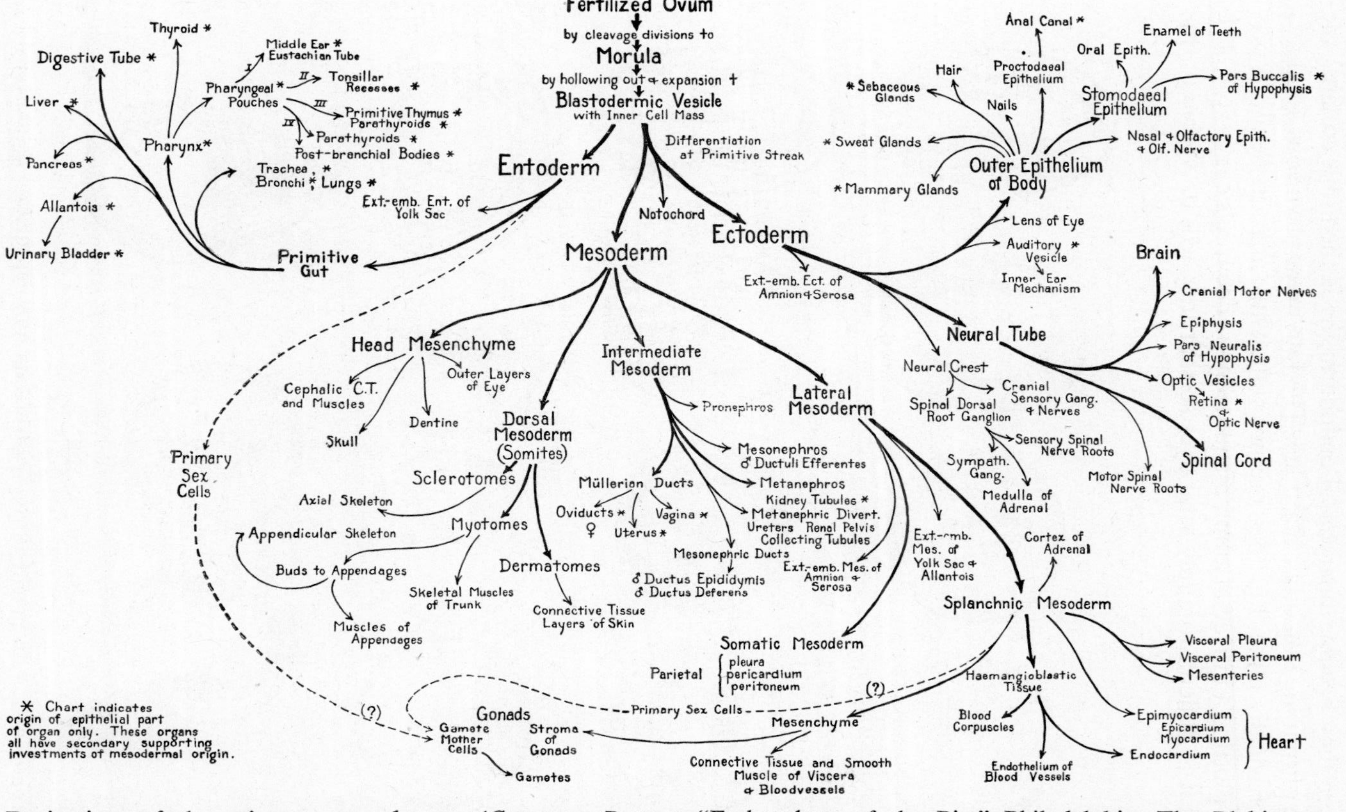

Derivatives of the primary germ layers. (Courtesy, Patten: "Embryology of the Pig," Philadelphia, The Blakiston Company.)

where they become pharyngeal endoderm, he is then able to label the fate of that area on other blastulae. The fate maps of various amphibia are basically alike, but they are not sufficiently alike in detail to permit plotting a universal amphibian fate map. The frog's egg is very dark and it is difficult to apply vital dyes so that they will be visible on the

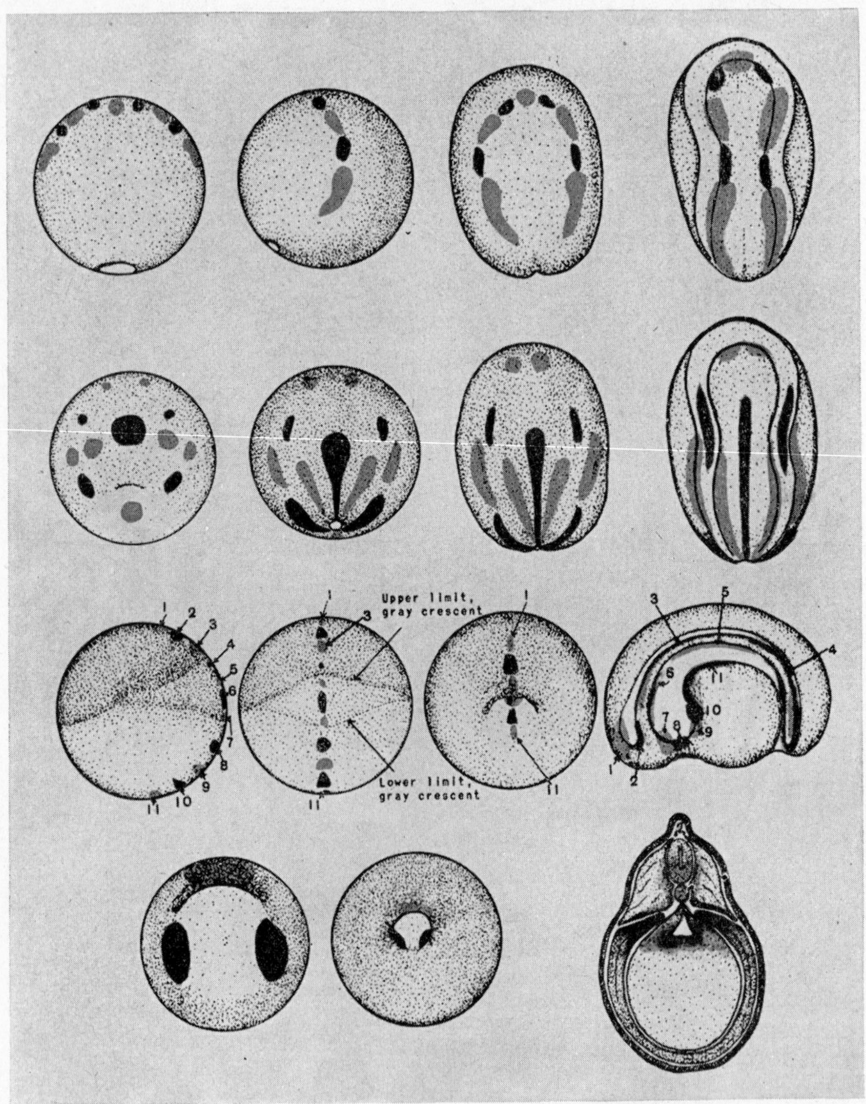

Morphogenetic movements during gastrulation and neurulation as indicated by changes in position of applied vital dyes.

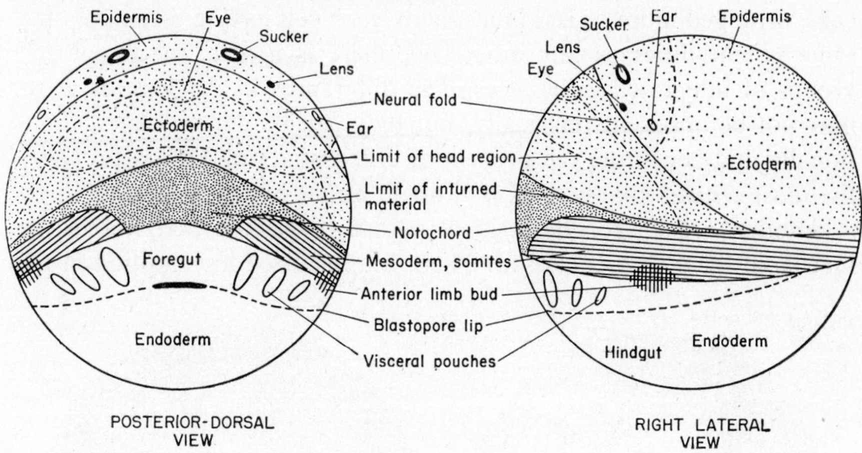

Fate map showing presumptive regions of the anuran blastula. (Adapted from Vogt: 1929.)

frog blastula. However, the fate maps of closely related species have been worked out and, combined with circumstantial experimental evidence on the frog's egg, we are able to supply what is believed to be a reasonably accurate fate map of the frog blastula.

Under conditions of normal development, the ectoderm of the frog is derived in part from the cells of the animal hemisphere and in part from the intermediate or equatorial plate cells. These are the regions on the fate map designated as presumptive ectoderm. The endoderm comes partly from the intermediate zone but largely from the vegetal hemisphere area (i.e., the presumptive endoderm on the fate map). The mesoderm and the notochord have a dual origin, arising between the ectoderm and the endoderm, largely from the region known as the lips of the blastopore. The student is advised to study carefully the accompanying fate maps.

Gastrulation as a Critical Stage in Development

One of the reasons for the fact that gastrulation is such a critical stage in embryonic development is that not only do the cells divide but also various cell areas take on special significance which they did not previously have. This special significance is shown by the mere fact that fate maps have been derived. There is a new independence, as well as interdependence, of various areas of the embryo. This change is designated as differentiation. Instead of a group of somewhat similar cells, arranged more or less in a sphere, each cell having essentially the same potentialities as any other cell, there is now a mosaic of cell groups of integrated differences. The differences in the various areas may not be apparent physically, but they can be demonstrated functionally and constitute the process of differentiation. This is probably the most critical change that is brought about by gastrulation.

Another reason for the critical nature of gastrulation lies in the mechanics of the process itself. There is a localized interruption in the

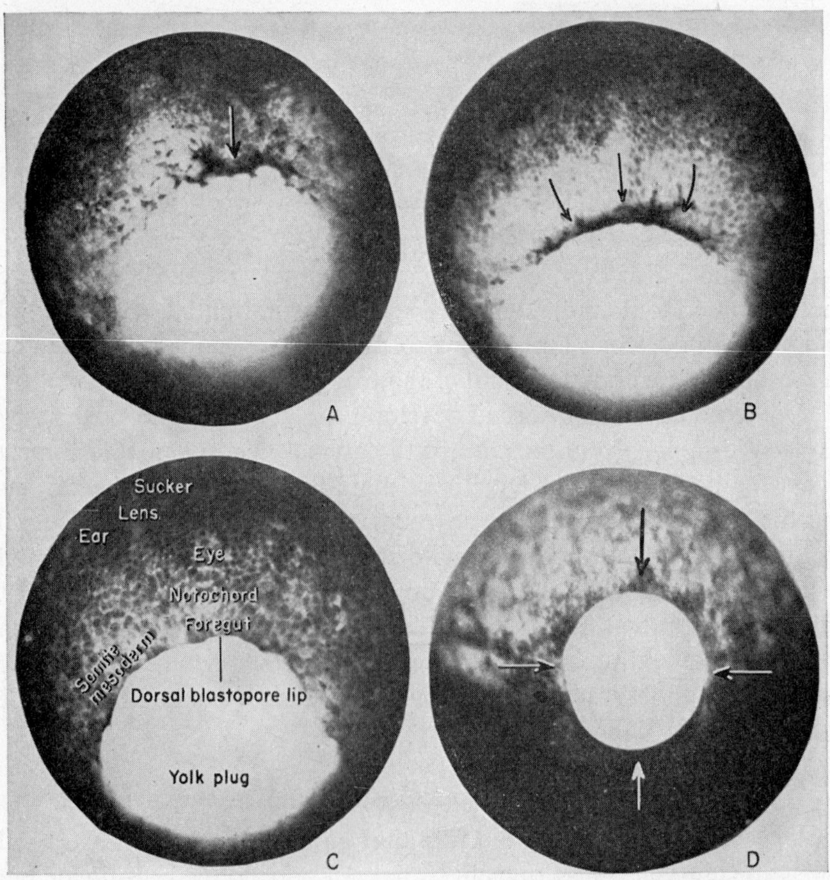

Gastrulation in the frog, *Rana pipiens* (photographs). (A) Initial involution at the dorsal lip. (B) Crescent-shaped lips of the blastopore extending laterally along the margin of the germ wall. (C) Half-moon–shaped involuted dorsal and lateral lips of the blastopore. Presumptive areas or organ anlagen indicated. (D) Lips of the blastopore completely encircle the exposed yolk plug. Rotation of the entire embryo through 90°.

continuity of the epibolic movement of the surface coat toward the vegetal hemisphere. This is only an apparent interruption, since it involves an inturning of cells at a very specific region of the marginal zone, or the most ventral limit of the pigmented animal hemisphere cells. This specific region is the ventral limit of the original gray crescent, destined (at the time of fertilization) to become the region of formation of the dorsal lip of the blastopore, with all of its implications.

Cells which lie on the lateral surface of the late blastula begin to roll inwardly, first only a few cells and then, by a sort of contagion, the contiguous cells of the more lateral marginal zone. It is this infolding process which marks the actual, observable process of gastrulation. It must be emphasized that these observable changes are probably long anticipated, as will be suggested by the detailed description below. If there is interference with this inturning movement of cells, any subsequent development is apt to be abnormal or incomplete if, in fact, it occurs at all. Embryos at the time of gastrulation are indeed hypersensitive to physical changes in the environment, and to genetic incompatibilities within the chromosomes of the involuting cells. Embryos which survive this process may reasonably be expected to achieve the next major step, namely neurulation.

Pre-gastrulation Stages

There is no clear-cut demarcation between the blastula and the gastrula stages, unless one accepts the initial involution of the dorsal lip cells. Some investigators have pointed out that there is a disproportionate ratio of the yolk and cytoplasm to the nucleus of the fertilized egg, as compared with the ratio in the somatic cell. This suggests to them that cleavage results in a progressive approach to the somatic ratio of nuclear volume to cytoplasmic volume. When the ratio is reached whereby the nucleus can properly control its cytoplasmic sphere of influence, then the latent influence can begin to exert itself and the process of differentiation begins. Such a situation occurs at the beginning of the gastrula stage. Cleavage continues, of course, but it has been proved beyond a doubt that cell areas are no longer of equivalent potency with regard to ultimate development. It has been suggested, therefore, that the blastula stage is monodermic (one principal outer layer of cells, generally arranged somewhat spherically) and contains a blastocoel. The end of the blastula stage is reached when the nuclear to cytoplasmic volume relationship of the constituent cells becomes most efficient, differentiation begins, and we can observe the movements and surface changes attendant upon gastrulation.

Until recently the yolk hemisphere of the early cleavage stages of the amphibian embryo was considered to be relatively inert. It was even considered a deterrent to morphogenetic movements of gastrulation. The vegetal hemisphere becomes cellular, but more slowly than does the animal hemisphere. The cells are larger and always contain abundant yolk. Nicholas (1945) wrote: "The concept of the inertness of the yolk mass probably inhibited our realization of its possible import." This attitude is now subject to change.

By applying vital dyes to the yolk hemisphere of the early and late blastula stages, Nicholas has found positive activity on the part of these yolk-laden vegetal pole cells, suggesting that they are concerned with the formation of the blastocoel, with the process of ingression, and also with the changes in water balance and later rotation. It now seems that the yolk assumes a dynamic rather than a passive role both in the process of blastulation and in anticipating the changes prerequisite to gastrulation.

In an exhaustive series of studies, Holtfreter and Schechtman have attempted independently to analyze the morphogenetic movements both before and during the gastrulation process in the amphibia. It is very probable that the formative influences so evident at the time of gastrulation are present long before the initial involution of cells to form the dorsal lip of the blastopore. The following description is based largely on the studies of these investigators and is supported by direct observation, available to anyone.

There is a protein-like surface coating or film on amphibian eggs, present from the beginning. It has plastic elasticity, is not sticky on its outer surface, but is an integral syncytial part of the living egg. This coat persists and its strength increases during development. It is involved in matters of cellular elasticity, cell aggregation, cell polarity, cell permeability, resistance to external media, osmotic regulation, and tissue affinity—all physical phenomena which are important in gastrulation movements.

This surface coating is divided only superficially by the segmenting blastomeres of the early embryo and yet (Holtfreter): "the syncytial coat thus represents at least one, and perhaps the most significant one, of the effective forces that make for a morphogenetic integration of the dynamic functions of the single cells into a cooperative unity." Embryologists have long been in search of a controlling supercellular physical force which might explain at least the initiation of the movements leading to gastrulation. This surface coat of Holtfreter may well be that controlling and integrating force. He suggests further that probably all of the non-adhesive epithelial linings of the larva can be traced back to this original surface coat.

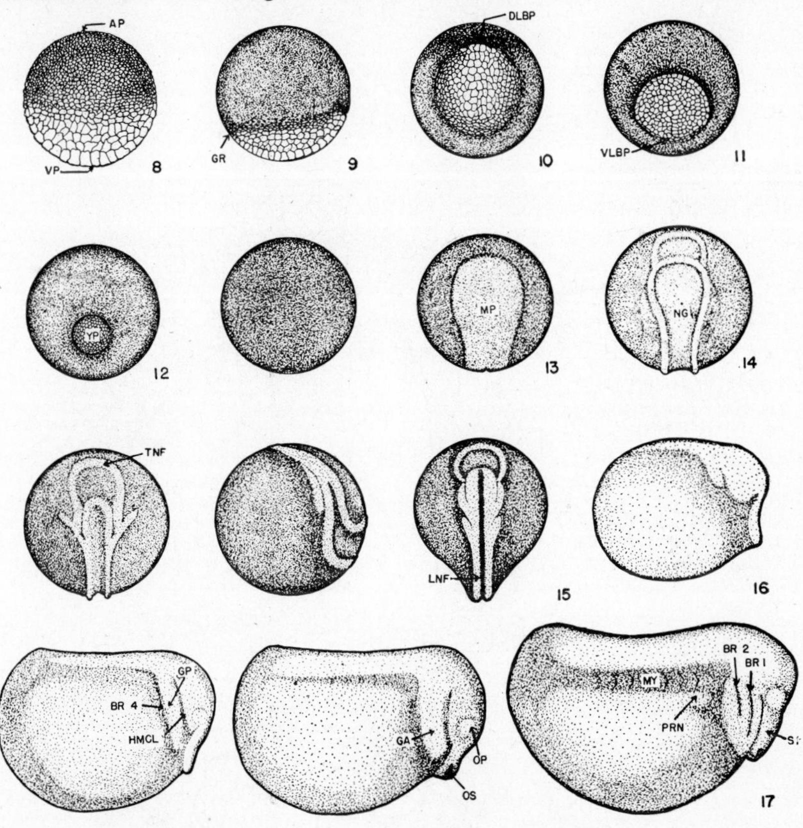

Blastula to tail bud stages. (AP) Animal pole. (BR 1) First branchial cleft. (BR 2) Second branchial cleft. (BR 4) Fourth branchial cleft. (DLBP) Dorsal blastopore lip. (GA) Gill anlage. (GP) Gill plate. (GR) Germ ring. (HMCL) Hyomandibular cleft. (LNF) Lateral neural fold. (MP) Medullary plate. (MY) Myotome. (NG) Neural groove. (OP) Optic vesicle. (OS) Oral sucker. (PRN) Pronephric region. (SP) Sense plate. (TNF) Transverse neural fold. (VP) Vegetal pole. (VLBP) Ventral blastopore lip. (YP) Yolk plug.

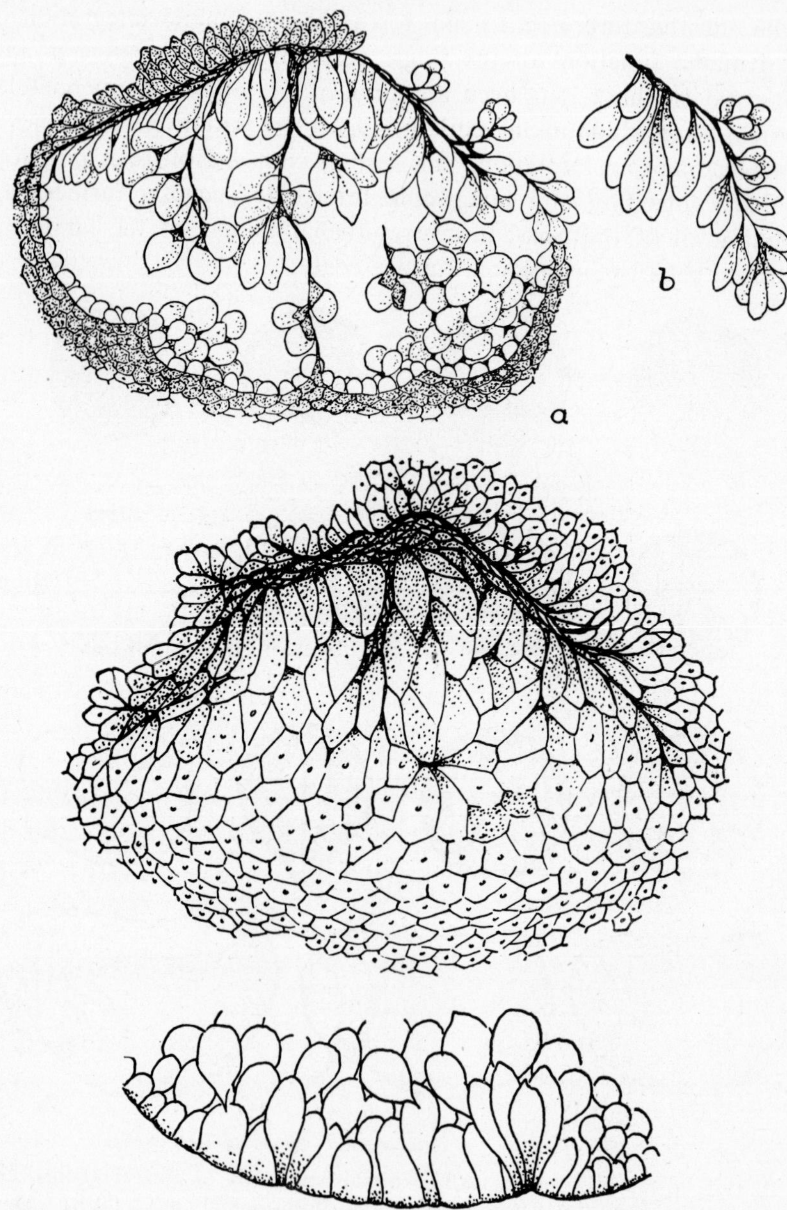

(*Top*) *Triturus torosus,* gastrula. (a) Surface view of the blastoporal region after part of the surface layer has been removed. (b) Isolated bunch of flask cells from the lateral blastoporus lip, containing larger endodermal and smaller mesodermal cells. (*Center*) *A. punctatum,* gastrula. Surface view of the blasto-

(*Continued on facing page.*)

The blastula stage is held to a spherical aggregate by the presence of this surface coating. However, since the coating is not itself divided with each cleavage, but simply folds into the furrows between blastomeres, the inner boundaries of the cells do not have the same dominating force that is present on the outer surface. Such cells are found to be interconnected by slender and temporary processes. The formation of cells, once thought to be the cause of gastrular movements, is now thought to be merely a convenience for the execution of such movements.

Epiboly in the frog is the concern of this surface coat rather than of individual cells. It is due to the expansive nature of the surface coating while it is in contact with a suitable substratum. The potential ectoderm (animal hemisphere cells) and the potential endoderm (vegetal hemisphere cells) are, in fact, competitors in the tendency to cover the surface area. The driving force is this surface coat, and for some reason the potential of the animal hemisphere portion of it is greater than the potential of the surface coat of the vegetal hemisphere.

Definition of the Major Processes of Gastrulation

Gastrulation is now recognized as an extremely complicated but highly integrated and dynamic change in the embryo, brought about by a combination of physical and chemical forces arising intrinsically but subject to extrinsic factors. We do not yet fully understand the process in any animal, particularly because of the elusive nature of the forces involved. Gastrulation is concerned with cell movements, changes in physical tension, and in the metabolism of carbohydrates, proteins, and possibly even the lipids.

Before attempting to describe the process as it occurs in the frog, it would be well for us to have a clear-cut understanding of the meaning of the various terms often encountered in such a description. The student is advised to consult frequently the Glossary at the end of this text, not only while reading this section but also throughout the discussion of embryology as a scientific subject.

(*Continued from opposite page.*)

pore showing the accumulation of pigment and the stretching of the cells toward the lines of invagination. (*Bottom*) *A. punctatum,* blastula. Section of the prospective blastoporal region. Note the black streaks of condensed coat material, and the flask cells attached to it. (Courtesy, Holtfreter, **1943,** *J. Exper. Zoöl.,* **94**:261.)

Invagination—As used by Vogt, this term means insinking (Einstulping in German) of the egg surface followed by the forward migration (Vordringen) which involves the displacement of inner materials. Schechtman uses the term to mean an inward movement, without any reference to whether there is pulling, pushing, or autonomous movement. There is probably some invagination in gastrulation of the frog's egg.

Involution—As used by Vogt, this term means a turning inward, a rotation of material upon itself so that the movement is directed toward the interior of the egg. Involution does occur in the frog's egg gastrulation.

Delamination—This is a splitting-off process whereby the outer layer of ectoderm gives rise to an inner sheet of cells known as the endoderm. It does not occur in the frog's egg gastrulation.

Epiboly—This is a progressive extension of the cortical layer of the animal hemisphere toward the vegetal hemisphere, or a sort of expansion from animal toward the vegetal hemisphere. In some eggs (e.g., the mollusk Crepidula) it actually involves an overgrowth by smaller cells over the larger vegetal hemisphere cells. The extension type of epiboly does occur in the frog's egg gastrulation.

Extension—This term is used by Schechtman to describe in amphibia the self-stretching process which seems intrinsic within certain cell areas, particularly in the dorsal region of the marginal zone. It is

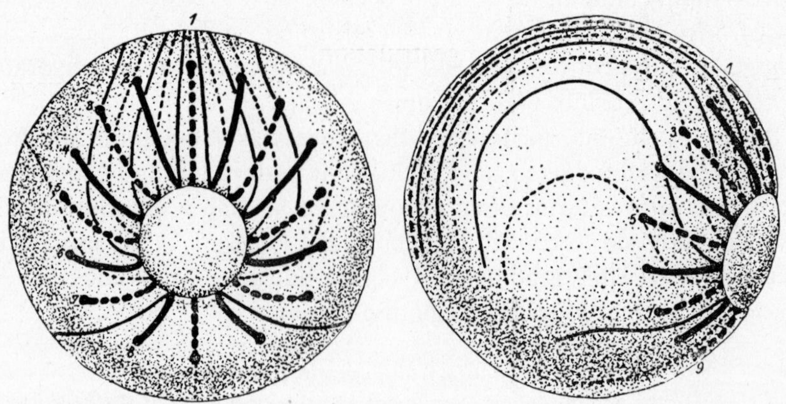

Diagrams to show the directions of movement and the displacement of the parts of the blastula in the process of gastrulation in amphibia. (After W. Vogt, 1929b. From Spemann: "Embryonic Development and Induction," New Haven, Yale University Press.)

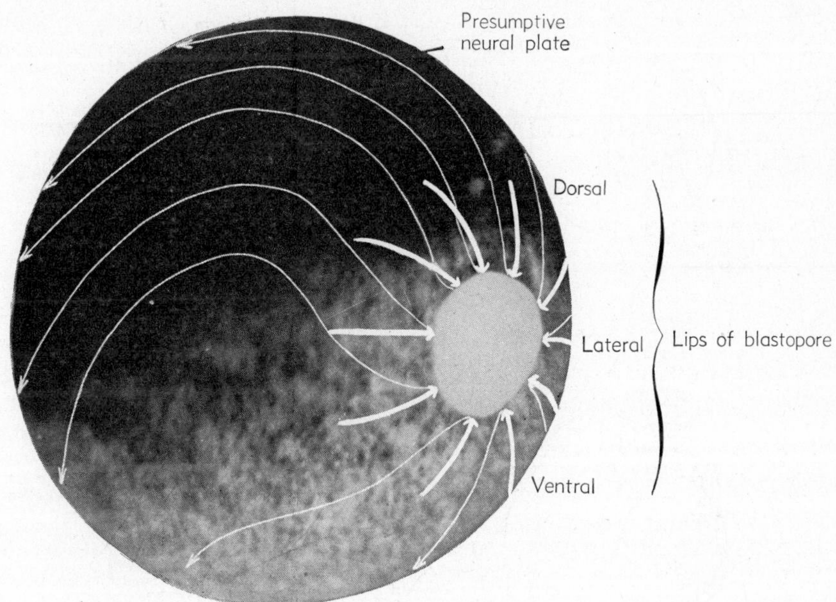

Involutional movements during gastrulation outlined on the living gastrula.

synonymous with elongation (or Strekung of Vogt), and probably occurs in the frog's egg gastrulation.

Constriction—This term is used to describe the convergence of cell areas resulting in the gradual closure of the blastopore. It is due to a narrowing of the marginal zone and a pull, or tension, of the dorsal lip. This occurs in the frog's egg gastrulation.

Dorsal convergence—This is the dorsal Raffung of Vogt, used to describe the movement of the marginal zone cell areas toward the dorsal mid-line during involution and invagination.

With this general introduction to a very fascinating but, as yet, little understood phase of embryological development, we shall retrace the steps to the late blastula stage and endeavor to anticipate the process of gastrulation in the frog.

Gastrulation Proper

To understand the processes to be described as gastrulation, let us list in succession the changes that may be observed in the frog embryo.

1. *Thinning of the gray crescent side of the blastula wall.* There appears to be an actual migration of cells from the deeper layers

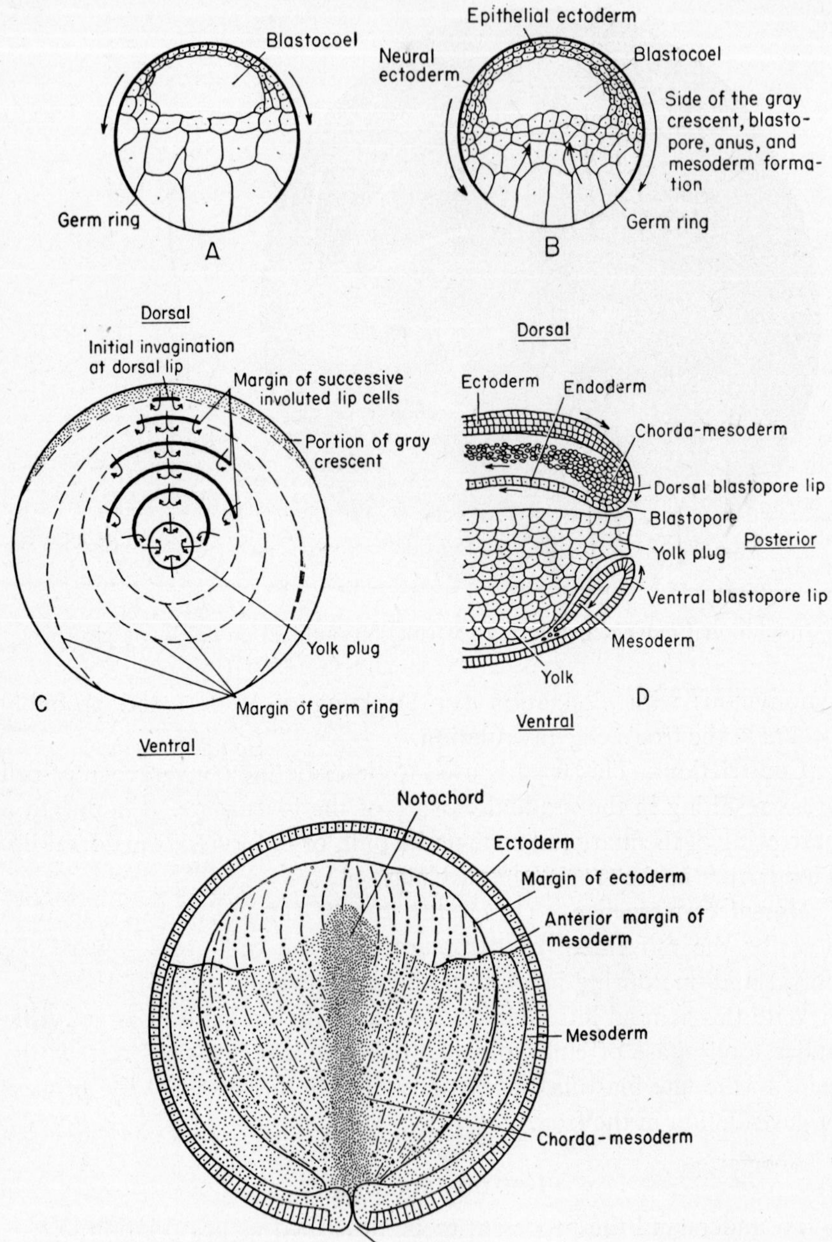

The process of gastrulation. (A) The blastula stage, prior to any gastrulation movement. (B) Movement of the blastula cells preliminary to gastrulation. (*Continued on facing page.*)

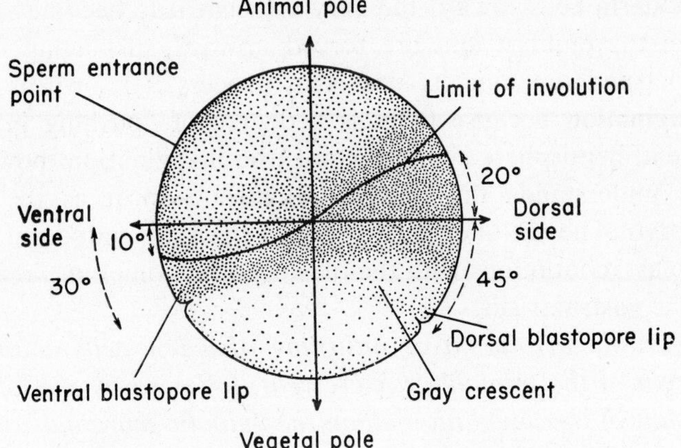

Surface changes during gastrulation. (Modified from Pasteels.)

of the blastula away from the original site of the gray crescent. This is the region where involution will first take place, the region which will come to be known as the dorsal lip of the blastopore. The blastula wall which is equatorially opposite to the gray crescent side may, in consequence, become several cells thicker.

2. *Continued epiboly or extension of the marginal cell zone toward the vegetal hemisphere, so that the diameter of the marginal zone becomes progressively smaller as it passes below the equator.* The marginal zone attains increasing rigidity so that it exerts an inward pressure on the yolk cells which are being encircled, causing them to be arched upward toward the blastocoel. One might draw the simile of an overlapping rubber membrane being drawn down over a mass of slightly less resistant material, toward the center of which there is a cavity. The yolk

---

(*Continued from opposite page.*)

(C) Blastoporal view of successive phases of gastrulation; (*solid line*) lip of blastopore, (*dotted line*) germ ring, to be subsequently incorporated into the blastoporal lips. (D) Lateral view of sagittal section during late gastrulation showing the origin of the mesial notochord, and the lateral mesoderm from the proliferated chorda-mesoderm cells at the dorsal lip. (E) Composite drawing to illustrate the germ layer relations in the later gastrula of the frog. The medullary plate (ectoderm) is not indicated; (*alternate dots and dashes*) notochord, (*heavy stippling*) notochord, (*sparse stippling*) mesoderm, (cellular markings) ectoderm.

endoderm cells toward the gray crescent side become separated from the epiblast and are forced upward, displacing the blastocoel and reducing its size. This process is known as **pseudo-invagination** because there is a degree of "pushing in" of the vegetal hemisphere cells. It is not true invagination, however, as one understands the process in such a form as the starfish embryo. The slit-like space between the yolk endoderm and the epiblast, continuous with the blastocoel, is sometimes referred to as the **gastrular slit.**

3. *The initial involution or inturning of a few cells at the lower margin of the original gray crescent, followed by the lateral extension of this involution along the epibolic marginal zone.* This region of initial involution becomes the dorsal lip of the blastopore. The marginal zone cells become separated from the more ventral and lighter colored yolk cells. The first cells to involute do not lose continuity with their neighbors, but carry with them the adjacent, contiguous lateral cells of the marginal zone. The infolding or inturning process therefore begins at one point but is continued around the marginal zone.
4. *Further epiboly of the entire marginal zone toward the vegetal hemisphere, apparently interrupted only at the levels of involution.* The inturning cells are rolling under themselves like an oncoming wave. The margin of the wave continues, through epiboly, to move toward the vegetal hemisphere but at a rate which seems slower than that of the marginal zone which has not yet involuted (i.e., opposite the dorsal lip cells). In other words, cells are moving inwardly over the dorsal lip of the blastopore, but the margin of the lip itself is moving vegetally as a result of epibolic extension. Some epibolic movement is absorbed in involution.
5. *The piling up or confluence of animal hemisphere cells, many of which are destined to move inside over the blastoporal lips.*
6. *The continued lateral extension of the involuting marginal zone cells so that there is eventually a circumferential meeting of the blastoporal lips.* These comprise the dorsal, lateral, and ventral lips of the blastopore, not clearly demarked. The vegetal hemisphere cells, which are now exposed within a ring of involuted marginal zone (lip) cells, are collectively known as the "yolk plug." The term yolk plug is used because the cells of the pig-

mented marginal zone (blastoporal lips) are in sharp contrast with the surrounded vegetal pole yolk-laden cells.

7. *The future epiboly of the marginal zone, accompanying involution at all points, resulting in a continued reduction in the size of the circumblastoporal lips and of the exposed yolk plug.* The margins of the yolk plug are at first round, then vertically oval, and finally the lateral lips of the blastopore approach each other to form a vertical slit as the yolk plug is closed over and disappears within.
8. *The origin of the internal or second layer of cells, arising from the involuted dorsal lip cells and collectively known as the* **endoderm.** This sheet of cells fans out within the embryo to give rise very soon to a new cavity, the **gastrocoel** or **archenteron.** Since these inturning cells give rise largely to the roof and lateral walls of the archenteron, those parts of the cavity will be lined with somewhat pigmented cells from the original epiblast. There is a gradation or lessening of this pigment in the archenteric roof cells as one progresses anteriorly in the gastrula.
9. *Simultaneously with the origin of the inner layer of endoderm, some cells are proliferated off into the gastrular slit, between the roof of the archenteron and the dorsal epiblast, which cells will become the notochord.* Before differentiation these cells are called chorda-mesoderm. Since the lips of the blastopore are circular, this proliferated mass of cells also becomes circular. The more lateral and also the ventral proliferations become mesoderm. There arises, therefore, the dorsal notochord and the lateral and ventral mesoderm as a circle of tissue within the fold of the blastoporal lips, occupying the space between the epiblast and either the inner endoderm or yolk endoderm.

By this time the student must have realized that gastrulation is a highly integrated mosaic of motions which are purposeful in that they achieve the state of the completed gastrula. Spemann aptly wrote:

However harmonious the process of motion may be by which the material for the chief organs arrives at the final place, and however accurately the single movements may fit together . . . they are nevertheless no longer causally connected, at least from the beginning of gastrulation onward. Rather, each part has already previously had impressed upon it in some way or other, direction and limitation of movement. The movements are regulated, not in a coarse mechanical manner, through pressure and pull of simple parts—but they are ordered according to a definite plan. After an

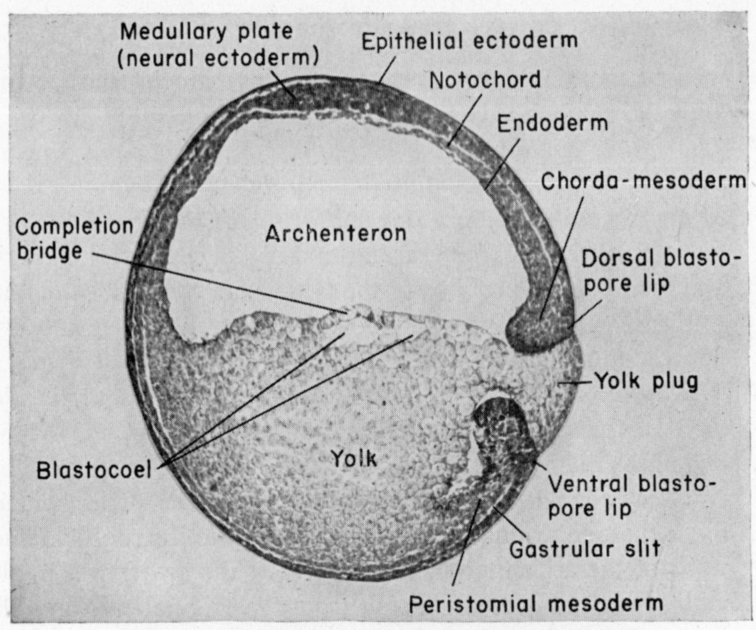

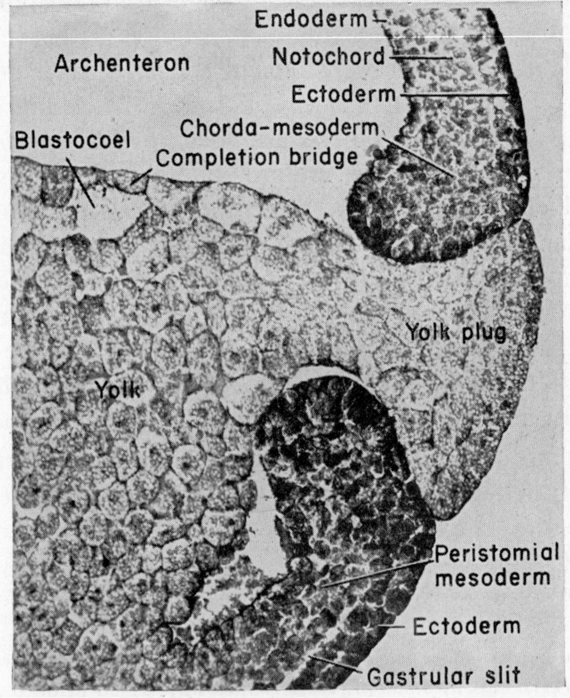

Gastrulation and mesoderm formation. (*Top*) Photograph of sagittal section through the blastopore. (*Bottom*) Enlarged photograph similar to above illustration. Note the continuity of the ventral ectoderm and peristomial mesoderm. (*Continued on facing page.*)

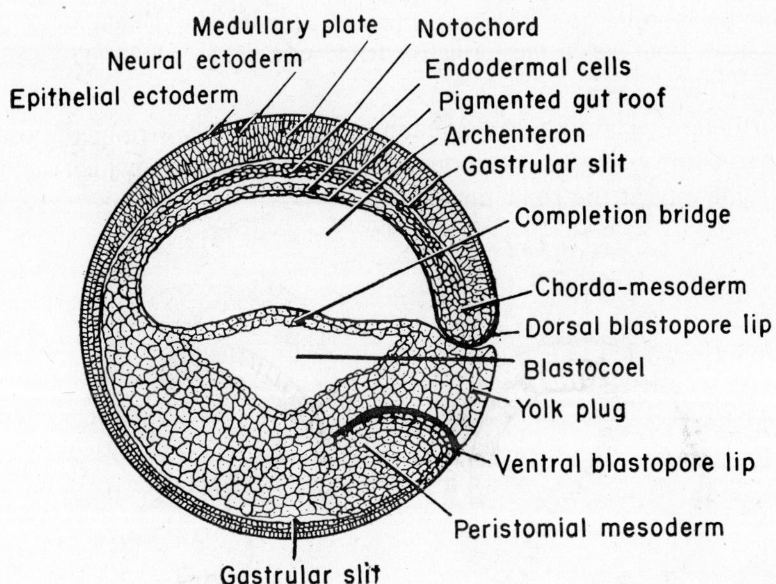

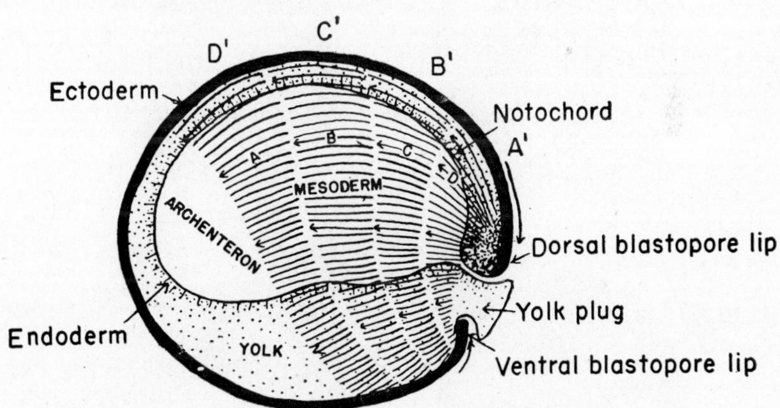

Gastrulation and mesoderm formation—(*Continued*). (*Top*) Drawing to be compared with top illustration on facing page. (*Bottom*) Schematic diagram to show progression, internally, of the mesoderm.

exact patterned arrangement, they take their course according to independent formative tendencies *which originate in the parts themselves.* Thus we find in the gastrula stage a mosaic, a pattern of parts with definite formative tendencies from which the formative tendencies of the whole must necessarily follow.

Gastrulation, according to Spemann, is an intricately arranged mosaic of parts possessing autonomous movement potentials which act in the right way at the right time.

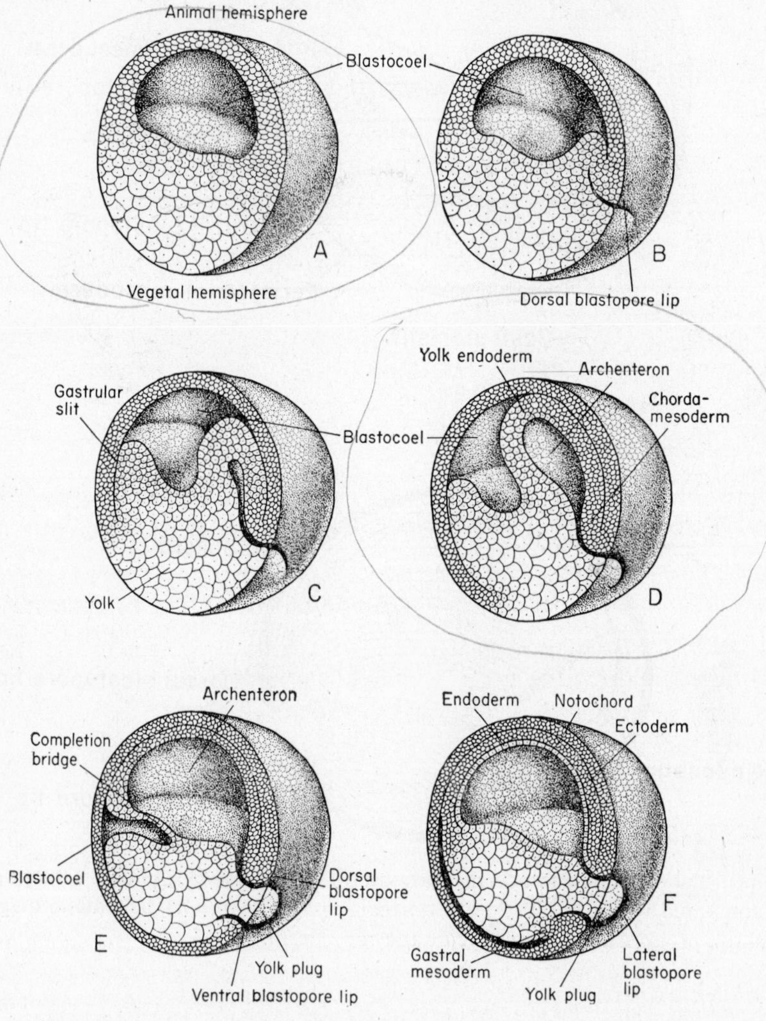

Blastula to gastrula stages in the frog. Shown by stereograms.

(*Continued on facing page.*)

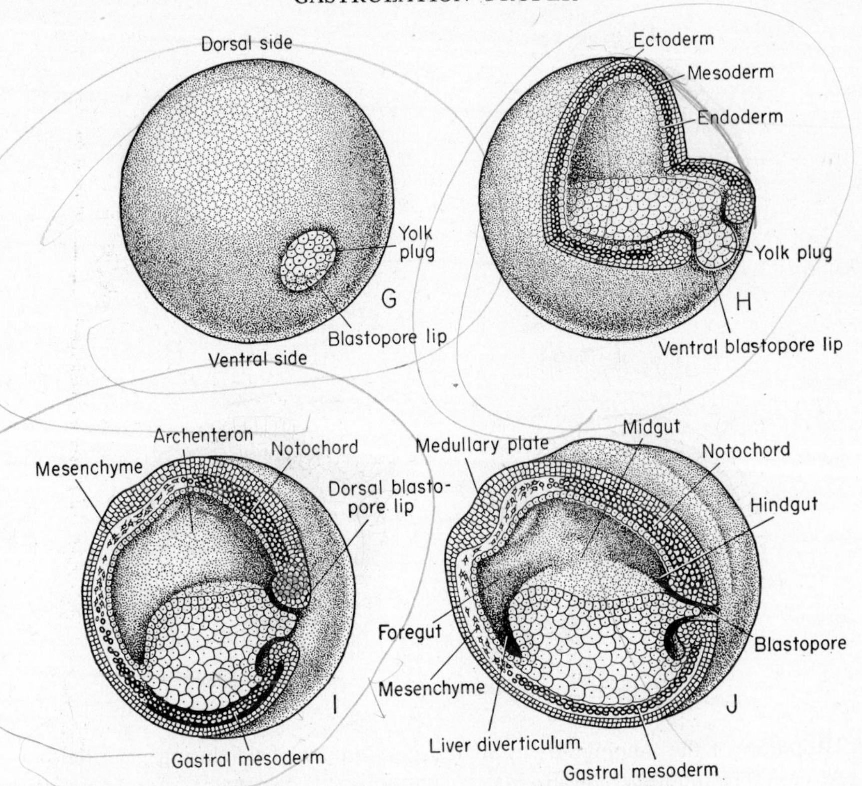

Blastula to gastrula stages in the frog—(*Continued*) Shown by stereograms. (Modified and redrawn from Huettner.)

The forces which bring about the initial involution or inturning of cells at a specific point of the marginal zone to form the dorsal lip of the blastopore have not yet been identified. The nearest approach to a valid explanation is that of Holtfreter. He says:

> The alkalinity of the blastocoel can be assumed to be strong enough to establish, in cooperation with the suspended protein particles, an efficient gradient of surface tension between the internal and external medium, as envisaged by Rhumbler. Those cells which are in interfacial contact with both media would be primarily affected by it. They will tend to move in the direction of the surface tension lowering alkaline medium, and to reduce their contact area with the external medium having a higher surface tension. Being, however, attached to the peripheral coat they can only stretch along the gradient, assuming a shape which can be expected to correspond to those claviform cells which we find in all cases where invagination takes place. The perpendicular stretching will have to continue as long as the gradient

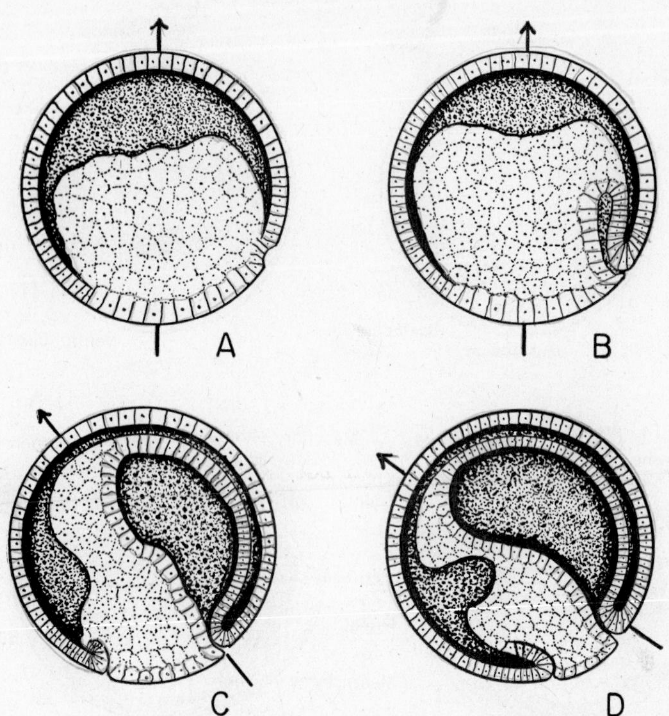

Rotation of the amphibian egg in the gravitational field during gastrulation. (After V. Hamburger and B. Mayer, unpublished. Redrawn from Spemann: "Embryonic Development and Induction," New Haven, Yale University Press.)

persists and until the cells have attained a position where their potential energy is lowered to a least possible value. This movement is, however, conditioned by the cellular plasticity which is restricted. Thanks to the tensile strength of the cell wall, the attenuated neck portion is subjected to an increasing mechanical stress. *The surface yields and is pulled inside in the form of the archenteron.*

Schechtman (1942) calls involution an "insinking" and then explains what follows, after having demonstrated that various areas of the pre-gastrula have various types of autonomous movement. He says:

Gastrulation begins with autonomous movements; the in-sinking of the presumptive pharyngeal endoderm, the stretching of the marginal zone toward the blastoporal groove, the forward migration of the internally situated marginal material along the underside of the animal hemisphere. As the stretching presumptive chordal region comes to the edge of the blastoporal lip, it is progressively carried under by the invagination and involution of the adjacent portions of the marginal zone. This insures that the presumptive chorda is in a position to exert a double effect by means of its extension, for it will not only pull the lateral marginal zones dorsalward, but will also carry them forward in a dorsal position. Meanwhile the blastoporal lips are constricted, since there is progressive withdrawal of marginal zone material by the process of dorsalward convergence somewhat as the mouth of a purse is constricted when the purse string is pulled. The tendency of constriction is augmented further by the forward migration of the internal portions of the marginal zone, for this movement also tends to withdraw material from the region of the blastoporal lips.

In summary, Schechtman believes:

1. The presumptive chorda is invaginated by the inwardly directed tension or pull exerted by the invagination and involution of the lateral marginal zone, with which it is continuous.
2. The lateral marginal zones are then pulled dorsalward and inward in the dorsal position by the autonomous stretching and simultaneous narrowing of the presumptive chorda.
3. The constriction of the blastoporal lips over the yolk mass is affected by the progressive withdrawal of marginal zone material by dorsalward convergence.

Internally the involuted cells extend anteriorly, away from the point of involution or the dorsal lip of the blastopore. The inturned endoderm surrounds the new cavity, which is at first no more than a slit. The cavity (archenteron) rapidly expands in all directions so that the blastocoel, originally in a dorsal position, becomes progressively displaced anteriorly or away from the side of the blastopore formation. The blastocoel is later displaced antero-ventrally by this expanding archenteron. It also becomes reduced in size until finally it is found only as the slit between the endoderm and the yolk, referred to as the gastrular slit. Sometimes there is a remnant of the blastocoel, separated from the archenteron by a single layer of cells called the **completion bridge.** This bridge is of no consequence, and frequently ruptures to merge the contents of the blastocoel and the gastrocoel.

These movements of involuting cells and expanding endoderm result in an enlarged archenteron (gastrocoel), entirely lined with endoderm. As stated, the roof and lateral wall cells are more pigmented than the yolk endoderm floor cells of the archenteron. The opening beneath the dorsal lip of the blastopore, and into the archenteron, is called the blastopore. This is an incorrect term, however, for

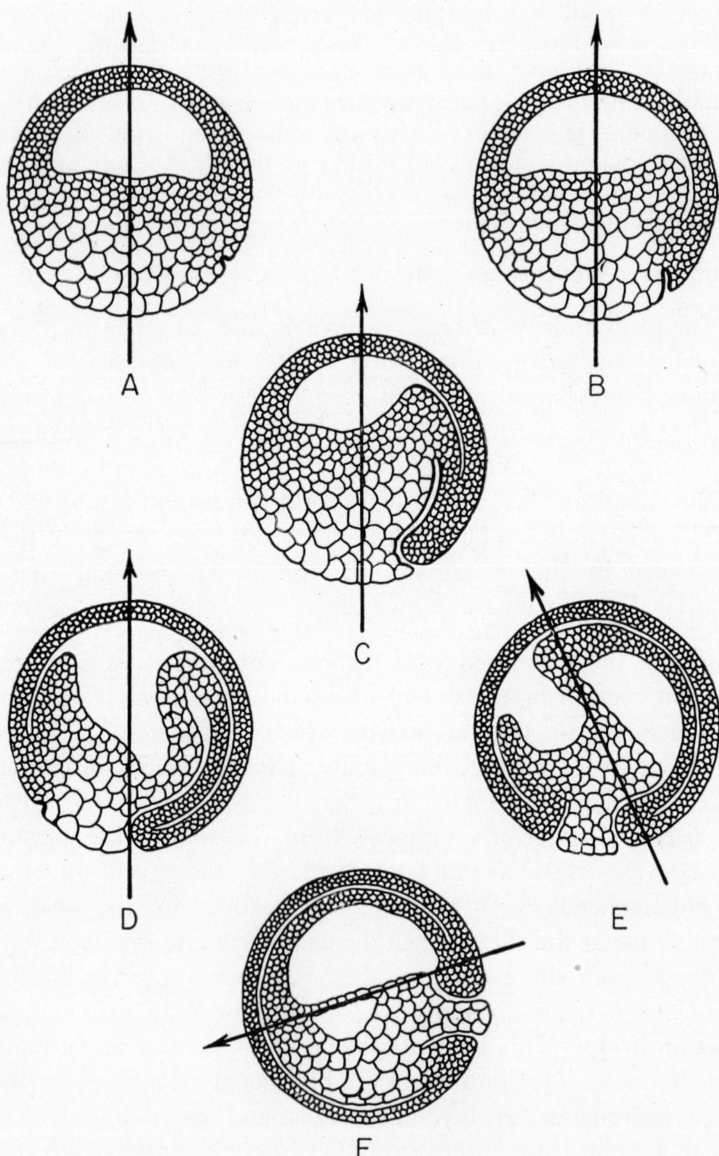

Rotation of the amphibian egg during gastrulation, due to the development of the internal cavity, the archenteron. (Redrawn from Kopsch.)

the pore opens into the gastrocoel and not into the blastocoel. The blastopore is occluded by the yolk endoderm cells but later opens into the perivitelline space by the withdrawal of the yolk plug. It will close ultimately with the development of tail mesoderm.

The reduction of the blastocoel and the enlargement of the archenteron together alter the gravitational axis of the entire embryonic mass, shifting it about 90° away from the position of the blastopore. The yolk plug, instead of remaining in a ventral position, comes to lie about the level of the original equator. This all occurs while the embryo lies free within its fertilization membrane. Further, the presence of the archenteric roof and the chorda-mesoderm cells above it cause the overlying ectoderm to thicken and the whole embryo becomes elongated in an antero-posterior direction, more or less horizontal to the revised center of gravity. The yolk plug now marks the posterior region of the future embryo.

It must be emphasized that, during this shift in the gravitational axis, there has not been a comparable shifting of the internal relationships of the embryo. The blastopore and all related parts of the embryo have been rotated dorsally, within the enveloping fertilization membrane. The axis of the gastrula is simply altered by the development of this new cavity, the archenteron, with its consequent obliteration of the blastocoel.

CHAPTER EIGHT

Neurulation and Early Organogeny

Neurulation

The axes of the embryo are altered by the development of the archenteron. The **antero-posterior axis** is made obvious by the development of the neural axis. Either the roof of the archenteron and/or the notochord induces, in the overlying ectoderm, the formation of a thickening, limited to the nervous layer. This becomes the **medullary** (or neural) **plate** which extends from the dorsal lip of the blastopore in an anterior direction as a median band of thickened ectoderm which widens anteriorly where the brain will develop.

Shortly the more or less parallel lateral margins of the thickened medullary plate become even more thickened as the **lateral folds** or ridges, and are continued anteriorly as the **transverse neural fold** or ridge. A longitudinal **neural groove** or depression appears in the center of the medullary plate, so that the height of the neural folds appears to be accentuated. This is the very beginning of the formation of the **central nervous system,** induced by the presence beneath of the archenteric roof and/or the notochord.

The following description covers the period from the time the medullary plate first thickens until about the time the embryo reaches the 2.5 mm. stage. At this time the embryo shows ciliary movement within its jelly capsule. These cilia are lost, except on the tail, by the time the 11 mm. stage is reached.

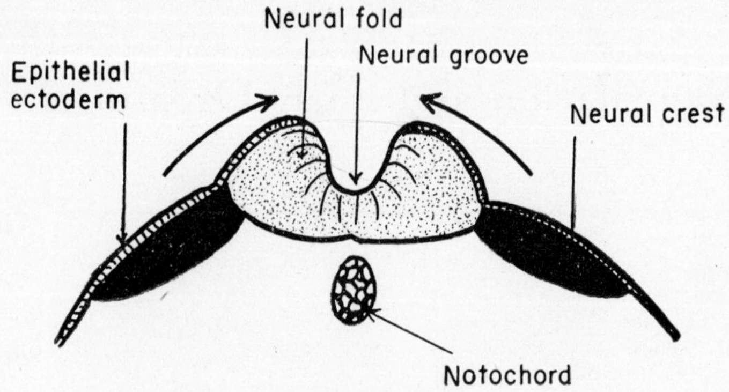

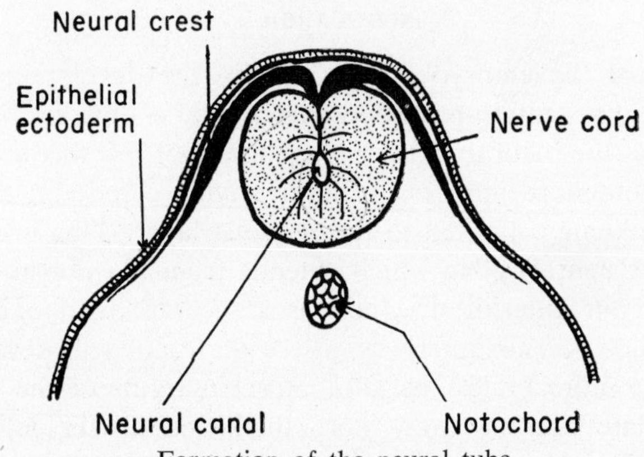

Formation of the neural tube.

Early Organogeny

Surface Changes

The oval-shaped gastrula quickly becomes elongated and the medullary plate provides a slightly elevated (convex) dorsal surface. This soon changes to a flattened and then a concave upper surface, as the development of the central nervous system proceeds. At this time the embryo acquires a distinct head and a body which is ovoid because of the mass of contained yolk.

The appearance of the thickened and elongating medullary plate and the subsequent formation of a **neural tube** is the main causal factor in the change in shape of the embryo, which follows upon gastrulation. In fact, it may well be the autonomous powers of elongation of the presumptive notochord that are responsible for

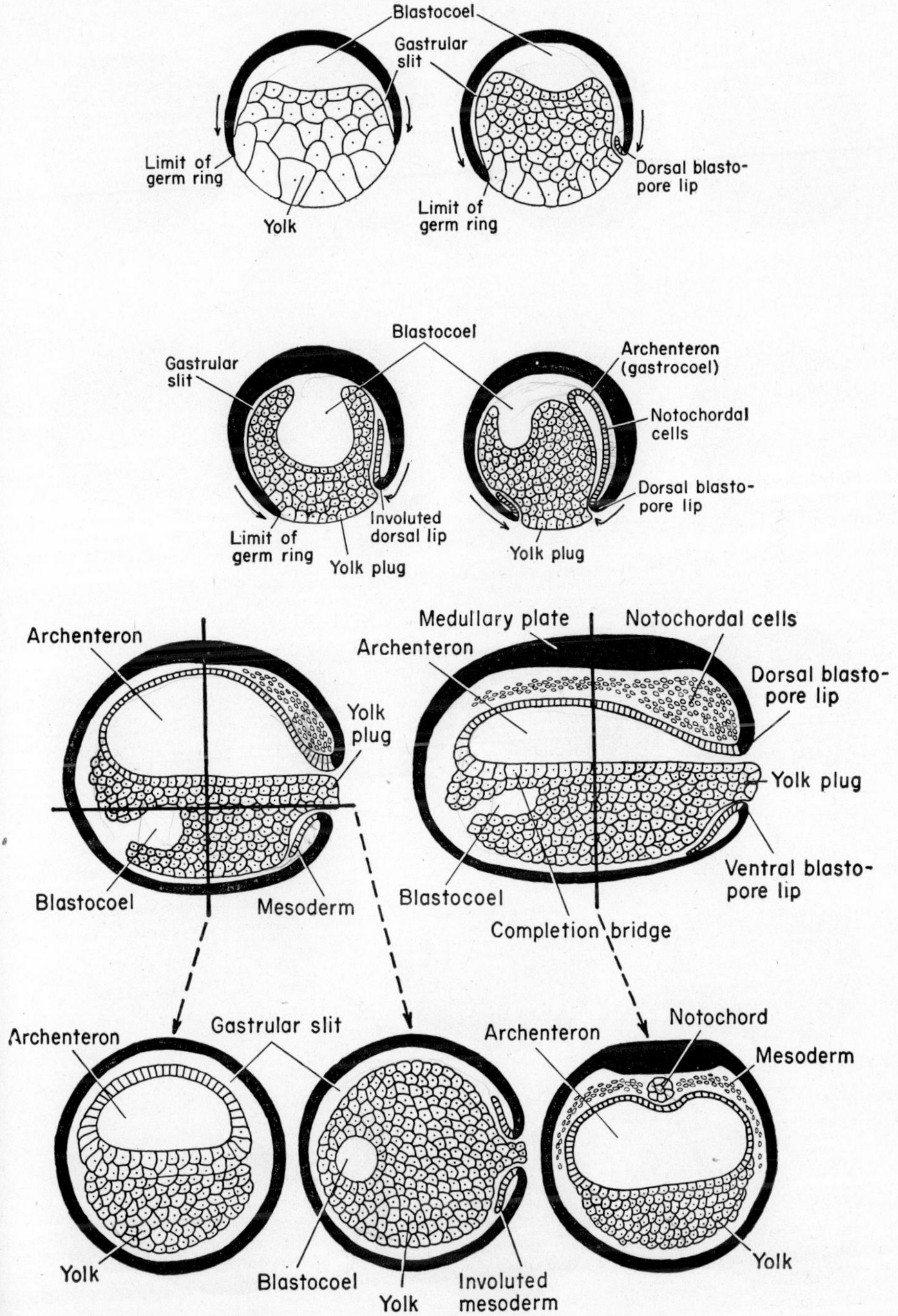

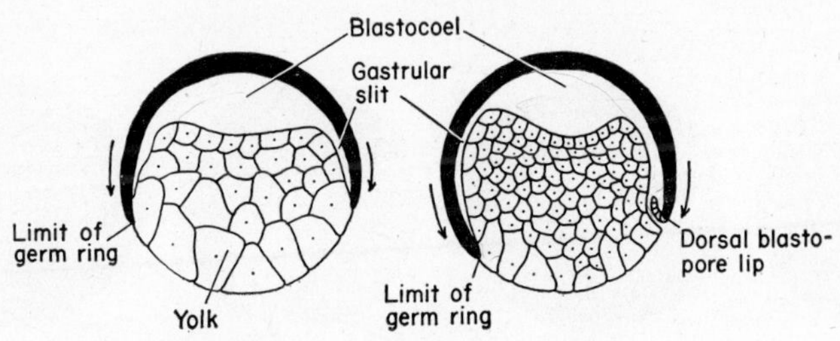

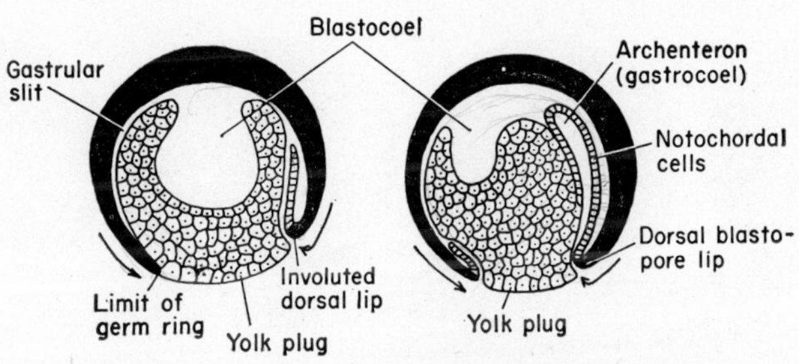

Gastrulation and early neurulation in the frog; (*solid*) ectoderm, (*cellular*) endoderm and yolk, (*striated*) mesoderm, (*circles*) presumptive notochord and mesoderm.

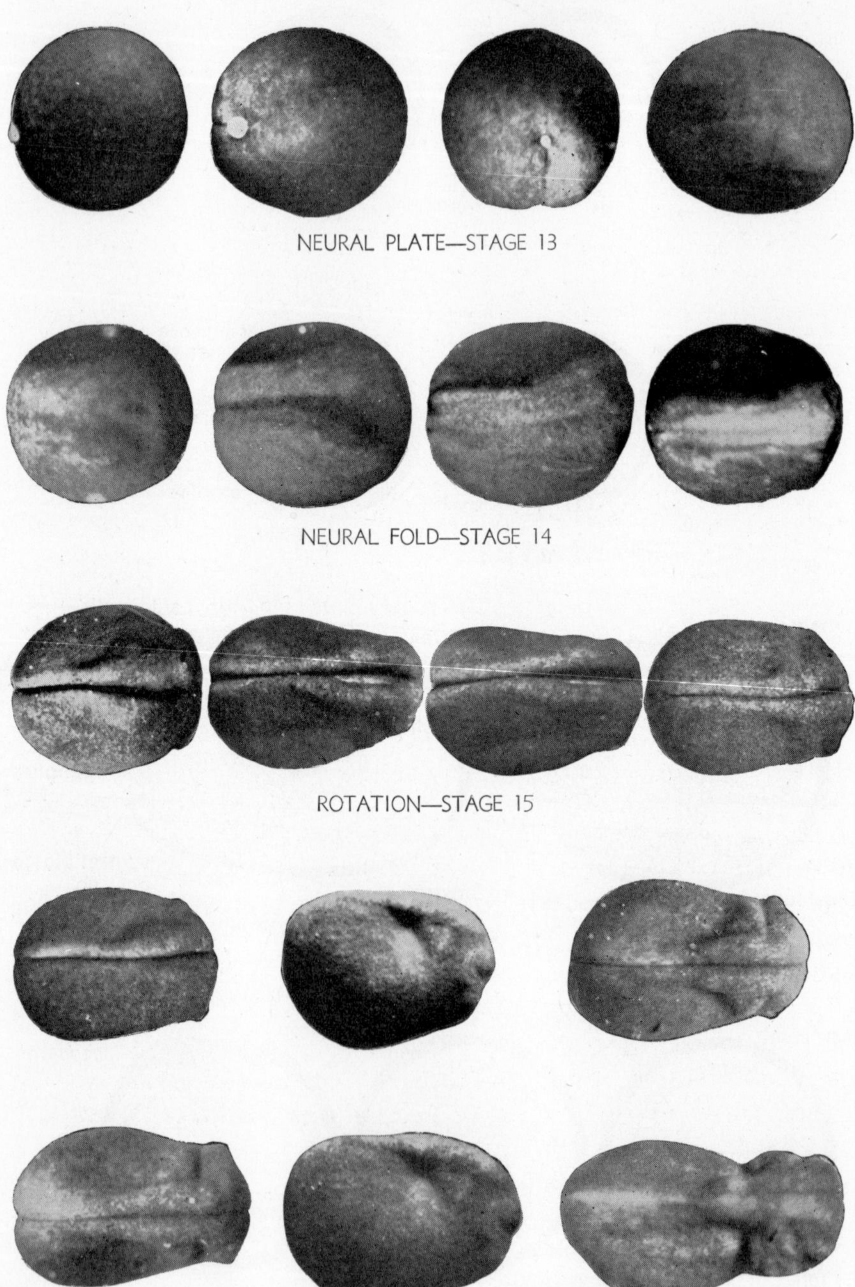

Development of the frog (*Rana pipiens*) from the yolk plug stage to the neurula.

the general elongation of the entire embryo and its contained archenteron. At this stage, when the primary nervous structures are being formed, the embryo is known as a **neurula.**

The medullary or neural plate extends from the dorsal lip of the blastopore to the anterior limit of the developing embryo, where it appears somewhat rounded in contour. The elevated neural folds are therefore continuous around the margins of this thickened medullary plate, the anterior junction of the folds being designated as the **transverse neural fold** to distinguish it from the paired, extensive and more posterior **lateral neural folds.** This transverse neural fold represents, then, the anterior extremity of the developing brain. The regions of the lateral neural folds represent the posterior parts of the brain and the spinal cord levels.

These lateral neural folds move toward each other and first make contact at a point slightly anterior to the center of the original medullary plate, a region which will be identified later as the level of the **medulla** of the brain. From this initial point of contact the neural folds come together and fuse in both an anterior and a posterior direction, thus converting a groove into a closed canal, the medullary (neural) tube or **neurocoel.** Obviously, fusion will occur last at the extremities, the anterior one being called the **anterior neuropore** and the posterior one the **blastopore.** At the posterior end the medullary (neural) folds merge into the sides of the blastopore. As the folds meet they cover over this blastopore and the enteron is therefore no longer opened to the exterior (by way of the blastopore) but into the posterior end of the neurocoel. The original blastopore then becomes a temporary tube-like connection between the gut and the nervous system, known as the **neurenteric canal.**

As the neural folds fuse and the neurocoel becomes constricted off from the dorsal ectoderm, the latter becomes a continuous sheet of cells above the mid-dorsal line. The enclosed canal, lined with ciliated and pigmented ectoderm, is the neural canal or neurocoel which is found as the much-reduced **central canal** of the spinal cord and brain of the adult frog.

Slightly ventral to the anterior end of the closing neural folds there appears a semicircular elevated ridge of **ectoderm,** the two extensions of the elevation merging with the lateral limits of the transverse neural fold. This is called the **sense plate** which contains the material of the fifth and seventh cranial nerve ganglia. As the neural folds come to-

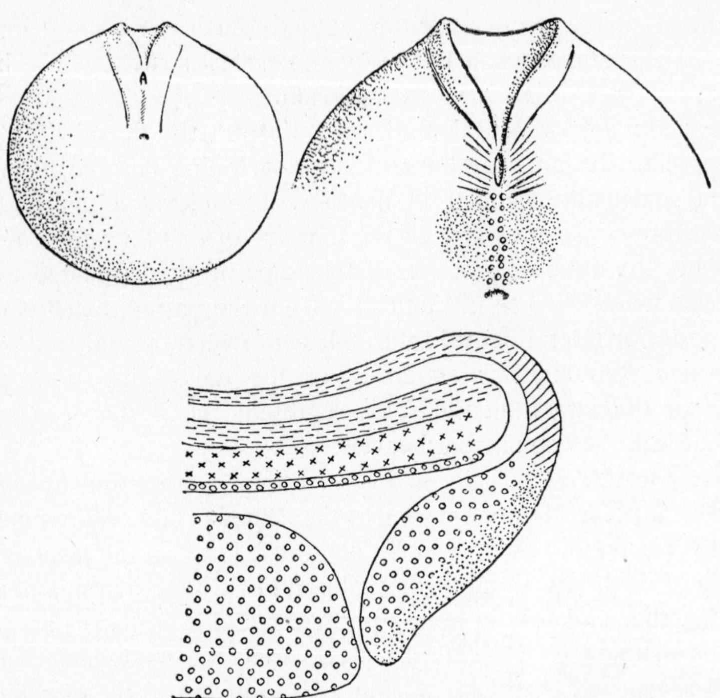

Early development of caudal structures. (*Top, left*) Posterior view of late neurula. (*Top, right*) Enlargement of illustration at top, left. (*Bottom*) Sagittal section through the posterior end; (*dashes*) nervous, (*circles*) entoblast (presumptive endoderm), (*crosses*) notochord, (*dots*) mesenchyme (presumptive mesoderm). (Pasteels, Jean, **1943,** Fermeture du blastopore, anus et intestin caudal chez les Amphibiens Anoures, *Acta Neerland. morphol.,* **5**:11.)

gether, this sense plate remains distinct (i.e., the sides do not become fused as do the neural folds), but its posterior limits merge with the outer margins of the lateral neural folds even after the fusion of the latter structures. These sense plates will give rise to the mandibular (first visceral) arches, lens of the eyes, nasal placodes, and oral suckers. The ridges are formed largely from **mesoderm** and will give rise to parts of the jaw apparatus. The superficial **suckers** are paired larval organs that take the shape of an inverted "U." They become glandular and form a mucous secretion which the larva uses to adhere to objects after hatching.

The anterior median level of the sense plate will shortly develop a vertical groove, the **stomodeal cleft,** which separates the two **mandibular ridges** (arches) or primordia of the right and left sides of the

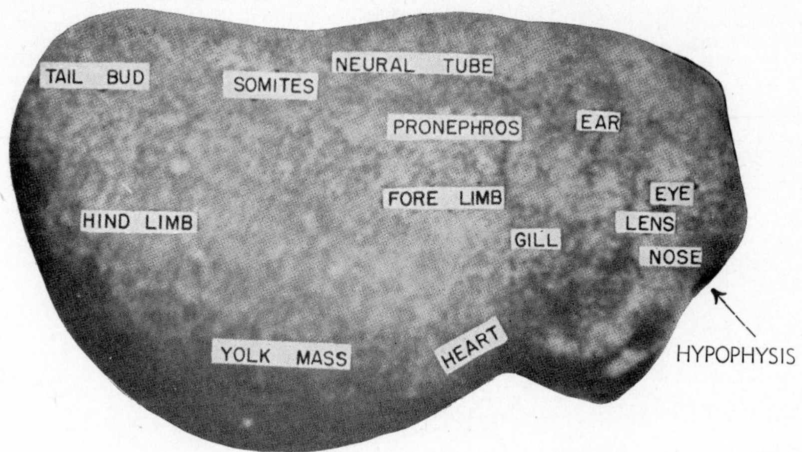

Organ fields or anlagen of the closed neural tube stage.

jaw. The **oral suckers** appear as V-shaped, pigmented, adhesive, mucus-secreting glands at the ventral end of each sense plate. They reach their maximum development at the 6 mm. stage and then begin

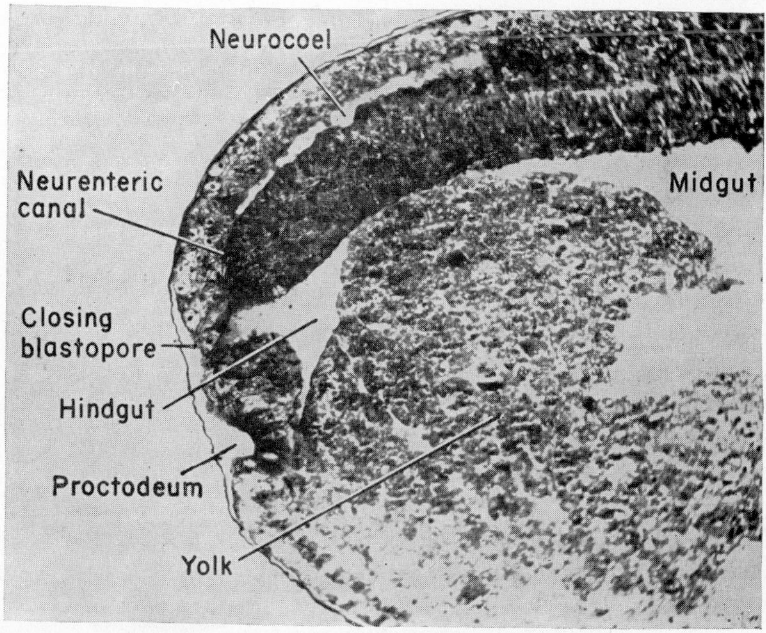

Photograph of the neurenteric canal of the late neurula stage in the frog: sagittal section.

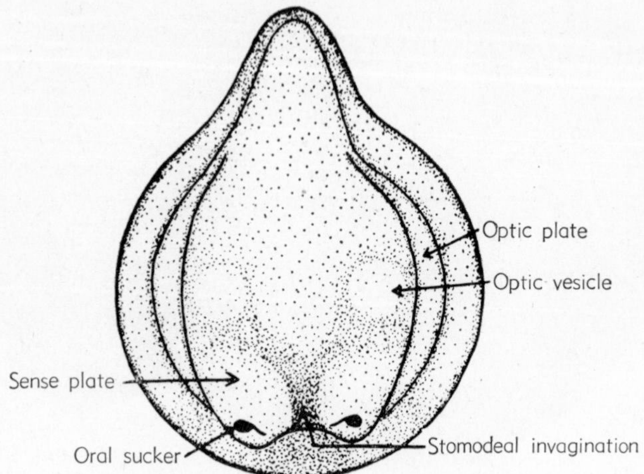

A face view of the 5 mm. frog tadpole.

to degenerate. The ventral limit of the vertical groove becomes the ectodermal **stomodeum** when it breaks through to the endodermal pharynx to form the mouth. That part of the mouth derived from the stomodeum will therefore be lined with ectoderm. The dorsal limit of the vertical groove becomes the hypophyseal invagination. Directly dorsal to each oral sucker, above and to either side of the stomodeal cleft, there develop large oval evaginations (bulbous out-

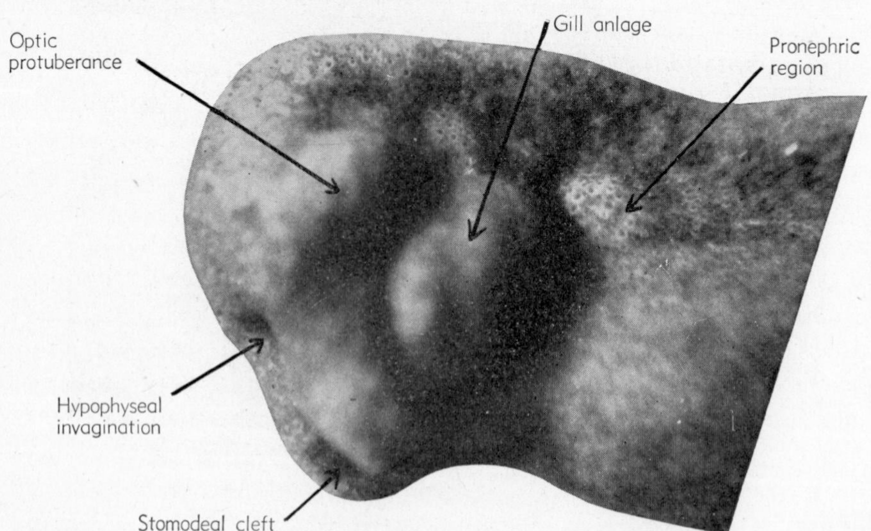

Anlagen of the head region: 5 mm. frog tadpole.

growths) which will be recognized as the external evidences of the internally enlarging **optic vesicles** or **opticoels.**

Visceral Arches

Parallel to the posterior margins of the sense plate there develops another thickened pair of elevations, directed forward. These are the **gill plates** which merge imperceptibly with the more posterior lateral folds of the sense plate and the closed neural folds. They contain the ninth and tenth cranial nerve ganglia and represent the forerunners of the gill or branchial arches. These are very important in the development of the external gills used for aquatic respiration in the tadpole. These gill plates acquire vertical grooves (furrows) which separate the intermediate bulges into three prominent vertical thickenings known as the **visceral** or **branchial arches.** The most anterior of the grooves appears between the mandibular arch of the sense plate and the first thickening of the gill plate and is known as the **hyomandibular groove** or **furrow.** This groove never really opens through from the outside to the pharynx as a cleft. Just posterior to this hyomandibular groove is the first gill thickening, the beginning of the **second visceral** or **hyoid arch** which will provide the mesodermal structures to the tongue and operculum. The fifth groove, the most posterior of all, is the next to develop. Then follow the third, fourth, and sixth visceral grooves (the fifth developing later), dividing the gill plate into vertical thickenings. The sixth is rudimentary and posterior to the gill plate. The visceral grooves appear in the sequence of I, II, III, IV, VI, V, counting from the anterior. The intermediate thickenings between the grooves are the visceral arches which remain rather solid, some of which will soon give rise to the external gills. Those which give rise to gills are sometimes referred to as branchial arches, the first of which is the third visceral arch.

The visceral arches, from the mandibular as the first, may be numbered in sequence in a posterior direction, and may be designated as visceral arches I to VI. However, since the third visceral arch becomes the first branchial arch because it is the most anterior arch to give rise to an external gill, to name the arches **"branchial"** one must begin with visceral arch III (called branchial arch I) and number them posteriorly as branchial arches I to IV.

The term "visceral arch" is used because of the homology of this structure with similar structures in other vertebrates, even though external gills are formed. In the frog, visceral arches III to VI develop external gills and they therefore can be properly called **"branchial arches."** A tabular comparison is given to clarify the distinction:

Original Structure	*Structure Formed*
Visceral arch I	Mandibular arch (jaw parts)
" " II	Hyoid arch (tongue and operculum)
" " III	Branchial arch I, first external gill
" " IV	" " II, second external gill
" " V	" " III, third external gill
" " VI	" " IV, rudimentary fourth external gill

Three, sometimes four, of the vertical (visceral) furrows will open through to the pharynx as clefts, functioning in gill respiration. They open in the following order: visceral clefts III, IV, II, and V. The presence and order of grooves therefore bears no relation to the break-through order of the clefts.

Following the hyomandibular groove in position, each is numbered in sequence as a **branchial cleft,** when all are developed. Branchial cleft I, for instance, is the slit from the outside to the pharynx just anterior to branchial arch II and immediately following the hyomandibular groove. Most of the arches are named for the gills to which they give rise. This is true except for the first (mandibular) and the second (hyoid). These do not give rise to gills but to jaw, tongue, and opercular parts. The confusion of the terms visceral and branchial need not be serious if we remember that all arches are visceral and are numbered from the anterior, while the third visceral arch is only the first branchial—i.e., the first to have gills.

Posterior to the dorsal limits of the gill plate will be seen (at the 2.5 mm. stage) a slightly elongated swelling in the direction of the embryonic axis. This is the surface indication of the internal enlargement of mesoderm known as the **pronephros** or head kidney. More posteriorly and slightly dorsal to this level may be seen the <-shaped surface indications of the internal, mesodermal **myotomes,** or muscle segments.

Origin of the Proctodeum and Tail

At the posterior end of the embryo in the neurula stage the neural folds converge, as do the lateral lips of the blastopore, so that they become confluent. The originally oval blastopore becomes a vertical slit, due to the active merging of the two lateral neural folds.

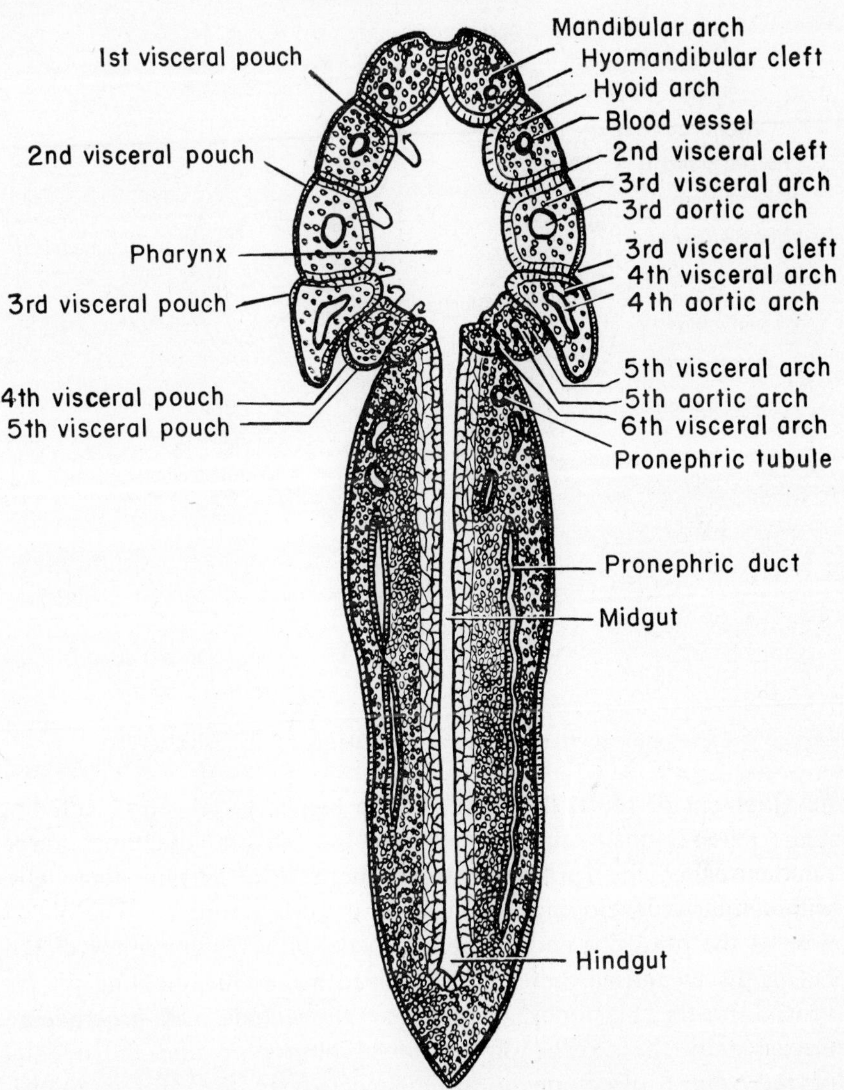

The 7 mm. frog tadpole: frontal section.

The lateral lips of the blastopore close together over the posterior end of the neurocoel above and the posterior end of the archenteron below. Internally this provides a temporary (about 1 hour) connection between the central nervous system (neurocoel) and the gut cavity (archenteron) known as the **neurenteric canal** or chorda-canal. Similar temporary connections of these two major systems are seen in the

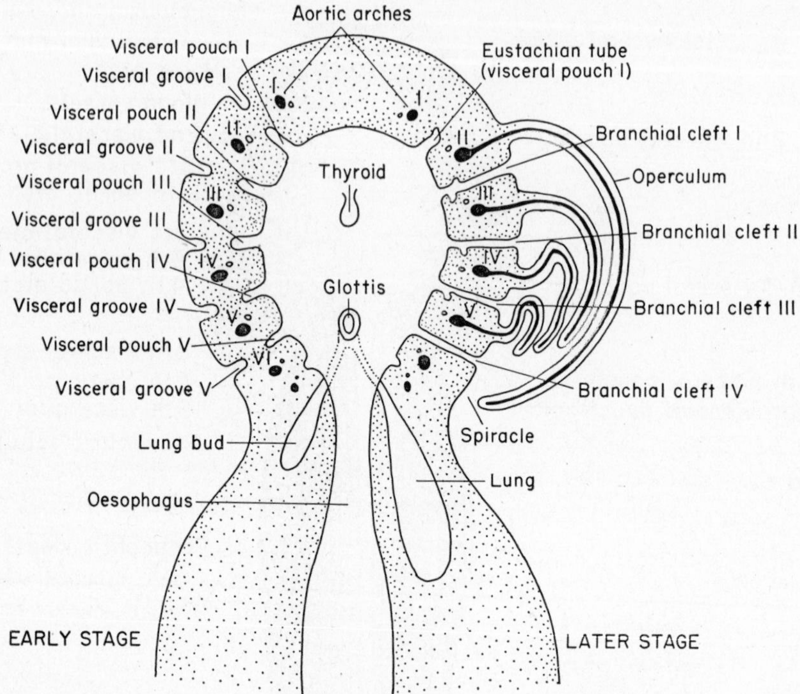

Development of the respiratory systems of the frog larvae.

development of most, if not all, of the higher vertebrates, including man. This region of approximation of the folds is sometimes unfortunately called the "primitive streak" because of certain homologies with similarly developing structures in the chick embryo. The blastopore at the posterior end of the neurocoel is now completely closed, but in the meantime there has developed a new invaginating pit just ventral to the blastopore, known as the ectodermal **proctodeum.** Occasionally the closing of the dorsal blastopore and the opening of the ventral proctodeum are connected by the aforementioned "primitive streak." The proctodeum is the primordium of the anus, and establishes a new ectodermally lined opening into the hindgut. The extent of the proctodeal ectoderm can be determined in sagittal sections by determining the limit of the invaginated and pigmented ectodermal cells.

The body of the neurula stage is laterally compressed along the dorsal surface but ventrally the belly region bulges with the large yolk endoderm cells. The **tail bud** is formed by a backward growth of

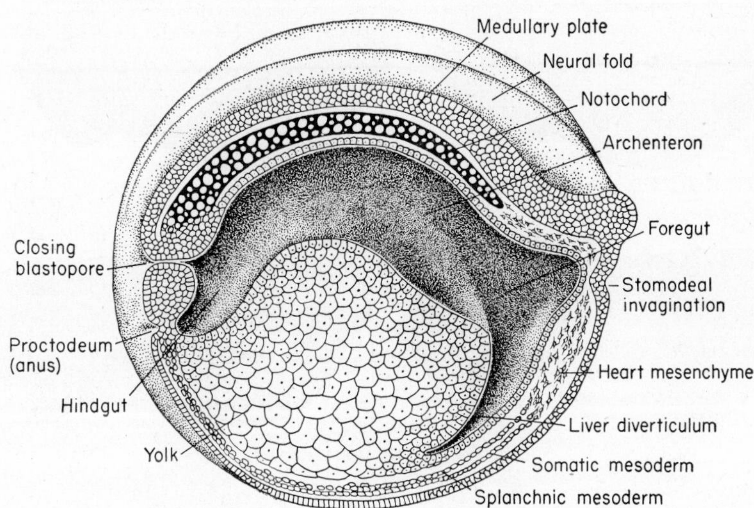

Sagittal section of the open neural fold stage. (Redrawn and modified after Huettner.)

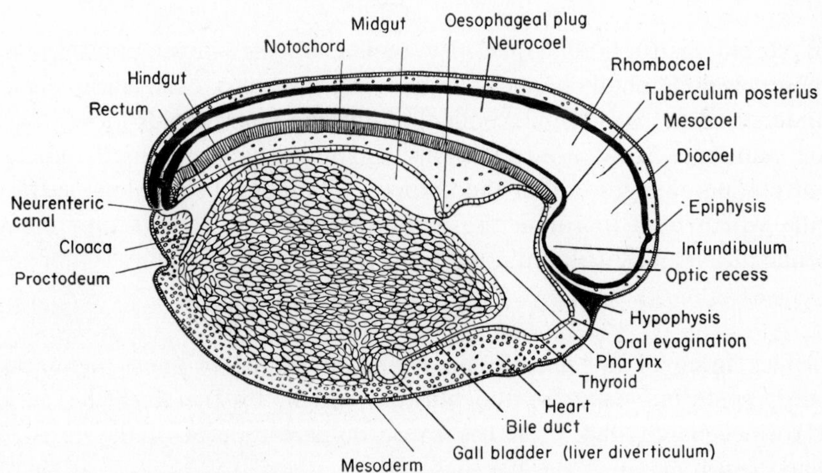

The 3 mm. frog tadpole: sagittal section.

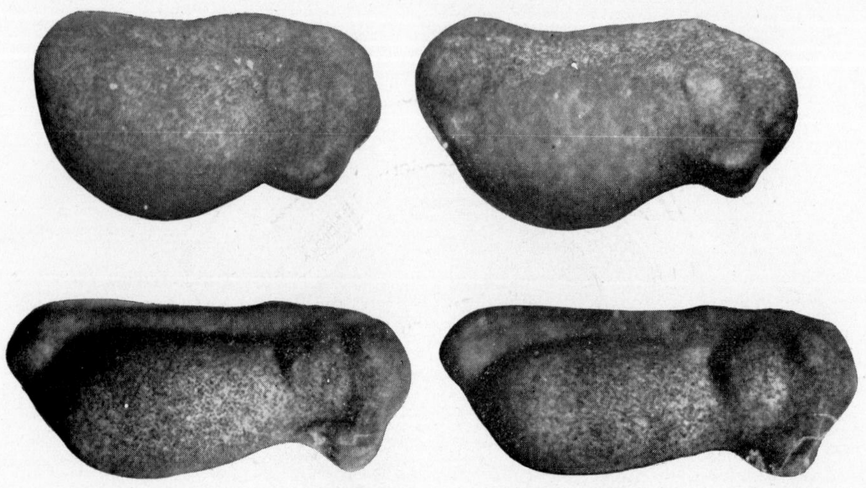

Formation of the tail bud.

tissue dorsal to the closed blastopore. As it is elongated it is provided with both a **dorsal** and a **ventral** fin, the dorsal fin being developed initially by the posterior growth of myotomes, with accompanying blood vessels and nerves, to form the tail bud.

The process of neurulation, or the formation of the central nervous system of the frog embryo, is too complicated to understand by means of verbal instructions alone. By means of time-lapse photography these developmental changes can be telescoped into a few minutes and understood more clearly. About the time the neural folds close, there are numerous surface evaginations and invaginations which indicate correlating changes within the embryo. The neurula develops surface cilia which tend to rotate the embryo within the fertilization membrane and its jelly (albuminous) coverings.

Internal Changes

The lining of the neural canal consists of the original pigmented outer epidermal layer of the blastula which, by the time the canal is formed, is ciliated, as is the entire outer ectoderm of the embryo. The central canal of the nervous system, when it is formed, is therefore lined with ciliated and pigmented cells, later to be identified as the **ependymal layer.** The bulk of the nervous system, however, is derived from the inner layers of polyhedral cells from the original nervous layer of ectoderm of the blastular roof. This properly named

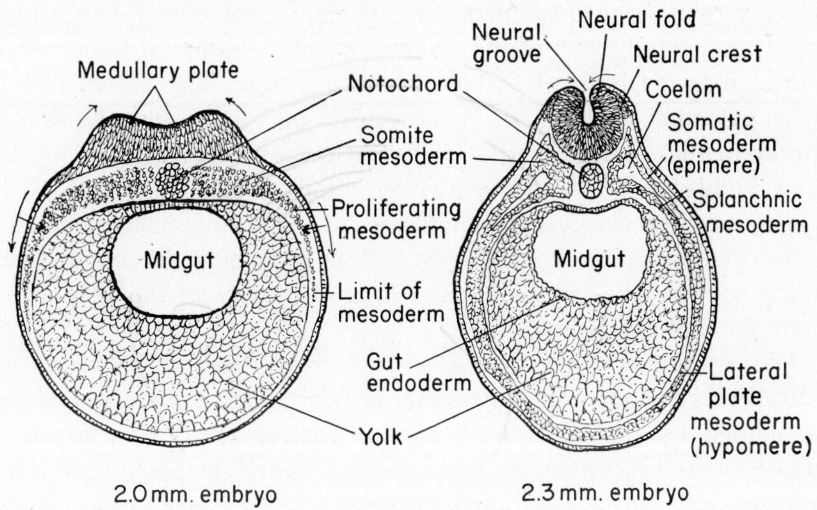

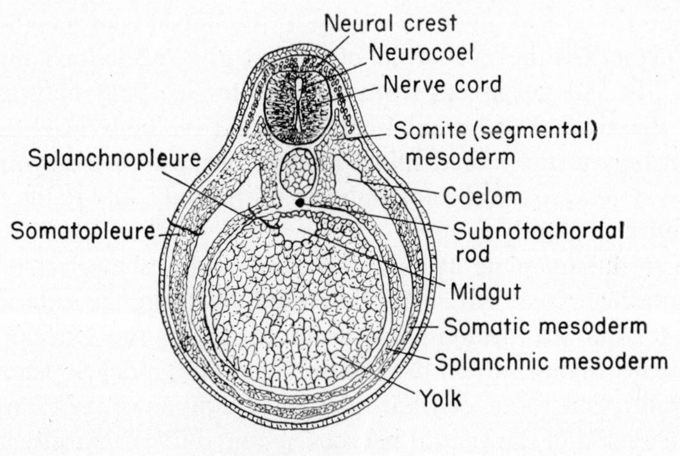

Formation of the neural groove and neural tube from the neural (medullary) plate.

"nervous ectoderm" gives rise to the neuroblasts of the central nervous system.

The roof and the floor of this neural tube are relatively thin, but due to this nervous layer the lateral walls are very thick. The roof is simply the region of the junction of the two neural folds. Some of this nervous layer, at the level of dorsal fusion, is pinched off on either side dorso-laterally to the neurocoel as the **neural crests.** The neural crests are actually part of the original ectodermal neural folds which do not form an integral part of the neural tube. The paired neural crests extend the full length of the central nervous system, lie dorso-lateral to that system, and will give rise to various ganglia of the central and sympathetic nervous systems and to chromatophores. Covering the central nervous system dorsally is the reconstituted ectoderm, derived by the fusion of ectoderm lateral to each of the neural folds which are brought together at the time of closure of the neurocoel, along the mid-dorsal line.

The continuous and paired neural crests, lodged between the neural folds and the overlying dorsal ectoderm, become metamerically subdivided by the developing somites. These crests are therefore neural from the beginning, but are extra-neural in position in that they are left outside the axial nervous system. These crests retain cellular connections with the dorso-lateral wall of the developing spinal cord and will give rise chiefly to the **dorsal root ganglia** of the spinal nerves. At the level of the brain they give rise to the ganglia and to the fifth and seventh to tenth roots inclusive. They may also give rise to the visceral and cranial cartilages. At the body level they give rise not only to the paired **spinal ganglia** but also to the **sympathetic nervous system,** to the **chromatophores** of the body, and to the **medulla of the adrenal gland.**

The medullary plate at its anterior extremity is the last region of the central nervous system to be closed off from the exterior. The opening from the presumptive brain region to the exterior is the **anterior neuropore,** which has a homologue in the development of all vertebrates. Due to the original spherical condition of the gastrula this anterior region of the central nervous system curves ventrally at about the level of the future midbrain, and this ventral curvature of the brain persists and is characteristic of all vertebrates. The notochord, which functions as an axial skeleton for the embryo, is ventral to the nervous system, and terminates just at this ventral curvature of the brain (i.e., at the **cranial flexure**). The anterior neuropore is then found at the anterior extremity of the embryo in the sagittal plane directly in line with the terminated notochord, but in the roof of the brain. Occasionally a sagittal section of a 2 mm. embryo will show a knot of cells in this region which represents the puckered closure of the anterior neuropore.

CHAPTER NINE

A Survey of the Major Developmental Changes in the Early Embryo

Primary Divisions of the Brain.

The anterior vesicular expansion of the central nervous system becomes constricted at certain levels and the walls begin to differentiate and may be used as identifying landmarks of the embryonic brain. It has just been stated that the brain floor bends ventrally (ventral or cranial flexure) around the tip end of the notochord. This flexure remains as a permanent feature of the brain. The brain floor at this region is known as the **tuberculum posterius** (posterior tubercle), and is in line with the notochord and the anterior neuropore, and will give rise to the floor of the **mesencephalon** or midbrain. Slightly anterior and dorsal to the tuberculum posterius the roof of the brain acquires a considerable thickening for a limited distance. This is known as the **dorsal thickening** and will be identified as the roof of the **mesencephalon,** later to give rise to the optic lobes. The primary brain very rapidly develops thinnings and thickenings of its walls, invaginations, and evaginations, all of which are part of its differentiation.

It is now possible to de-limit the three primary parts of the embryonic brain. These divisions are present in all vertebrate embryos of a comparable stage of development. They are the prosencephalon, mesencephalon, and rhombencephalon.

PROSENCEPHALON. This is the primary forebrain, consisting of all parts of the brain anterior to a line drawn from the tuberculum posterius to the anterior limit of the dorsal thickening, largely anterior and ventral to the notochord. This portion of the brain develops al-

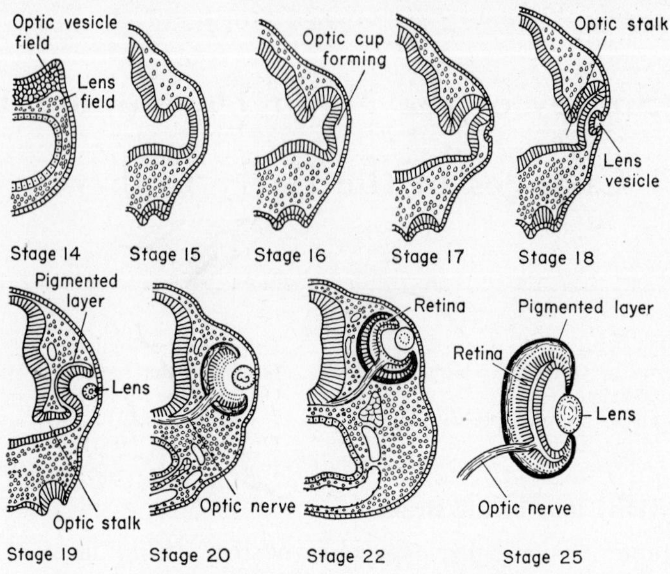

Development of the eye of the frog.

most immediately, giving rise to paired evaginations known as the optic vesicles, whose walls will give rise to the various ectodermal parts of the eye, exclusive of the lens and cornea.

MESENCEPHALON. This is the primary midbrain, or that portion of the primary brain bounded anteriorly and posteriorly by the limits of the dorsal thickening and lines drawn from these limits to the tuberculum posterius. It is located antero-dorsally to the tip of the notochord.

RHOMBENCEPHALON. This is the primary hindbrain, or that portion of the primary brain from the posterior limit of the mesencephalon to the spinal cord which, at this stage, is not clearly separated from the brain. The rhombencephalon lies entirely dorsal to the notochord, and in the frog it is never clearly divided further, as it is in higher forms.

DERIVATIVES OF FOREBRAIN. At this stage of development the forebrain alone has distinguishing derivatives. Ventral to the notochord there develops a vesicular outpocketing of the floor of the forebrain known as the **infundibulum.** Its cells will contribute later to the formation of the pituitary gland, in conjunction with a cluster of pigmented ectodermal cells seen between the infundibulum and the roof of the pharynx. This cluster of cells is known as the **epithelial hypophysis.**

It is believed that the more anterior infundibulum will form the pars nervosa or posterior pituitary gland. The more posterior hypophysis can be identified as contributing to the anterior pituitary gland (pars distalis, pars intermedia, and pars tuberalis of mammals). At the most ventral aspect of the forebrain, in the floor, is a pronounced

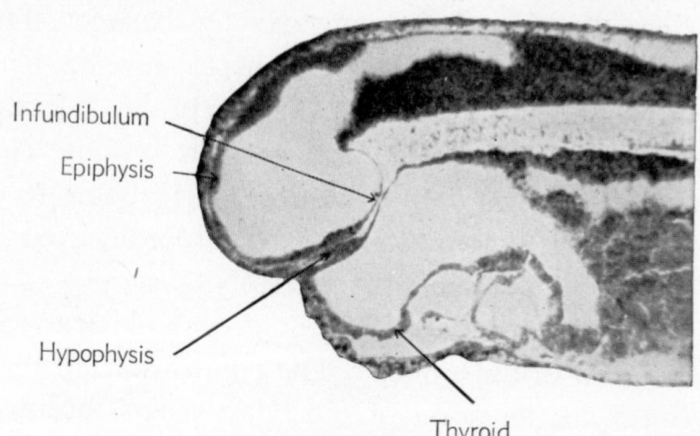

Photograph of endocrine anlagen at the 5 mm. stage of the frog tadpole.

thickening known as the **optic chiasma,** anterior to which is a depression associated with the lateral optic vesicles. The depression is the **optic recess** (recessus opticus) which is connected with the optic stalk. Anterior to this, also in the floor, is a second thickening known as the **torus transversus** which becomes the seat of the anterior and other commissures. This structure lies within the more extensive **lamina terminalis,** which represents the fused anterior neural folds

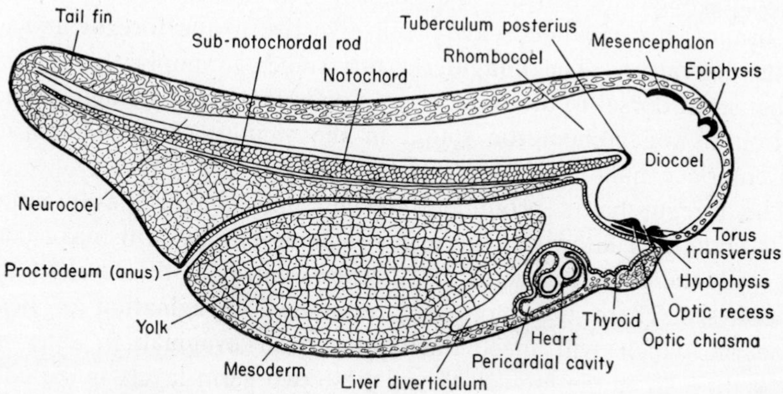

Reconstruction of the 5 mm. tadpole in sagittal section.

around the temporary anterior neuropore. More anteriorly, but in the roof of the forebrain, and slightly dorsal to a line drawn continuously from the notochord, one finds an evagination of the roof known as the **epiphysis.** This is the forerunner of the pineal body or gland. Anterior to the epiphysis the roof of the brain eventually becomes non-nervous, vascular, and folded as the **anterior choroid plexus.** Later the habenular ganglia and commissure develop between the epiphysis and choroid plexus. The only sense organs to develop by this stage (2.5 mm. length) are associated with the forebrain, a further indication of cephalization within the central nervous system. They are the **optic vesicles,** paired primordia of the eye, which begin to develop as paired lateral vesicular evaginations of the forebrain even before this portion of the brain is closed over dorsally. The presence of these vesicles was described previously as being dorso-lateral to the sense plate, in a facial view of the embryo. The connections of these vesicles with the forebrain, at the point of the optic recess, become partially constricted off into tubes known as the **optic stalks.**

At this stage the paired olfactory sense organs appear only as **olfactory placodes** or button-like thickenings of the pigmented surface ectoderm, each slightly ventral and mesial to the corresponding optic protuberances. The auditory placodes may be seen in slightly older stages as similar thickenings of the nervous ectoderm dorso-lateral to the level of the rhombencephalon (hindbrain).

The Enteron or Gut Cavity.

The anterior limit of the original archenteron expands both ventrally and laterally beneath the notochord and the infundibulum of the brain. This expanded cavity will give rise to the **foregut** and all of its derivatives. The **midgut,** at this stage, is simply the tubular archenteron dorsal to the mass of yolk endoderm. The **hindgut** is that portion of the archenteron found in the vicinity of the temporary neurenteric canal.

The foregut has a prominent median antero-ventral evagination of its endoderm known as the **oral evagination.** This will make contact with the head ectoderm just postero-ventral to the level of the hypophysis. There is an opposed **stomodeal invagination** of head ectoderm which will meet this endodermal evagination, later to break through as the mouth. When these two germ layers make contact, prior to the rupture, they constitute the **oral plate.**

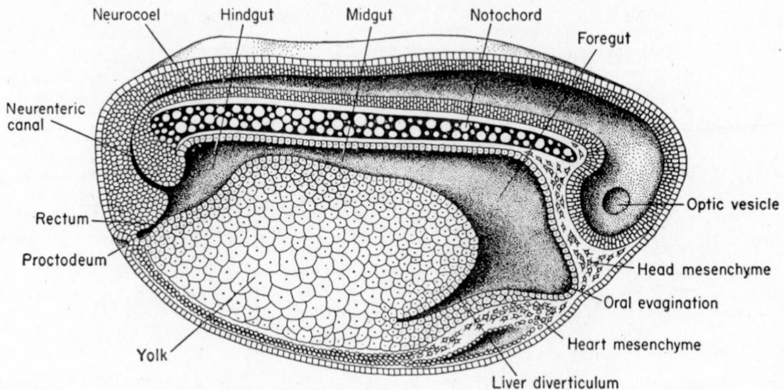

Three-dimensional representation of the late neurula stage of the frog, *Rana pipiens*. (Redrawn and modified after Huettner.)

The large cavity of the foregut is the **pharynx,** which expands laterally to form endodermally lined visceral pouches on either side of the developing vertical arches. These pouches are therefore vertically elongated endodermally lined sacs, at all times continuous with the pharynx. The most anterior pouch is called the hyomandibular because it comes to lie between the mandibular and the hyoid arches. Following this will be the first, second, and third **branchial** (gill) **pouches,** otherwise known as the second, third, and fourth visceral pouches. These all expand outwardly toward the opposed invaginations of the ectoderm which form external **visceral grooves.**

A medio-ventral and posteriorly directed pocket develops from the foregut, extending beneath the yolk a short distance. This is the **liver diverticulum,** the forerunner of the bile duct, the gallbladder, and the liver. This is the extent of gut development by the 2.5 mm. stage.

The Axial Skeleton.

The **notochord** was derived from cells indistinguishable from the mesoderm at the region of the dorsal lip. These cells very quickly expand and become vacuolated, and take on the appearance which they will manifest throughout development until they are displaced by bone of the vertebral column. Even the intercellular material of the notochord becomes vacuolated. The entire group of cells becomes enclosed in an outer elastic sheath and an inner fibrous sheath, both of which are classified as connective tissue.

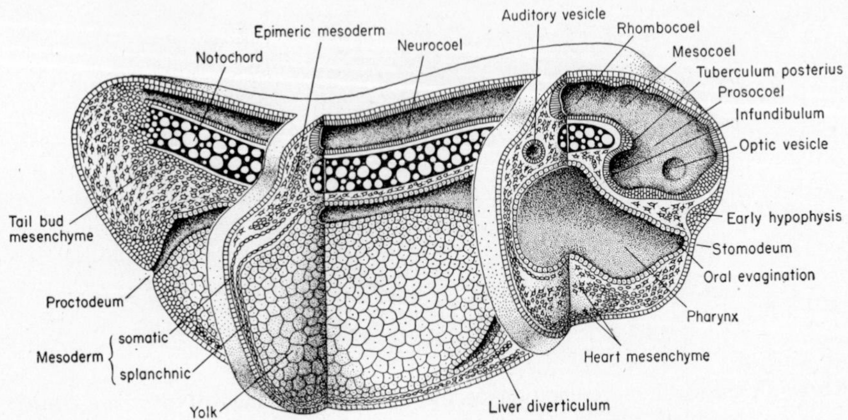

Three-dimensional representation of the tail bud stage of the frog embryo, *Rana pipiens.* (Redrawn and modified after Huettner.)

The Mesoderm and Its Derivatives.

Embryonic, loosely dispersed presumptive mesoderm is known as **mesenchyme.** At the end of gastrulation most of the frog mesoderm is in the form of sheets of such loose cells extending in all directions from the lips of the blastopore. However, the most anterior mesoderm, that found in the head and pharyngeal regions, is in the form of mesenchyme.

ORIGIN OF THE ARCHES. Lateral to the pharynx are developed vertical concentrations of mesoderm known as the **arches.** Subsequently most of these will contain blood vessels and nerves but at this stage they are merely condensations of mesenchyme. The most anterior arch is anterior to the first endodermal pouch and ectodermal groove, and is known as the **mandibular arch** associated with the development of the jaw muscles. This was first seen ventral to the sense plate on either side of the stomodeal and hypophyseal cleft. Posterior to this mandibular arch is a parallel **hyoid arch,** and between these arches is developed the rudimentary **hyomandibular groove** (ectodermal) and **pouch** (endodermal) which never break through to form the cleft. Posterior to the hyoid arch is the first endodermal branchial pouch followed by the **first mesodermal branchial arch;** the second branchial pouch followed by the **second branchial arch;** and so on as the more posterior derivatives develop. The second arch at this stage may not as yet have its mesenchyme clearly marked off from the succeeding arches.

ORIGIN OF THE SOMITES. The mesoderm posterior to the pharynx and lateral to the notochord (as seen in transverse section) takes an inverted horseshoe shape around the archenteron and the yolk. The uppermost level of this mesoderm, lateral to the nerve and noto-

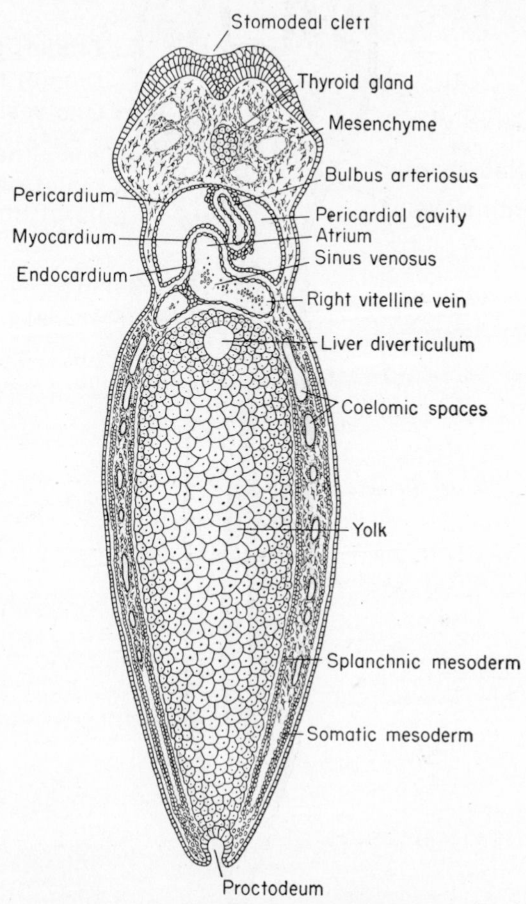

Frontal (horizontal) section of the 7 mm. frog larva at the level of the developing heart. (Redrawn and modified after Huettner.)

chord, is termed the segmental or **vertebral** plate and the more ventral portion of the same sheet of mesoderm is called the **lateral plate mesoderm.** This lateral plate extends continuously in a ventral direction and surrounds the yolk, just within the belly ectoderm. Shortly, all of this mesoderm will be separated off into a **dorsal somite mass**

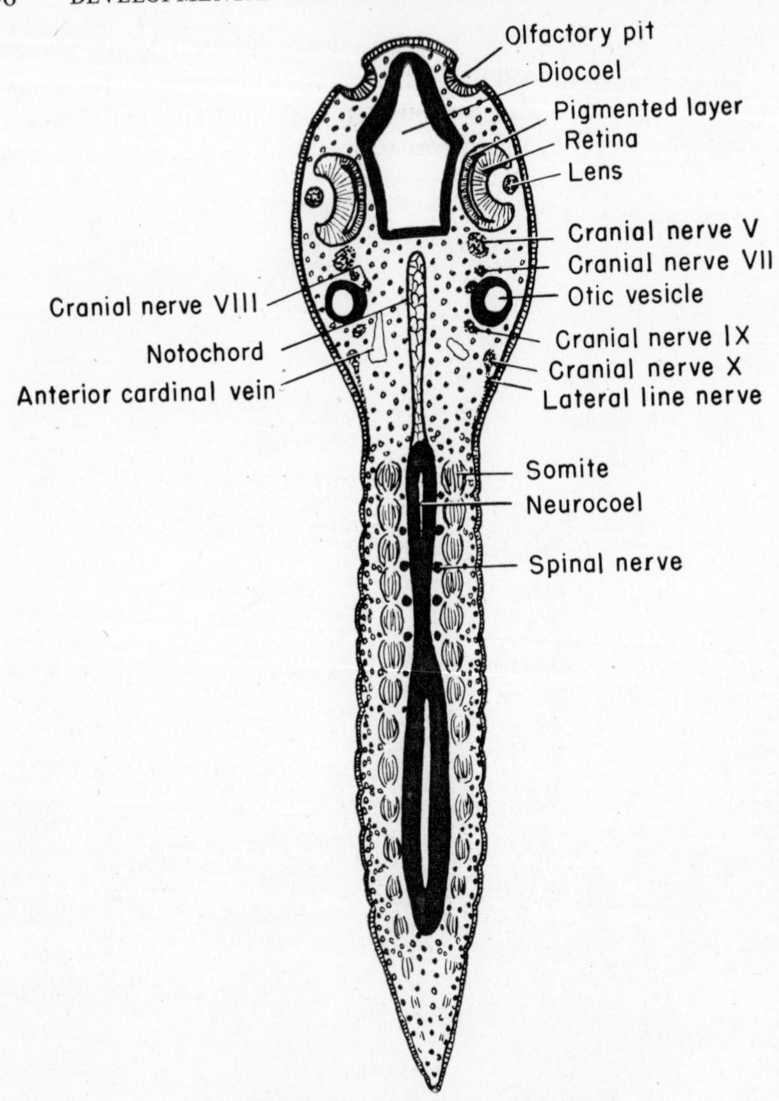

The 7 mm. frog tadpole: frontal section.

(**epimere**), an **intermediate cell mass** (**mesomere**), and a **lateral plate** (**hypomere**).

The epimere (segmental or vertebral plates) posterior to the pharynx becomes divided into sections known as the metameric **somites.** These are developed in sequence from the anterior to the posterior so that at any time in the development of an early embryo the anterior

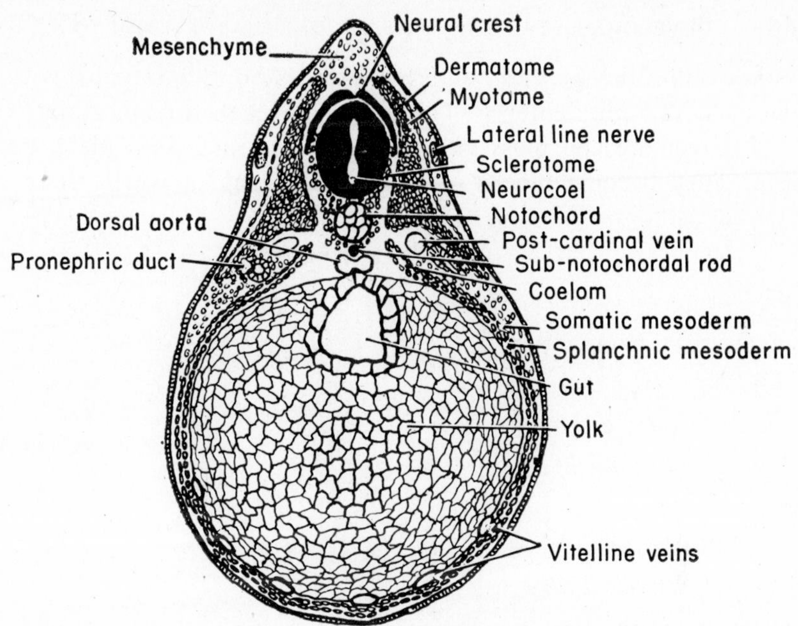

The 7 mm. frog tadpole: transverse sections. Through the mid-body level.

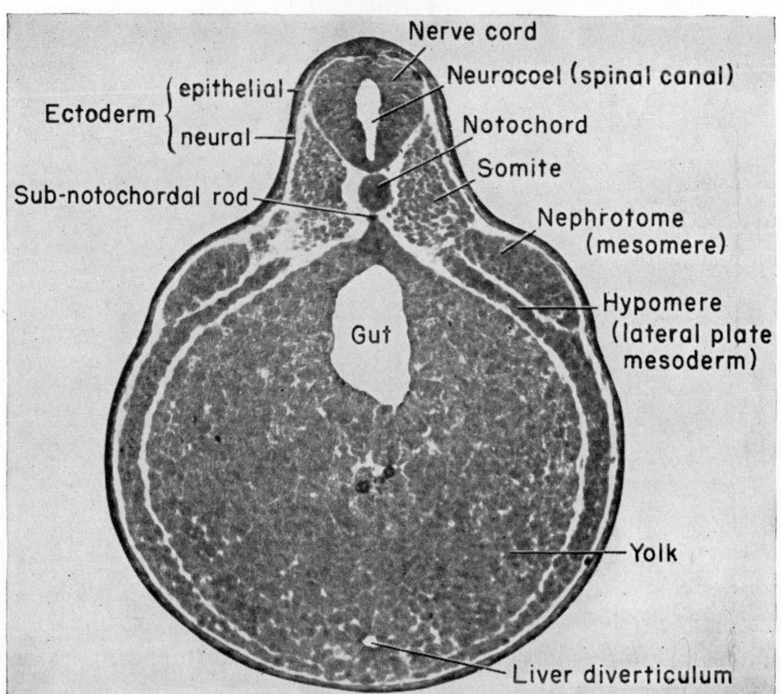

Early organogeny. The 5 mm. frog tadpole at mid-body level. Photograph of cross section.

somites show the greatest differentiation. About four pairs will be seen in the 2.5 mm. embryo. The somites sever their connections with the intermediate cell mass and the more ventral lateral plate mesoderm. They become blocks of cells within each of which there de-

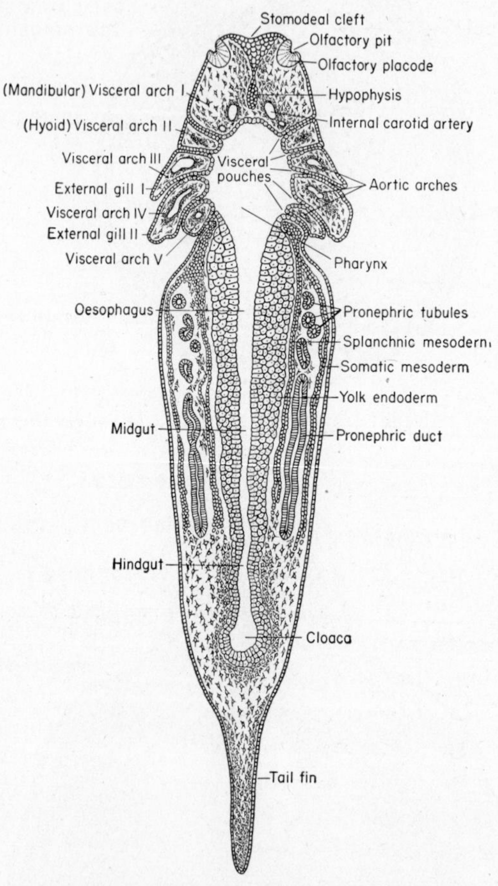

Frontal (horizontal) section of the 7 mm. frog larva at the level of the pharynx. (Redrawn and modified from Huettner.)

velops a cavity, the **myocoel.** This myocoel is eccentric in position, appearing displaced toward the lateral margin of the somite. As a result of this, the outer layer of somite cells is the thinner. It is known as the **dermatome,** or **cutis plate,** having to do with the derivatives of the dermis and of the appendage musculature. The inner layer of somite cells is thicker and will give rise to the skeletal muscles of the back and body. This portion is known as the **myotome.** A few

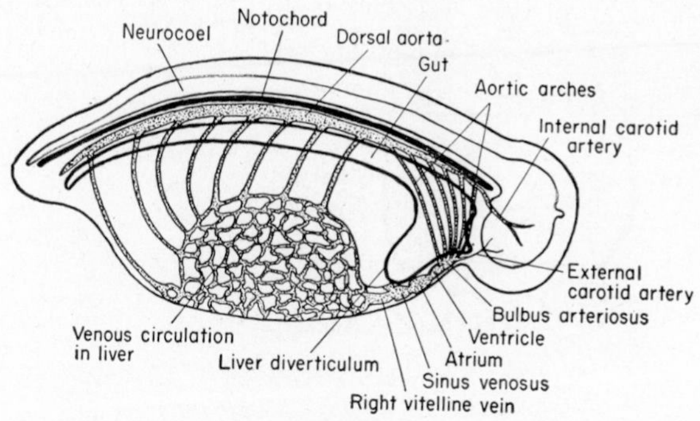

The earliest complete, closed blood vascular system of the frog embryo (found at the 4 mm. stage). Schematized drawing.

scattered cells may be seen between the myotome and the notochord, proliferating off from the somite. These are mesenchymal cells known as the **sclerotome.** They will give rise to the vertebral skeleton.

ORIGIN OF THE EXCRETORY SYSTEM. The **mesomere** and hypomere are still connected. The lateral plate (i.e., mesomere), separate from the epimere (somite), now develops along its dorsal border a continuous, antero-posterior band of mesoderm known as the **nephrotome.** This will give rise to parts of the larval and the adult excretory systems. The nephrotomal band enlarges in a lateral direction but maintains cellular connections with the remaining dorsal limit of the lateral plate mesoderm. The influence of the segmentation of the vertebral plate extends to the separated nephrotomal band, dividing it also into a series of metameric **nephrotomes.** This nephrotomal segmentation is transitory in

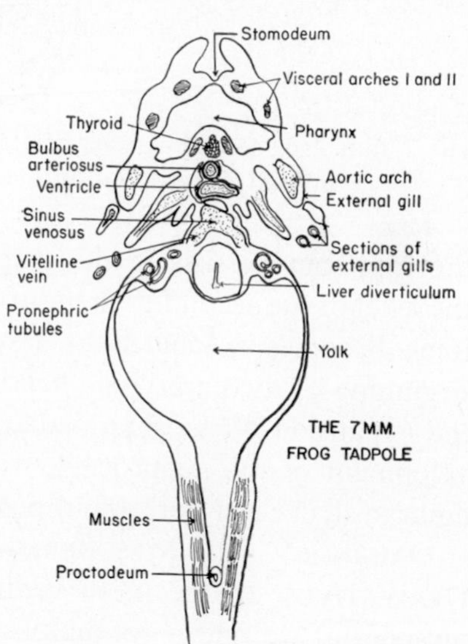

Frontal section through the level of the heart of the 7 mm. tadpole.

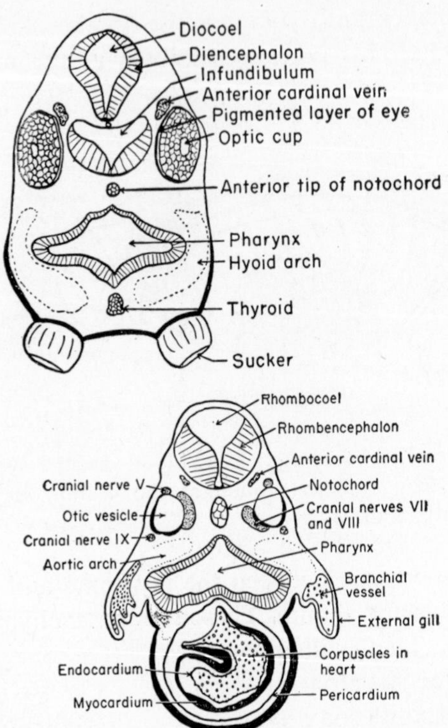

The 7 mm. frog tadpole: transverse sections. (*Top*) Through the level of the thyroid gland. (*Bottom*) Through the level of the heart.

the frog, but persists in the embryos of some vertebrates. At about the level of the second to the fourth somites, the center of each nephrotome becomes evacuated to develop a **nephrocoel.** This is the very beginning of the embryonic head kidney or **pronephros.** The effect of the expansion of the intermediate mass of mesoderm, due to the development of the nephrocoel, was seen on the surface of the earlier embryo, lying just dorsal and posterior to the gill plates.

ORIGIN OF THE MESODERMAL EPITHELIUM, COELOM, AND ITS DERIVATIVES. In the more ventrally placed **hypomere** (lateral plate mesoderm) we find a continuous split which separates the mesoderm into an outer, parietal or **somatic layer** and an inner, visceral or **splanchnic layer of mesoderm.** The outer somatic mesoderm, in conjunction with the adjacent body ectoderm, is called the **somatopleure,** and gives rise to the skin with its blood and connective tissue. The inner splanchnic mesoderm, in conjunction with the gut endoderm, with which it later becomes intimately associated, is called the splanchnopleure and gives rise to the lining epithelium, muscles, and blood vessels of the entire mid- and hindgut.

In between these two sheets of lateral plate mesoderm the cavity is known as the primary body cavity or **coelom.** Eventually the coelomic slit becomes continuous ventrally, from one side of the embryo to the other, forming a single visceral or coelomic cavity. Dorsally the junction of the lateral plates is interrupted by the notochord and the **sub-notochordal rod.** This latter structure, also known as the **hypochordal rod,** is a small rod of pigmented cells between the gut roof and the notochord. Presumably this represents a vestige of the connection between the two at the time of their simultaneous origin at the vicinity of the dorsal lip of the blastopore. It appears first at the 2.5 mm. stage.

Origin of the Heart. The lateral plate mesoderm extends into the head, ventral to the pharynx, as mesenchyme. This mesenchyme becomes organized into sheets, coextensive with the more posterior lateral plate sheets of somatic and splanchnic mesoderm. These will give rise to parts of the heart. As the coelomic split occurs at the body level, there is an extension of this split into the forming heart mesoderm, which will give rise to the **pericardial cavity.** The outer

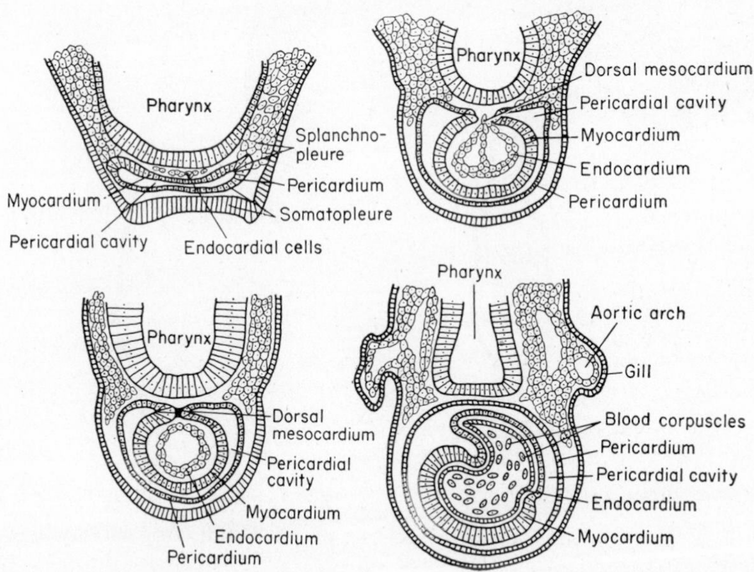

Development of the heart of the frog embryo.

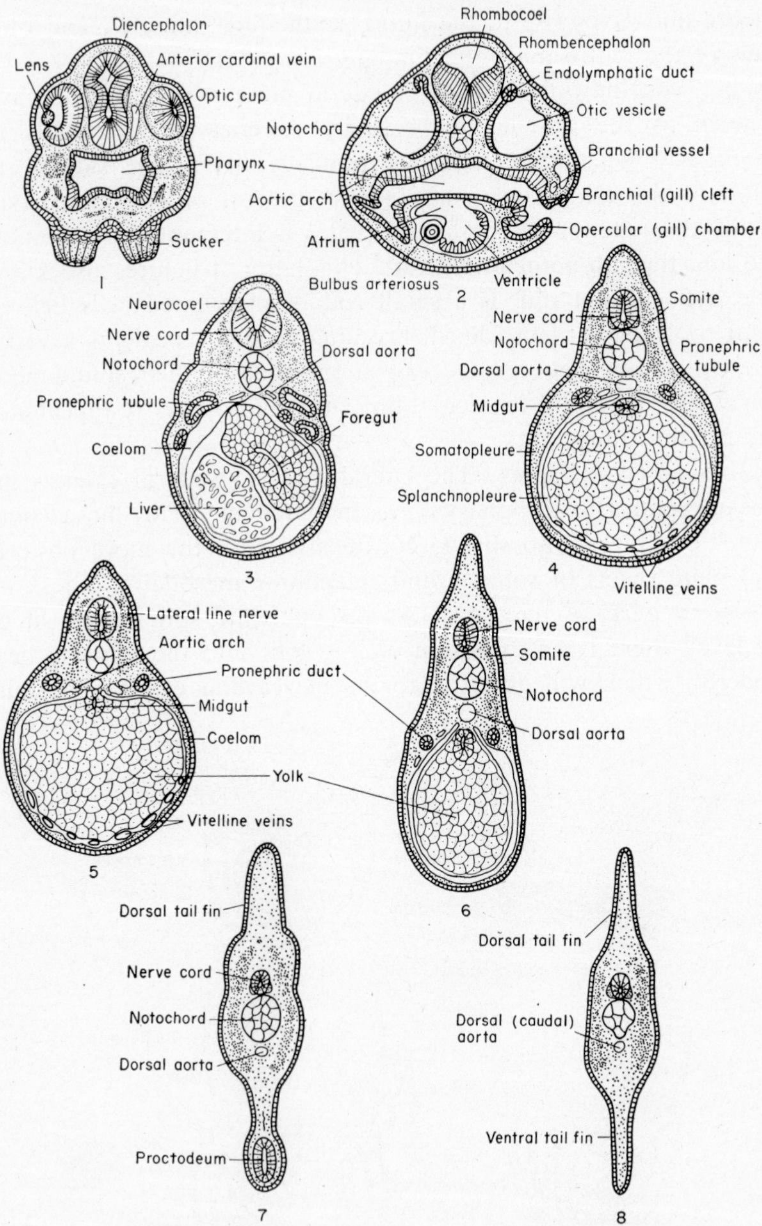

Representative transverse sections of an 8 mm. frog larva.

layer of mesoderm, corresponding to the body somatic layer, will become the **pericardial membrane.** The inner layer of mesoderm, corresponding to the body splanchnic layer, will become the **myocardium** or heart muscle. As in the body region, the mesoderm from the two sides grows together ventrally to fuse below the foregut. Both the coelom and the continuous and related pericardial cavity arise as bilateral cavities only to fuse and form single cavities around particular organs.

The **endocardium** or lining of the heart arises from scattered cells of mesodermal origin found beneath the pharynx. These cells become organized into a sheet of epithelium as they are enclosed by the bilateral folds of myocardium as they come together.

CHAPTER TEN

A Survey of the Later Embryo or Larva

External Features
Metamorphosis

External Features.

The external changes in shape of the frog embryo and early larva are continuous. The body is elongated and a posteriorly directed tail bud and tail develop, just dorsal to the original position of the blastopore. This tail carries with it an extension of the notochord, myotomes, and blood vessels as well as the pigmented epidermis of the body. It shows contractions of the <-shaped muscle blocks even before the time of hatching.

The previously described surface changes are further accentuated. The yolk mass accounts for the ventral bulge in the belly region. Anteriorly the pronephric and gill bulges are more prominent. The **olfactory pits** appear in the original placodes, dorsal and slightly lateral to the stomodeum. All four branchial grooves are developed and the rudiments of the external gills are beginning to grow from the upper levels of the first and second branchial arches.

The embryo hatches when it measures about 6 mm. in total length. Since no food is ingested during this period, the interval between the fertilization of the egg and hatching depends almost entirely upon the temperature of the environment during development. The hatching process probably is accomplished by the aid of temporary glands in the sucker region. These glands presumably elaborate an enzyme which aids in digesting away the surrounding jelly coverings, allowing the larva to escape. The jelly itself is not a food for the larvae, or tadpoles, even though after hatching they often are seen attached temporarily to the empty jelly capsules.

The pre-hatching embryos show constant swimming movements due to the presence of surface cilia. At this stage, and immediately after hatching, there is also considerable muscular movement and the entire larva (tadpole) may show occasional coil and S-shaped body contractions which are entirely muscular.

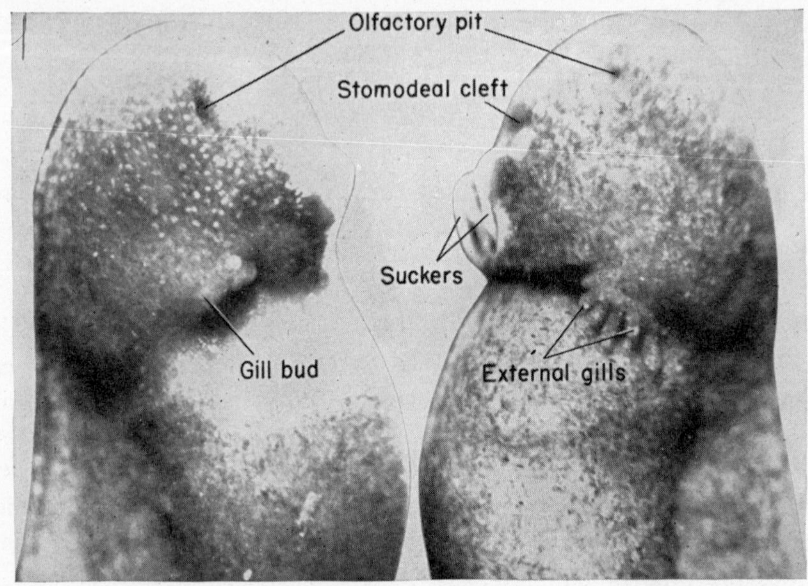

Development of the external gills of *Rana pipiens*.

Adaptations for respiration become a more and more important biological function as the embryo develops organ systems. Thus the third and fourth visceral arches develop finger-like external gills and the fifth visceral arch gives rise to a rudimentary pair of such gills. The mouth opens through to the gills and a constant current of water is taken into the mouth and pharynx. This water passes out through the second and third branchial clefts (otherwise designated as the fourth and fifth visceral clefts) and over the associated **external gills.** In this way these thin-walled, ectodermally covered, and highly vascular gills are able to exchange CO_2 and O_2. Subsequently, when the tadpole develops a set of internal gills, the hyoid arch gives rise to a posteriorly directed flap-like membrane which covers the degenerat-

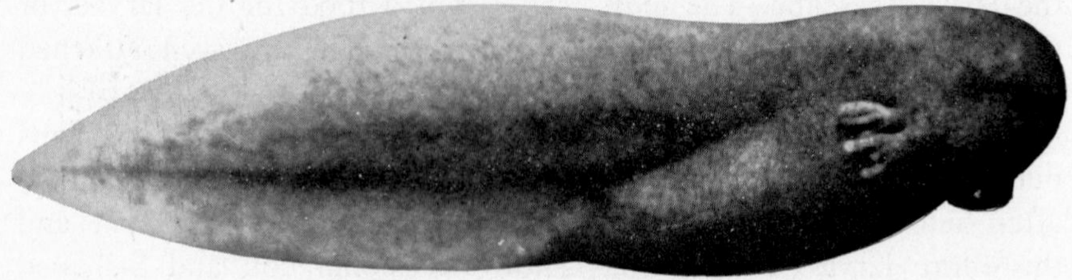

Tadpole with external gills.

ing external gills. This is called the **operculum.** On the left side of the head the operculum remains open at its posterior margin, to allow the egress of water. This opening is known as the **spiracle.** The opercular flaps from the two sides fuse ventrally to envelop the gill or **opercular** chamber within. Surrounding the mouth are a pair of **horny jaws** and **lips,** covered by **horny rasping papillae.** These are derived from the corneum and consist of rows of tooth-like horny denticles which are replaced frequently. Cornification begins at the 11 mm. stage.

Feeding becomes important as the yolk is being consumed more rapidly. The tadpole begins to use its oral accessories to obtain food, which is almost exclusively vegetation, until after metamorphosis. The intestine, developed from the midgut, is a long, thin, coiled tube having the appearance, through the thin abdominal wall, of a watch-spring. If stretched out straight, this larval gut often measures about nine times the length of the body of the tadpole.

Metamorphosis.

Under normal conditions of temperature (i.e., 20°–25° C.) and food supply, the tadpole of *Rana pipiens* will reach metamorphosis in 75 to 90 days. This period can be extended by keeping the larvae in an environment cooler than normal or it may be shortened by keeping them warmer and feeding them thyroid hormone or dilute iodine which tends to accelerate the changes attending metamorphosis.

There are four major areas of change during metamorphosis. First, the **respiratory system,** which has already gone through an external and an internal gill phase, now changes to a lung type of respiration. This develops concurrently with the change from an aquatic to a terrestrial environment or habitat, characteristic of amphibia. Second, the **horny jaws are lost,** the **mouth widens,** and the **gut shortens** to about two or three times the length of the body. There are parallel changes in the histology of the gut to take care of the change in diet. Third, the **two pairs of legs develop** and the **tail is lost** by regression. The hind legs appear some time before metamorphosis and the forelimbs are pushed through the opercular membrane just before emergence of the tadpole from the water. Fourth, **certain endocrine glands function actively** and the **definitive gonads appear.** There are also those changes which are necessary in the transforma-

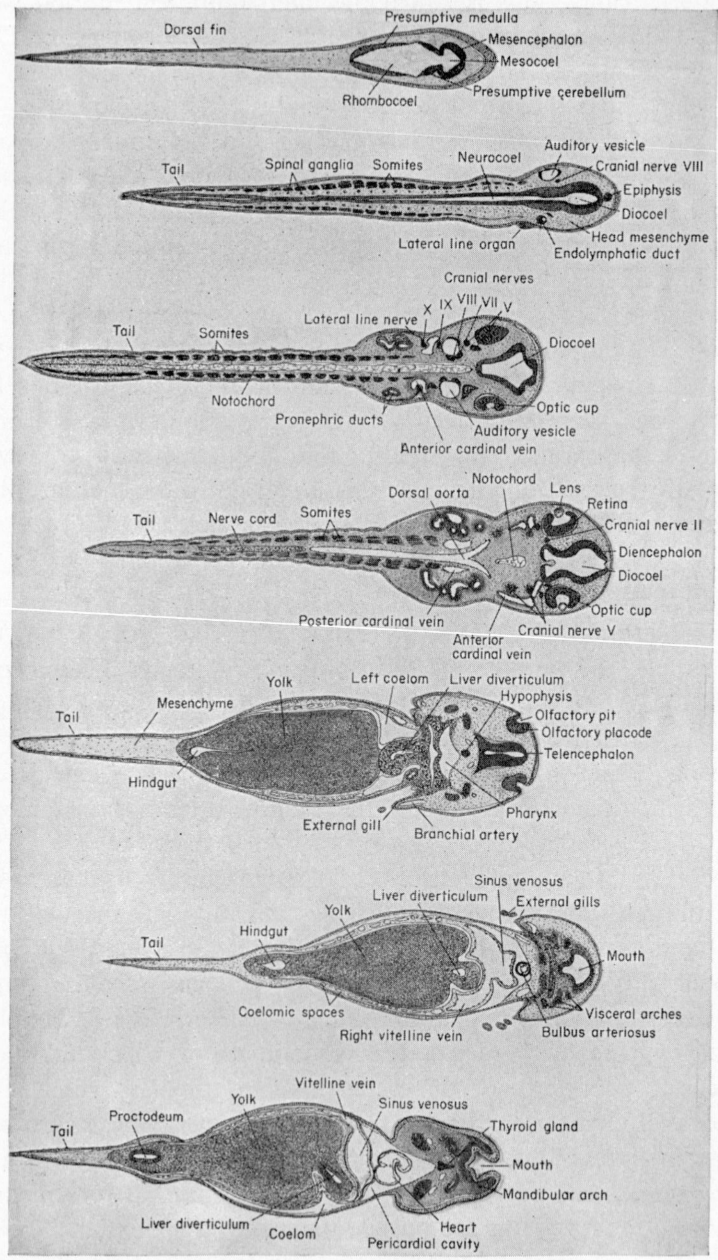

The 7 mm. frog larva in serial frontal sections.

tion of the tadpole into the frog. The larval skin is shed, along with the horny jaws. The mouth becomes a large horizontal slit instead of a simple oval opening. The gill clefts are all closed.

There is thus developed a frog in miniature, once metamorphosis is achieved and the embryonic stages of development are passed. It will be necessary now to return to the earlier developmental stages and treat the various derivatives of the three primary germ layers. The student is cautioned not to lose sight of the fact that the embryo is a composite whole, even though we are discussing the development of one or another of the various systems. There is functional integration which must be implied, while we are studying an isolated system in detail.

CHAPTER ELEVEN

The Germ Layer Derivatives

The Ectoderm and Its Derivatives

The Brain

The primary embryonic brain of the frog has three main subdivisions. The most anterior of these, the **prosencephalon,** alone becomes further subdivided into two regions, the **telencephalon** and the **diencephalon.** In the higher vertebrates but not the frog, the **rhombencephalon** (hindbrain) is also subdivided. The adult frog brain then has four major divisions, arbitrarily determined, for they merge into one another structurally and functionally. Each of these divisions has a specific set of characteristics and derivatives, which will be described in sequence from the most anterior to and including the spinal cord.

The Prosencephalon.

The Telencephalon (Secondary Forebrain). The most anterior division of the forebrain is the **telencephalon** with its original cavity, the **telocoel.** One may draw a line in a sagittal plane from a point just anterior to the **epiphysis** and extending through the brain cavity to the posterior wall of the thickened **torus transversus.** This

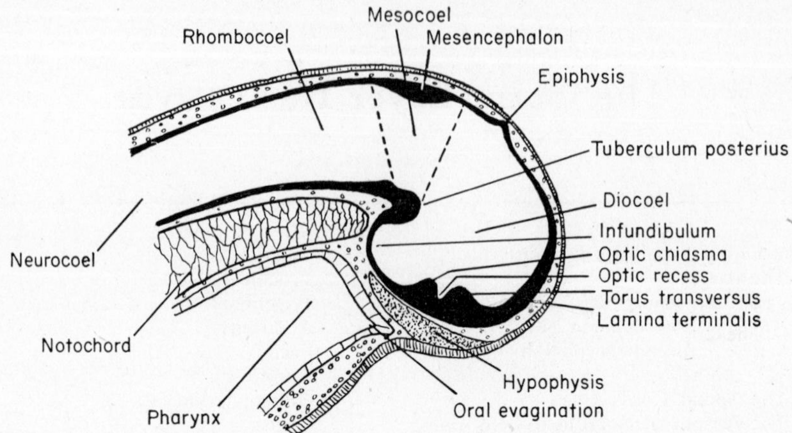

Early organogeny of the frog tadpole, showing the primary brain vesicles in sagittal section.

imaginary line separates the anterior telencephalon from the more posterior diencephalon of the forebrain. The telencephalon includes the fused anterior neural folds which comprise the **lamina terminalis.** This lamina will form a partition which will separate the paired cerebral hemispheres by a longitudinal groove.

The telencephalon is the embryonic **cerebrum.** Its cavity expands laterally to give rise to the right (first) and left (second) lateral **ventricles** and the surrounding thick-walled **cerebral hemispheres,** at about the 12 mm. stage. These ventricles are laterally compressed. In the frog the cerebral hemispheres are first differentiated at the 7 mm. stage but never become very large. The two telencephalic vesicles are partially constricted off from each other but remain connected by way of the tubular **foramen of Monro,** which opens into the common (intermediate) third ventricle, known as the **ventriculus impar.** The third ventricle overlaps and connects the telocoel and the diocoel. The nervous tissue of the cerebral hemispheres is connected transversely by the ventral **anterior commissure,** which is the original torus transversus, and the **anterior pallial commissure** found postero-mesially. The cerebral hemispheres become greatly thickened with consequent enlargement and there is a parallel reduction in the size of the contained ventricles. Antero-ventrally each grows out toward the anteriorly placed olfactory placodes to establish connections known as the **olfactory lobes** and **nerves.** The olfactory lobes arise as a pair but subsequently become fused mesially. These are rather prominent brain structures in the adult frog. They seem to originate together and become separated only at the point of origin of the **olfactory nerves.** However, each originates from the telencephalon on its side of the brain.

Dorsal to the **anterior pallial commissure** is the single median **anterior choroid plexus** which develops as a thin and highly vascular invagination from the roof just at the junction of the telencephalon

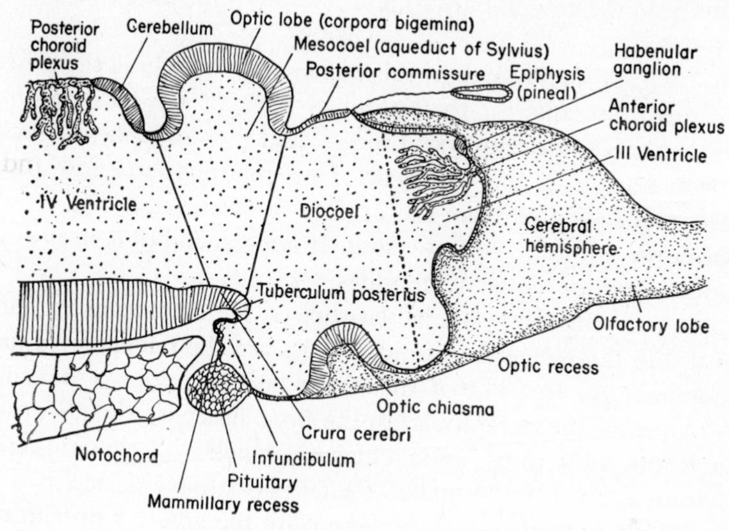

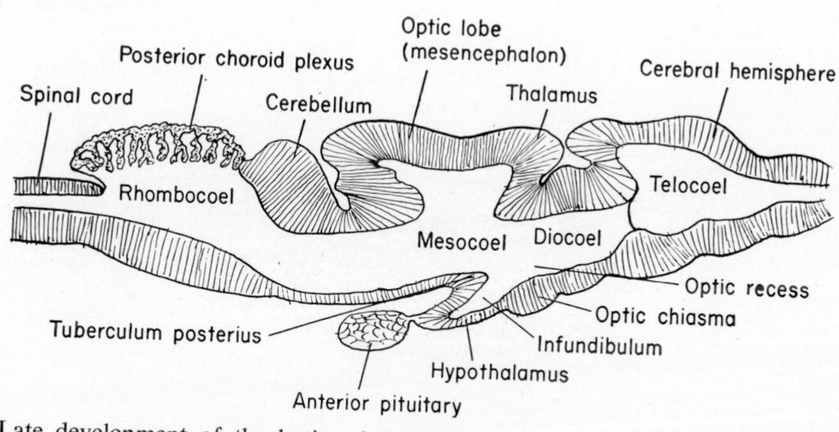

Late development of the brain of the frog tadpole. (*Top*) Pre-metamorphic stage. (*Bottom*) Adult brain, schematized, reduced in size.

and the diencephalon. It extends into the diocoel and into the two telocoels, and is therefore tri-radiate.

THE DIENCEPHALON (THALAMENCEPHALON OR BETWEEN-BRAIN). The **third ventricle** is divided between the telencephalon and the diencephalon, but the enlarged portion found surrounded by the diencephalon is identified as the **diocoel.** This cavity extends antero-dorsally beneath the epiphysis, antero-ventrally into the optic recess, postero-ventrally into the infundibulum, and laterally into the relatively large **optic vesicles.**

The structural derivatives of this diencephalon include the **posterior commissure,** just anterior to the dorsal limit of the mesencephalon. Anterior to this is the **epiphyseal recess,** and the dorso-mesial saccular outgrowth known as the **epiphysis.** This continues to grow forward and becomes separated from the brain as a small knob of cells which remain in the adult as the **brow spot.** It is presumably homologous to the **pineal gland** of higher vertebrates.

Anterior to the epiphysis, in the roof of the diencephalon and between it and the anterior choroid plexus, are the **habenular ganglion** and **commissure.** In front of this there later develops a dorsal outgrowth know as the **paraphysis.** In the floor just posterior to the **optic recess** is the very thick **optic chiasma** which will contain crossed fibers from the two optic stalks. Posterior to this chiasma is a thin-walled pocket or trough projecting beneath the anterior tip end of the notochord, known as the **infundibulum.** The cells of the infundibulum

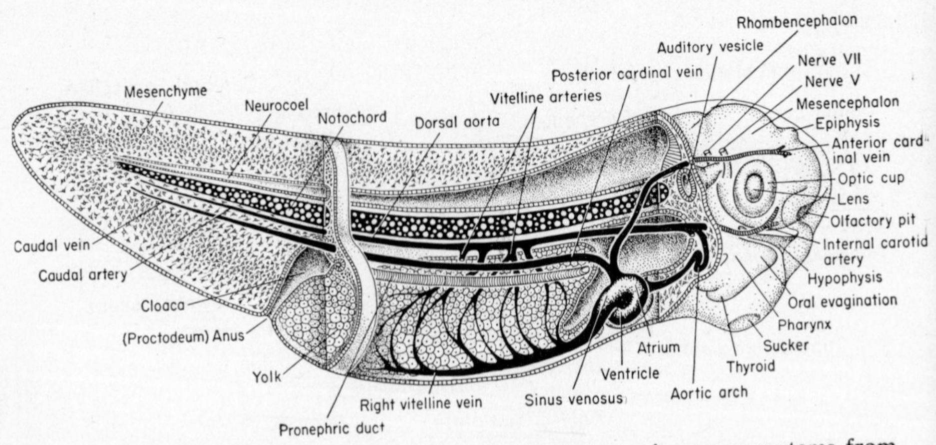

Reconstruction of the 7 mm. frog larva showing the major organ systems from the right side. (Redrawn and modified after Huettner.)

will combine with the approximated and pigmented cells of the ingrown **hypophysis** to form the **pituitary gland** of the adult. The infundibulum cells give rise to the posterior part of the pituitary gland and retain a hollow infundibular stalk connection with the brain. The hypophysis becomes the anterior part of the pituitary gland. During metamorphosis the individual lobes of the pituitary gland differ, both in gross morphology and in finer structure. The lateral and intermediate lobes show poor vascularization, a simple cellular structure,

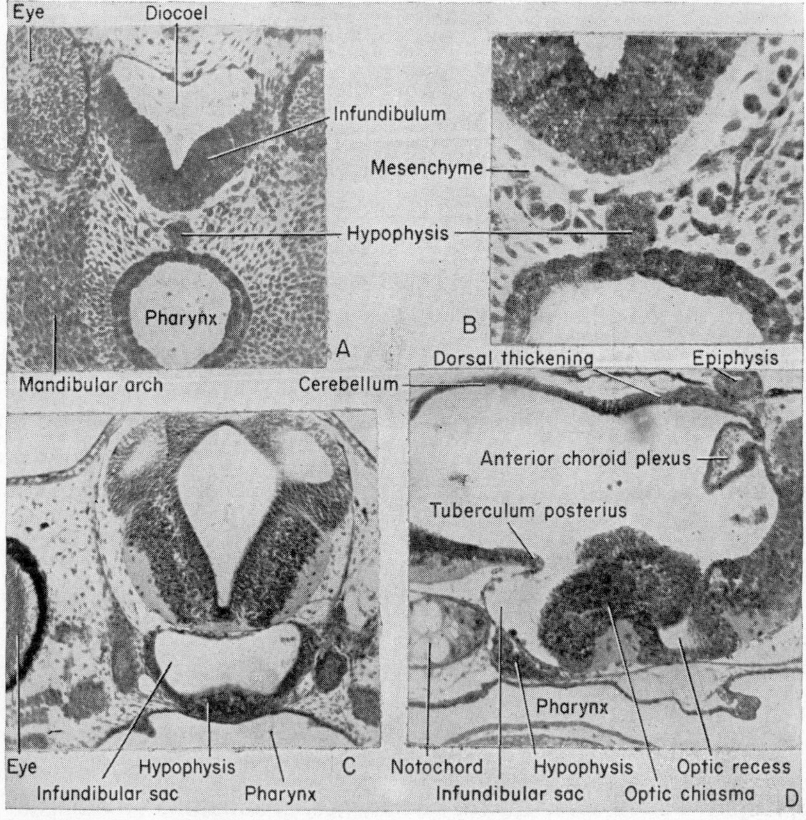

Development of the pituitary gland of the frog. (A) Relationship of the hypophysis to the infundibulum as seen in a cross section through the 5 mm. frog tadpole. (B) Same as "A" but enlarged to show the pigmented hypophyseal cells as distinct from the gut endoderm. (C) The approximation of the hypophysis and infundibulum as seen in a cross section through the 11 mm. stage. (D) Sagittal section of the 11 mm. stage to show the relation of the hypophysis and infundibulum to other parts of the brain and pharynx.

uniform staining reaction, and a rather static structural development. The anterior lobe becomes highly vascular, consists of several types of cells, and exhibits increasing complexity with further development. The acidophils of the anterior pituitary gland become highly differentiated and the basophils become poorly differentiated when the thyroid gland is either poorly developed or inactive. Conversely, thyroid activity is correlated with hyperactivity of the basophils of the anterior pituitary gland. This gland is formed from ectoderm, but some is epithelial and some is brain ectoderm. Between the infundibulum and the tuberculum posterius is a secondary and posteriorly directed pocket known as the **mammillary recess.**

The **optic vesicles** begin to develop very early as lateral outgrowths from a slightly ventral level of the diocoel. The expansion of the diocoel provides a temporary and slight thinning of the walls of the optic vesicles. However, as these vesicles make contact with the lateral head ectoderm, that portion of the vesicle in contact begins to thicken and then invaginate to form a 2-layered optic cup. The most lateral and invaginated portion of the cup will become the **retina,** the mesial layer will become the **pigmented layer** of the eye, and the connecting and somewhat constricted tube the **optic stalk.** The nervous elements of this optic stalk will join in the **optic chiasma** which contains the **optic nerve** fiber tracts from the two sides. The stalk will develop around an inverted groove (the choroid fissure) which will contain, within the groove, accessory nerves and blood vessels which feed the retina.

The Mesencephalon (Midbrain).

This portion of the brain functions largely as a pathway of nerve tracts between the anterior prosencephalon and the posterior rhombencephalon. These tracts are found principally within the paired ventro-lateral thickenings of the walls and floor on either side of the tuberculum posterius. They are known as the **crura cerebri.**

The original dorsal thickening becomes subdivided by a median fissure into paired dorso-lateral thickenings, at about the 10 mm. stage. These are known as the **optic lobes** or **corpora bigemina.** They do not reach their full development until the time of metamorphosis. Anterior to these lobes is the **posterior commissure.** From the posterior limits of the mesencephalon and optic lobes may be seen the **valvulae cerebelli** and the fourth pair of cranial nerves (**trochlear**) which emerge from the dorso-lateral wall. The original cavity of the midbrain (**mesocoel**) connects the **rhombocoel** (**fourth ventricle**) with the third ventricle which becomes narrow and is known as the **aqueduct of Sylvius** (also the iter e tertio ad quartum ventriculum).

The Rhombencephalon (Hindbrain).

This portion of the brain is clearly marked off from the mesencephalon by a transverse constriction in the roof of the brain, at the posterior limit of the dorsal thickening. It is not clearly divided farther. There appears a slight transverse thickening in the roof of the rhombencephalon which corresponds to the metencephalon of higher forms and develops into the small **cerebellum.** Posterior to this the roof becomes broad, thin, and vascular, and folds into the **rhombocoel** (fourth ventricle) as the **posterior choroid plexus.** The ventral and ventro-lateral walls of the rhombencephalon are known as the **medulla oblongata** from which arise the cranial nerves V to X inclusive. The walls become thickened by fibers which form numerous pathways from the brain and cord.

The rhombocoel or cavity of the hindbrain is known as the **fourth ventricle** which communicates posteriorly with the **central canal** of the spinal cord and anteriorly with the **aqueduct of Sylvius** of the mesencephalon.

The Spinal Cord

The neural or central canal (**neurocoel**) from the beginning of its development is laterally compressed by the thick lateral walls of the spinal cord derived from the original neural folds. The lining cells, coming from the dorsal epithelial ectoderm, retain both their pigment and their cilia, and are non-nervous in function. These cells, which continue to line the central canal of the adult, are known as the non-nervous **ependymal cells.** The thick lateral walls of the spinal cord are made up of the rapidly multiplying germinal **neuroblasts** (primitive or embryonic precursors of the neurons) and the supporting small and stellate cells known as the **glia** (**neuroglia**) cells. These cells have the function normally ascribed to connective tissue, namely support for the neuroblasts, but they are of ectodermal origin. The compact glia and neuroblasts close to the inner layer of ependyma comprise the **gray matter** of the cord. It is within this layer that the bulk of the cell bodies of neurons and the commissural fibers from one side of the cord to the other will be seen. As the cord develops further, the

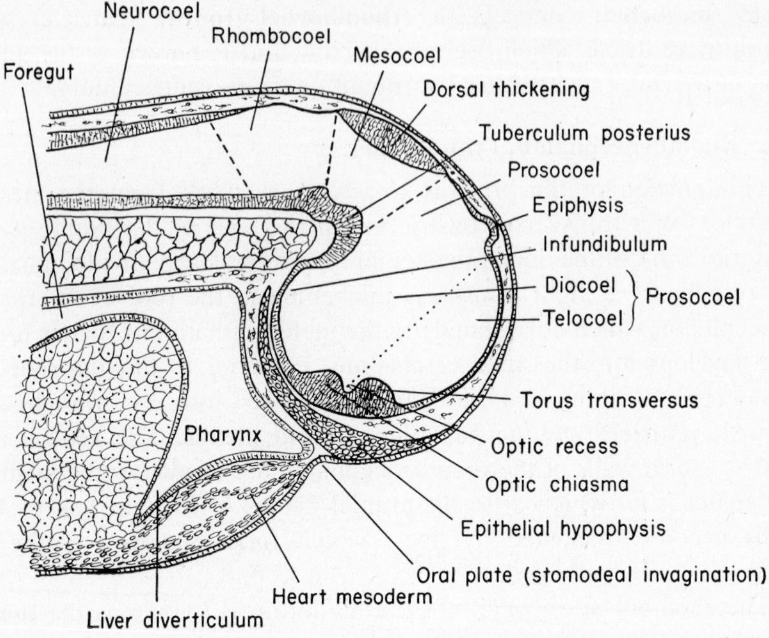

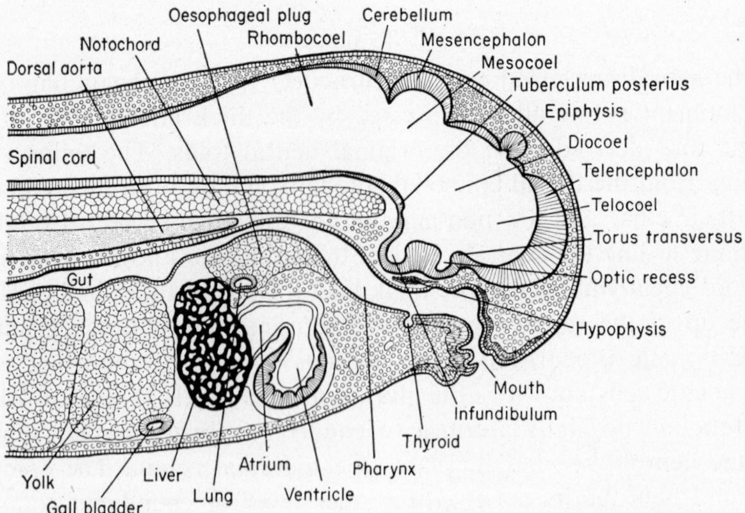

Development of the brain and anterior structures of the frog tadpole. (*Top*) Median sagittal section of the 7 mm. frog tadpole. (*Bottom*) Median sagittal section of the 11 mm. frog tadpole.

anterior and posteriorly directed fibers of the various neurons are concentrated more laterally so that only cross sections of axons will be seen. This peripheral area is then known as the **white matter,** to distinguish it from the more central and cellular gray matter of the cord.

In addition to the lateral walls of the cord, which are thick, the dorsal wall is also thick because it consists of the fused neural folds.

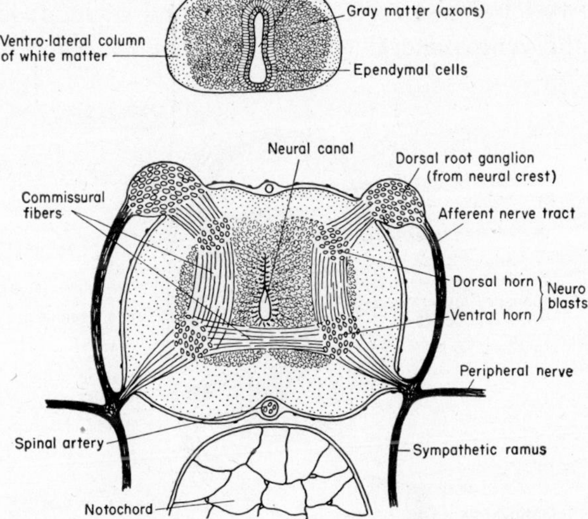

Development of the spinal cord of the frog. (*Top*) Spinal cord of the 7 mm. larva. (*Bottom*) Spinal cord just before metamorphosis.

The central canal or **neurocoel** is therefore displaced ventrally in the embryo and larva, but, as the cord is developed and more neuroblasts are formed, the neurocoel assumes a more central position. Within the enveloping connective tissue membrane which surrounds the spinal cord may be seen several blood vessels, principally the large **spinal artery** located in the mid-ventral (inverted) groove of the cord.

The Peripheral Nervous System

The development of this variegated portion of the nervous system will be treated in the following sequence, and the description will be continuous to the final stage of development:

1. Organs of special sense: optic, auditory, olfactory, and lateral line organs.

2. Cranial nerves I to X.
3. Spinal nerves.
4. Other neural crest derivatives: dorsal root ganglia, sympathetic nervous system, chromatophores, parts of the visceral and cranial cartilage, and the medullary portion of the adrenal glands.

The Organs of Special Sense

The Eye.

The **optic vesicles** arise early, by the tail-bud stage, as lateral diverticula from the ventro-lateral walls of the diocoel. The connection of

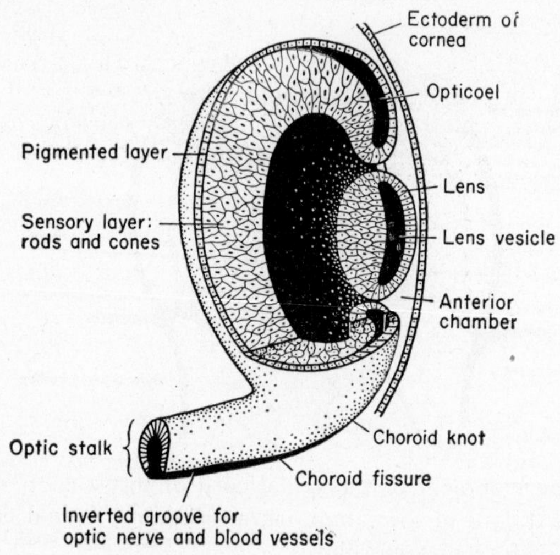

Schematic diagram of the developing eye parts of the frog.

the brain cavity with the optic vesicles becomes constricted, by the convergence of the surrounding mesenchyme, into a tube known as the **optic stalk.**

The dorso-lateral wall of each optic vesicle comes into contact with the head ectoderm, as it expands laterally, and it is then flattened and finally invaginated. This invagination begins ventro-laterally and is continued obliquely mesio-dorsally. This process of invagination is aided by a thickening of the vesicle wall between the dorsal and ventral limits. This is the region which will later form the retina. This thickening begins at the first point of contact (dorsal) and as a result the connecting optic stalk is moved to a more ventral position.

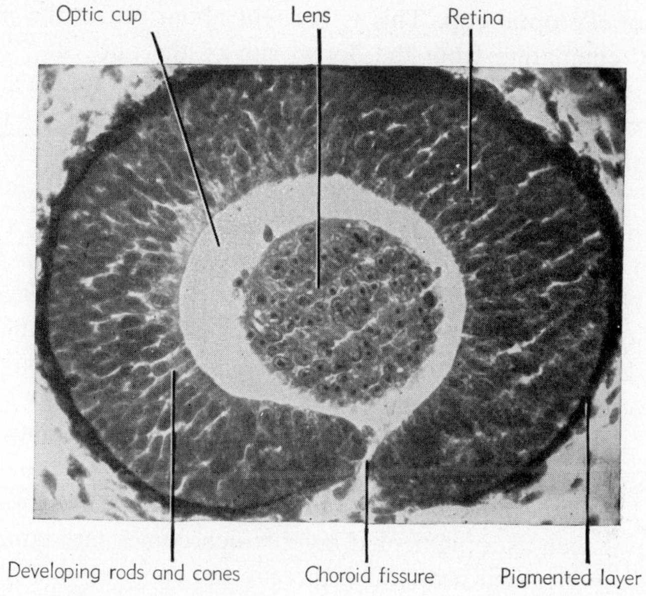

View into the larval eye. *Rana pipiens,* photograph.

The newly inverted cavity thus formed by the invagination of the lateral wall of the optic vesicle is known as the **optic cup.** The rim of the cup now exposes the **pupil.** The cup will invaginate further and grow in thickness until it all but obliterates the original optic vesicle (**opticoel**). The lateral (**retinal**) and the inner or mesial (**pigmented**) layers of the optic cup are therefore brought into close proximity with only a slit-like space remaining between, the remains of the original opticoel. Ventrally this double-layered optic cup is connected with the optic stalk.

The three-dimensional aspect of these changes must be understood. Transverse, sagittal, or horizontal (frontal) sections through the eye will appear to be essentially alike. The cup is circular with only a ventral cut-out where the inverted optic stalk is attached. If one could look directly into such a developing eye, after removal of the lens, the impression would be of a horseshoe-shaped cup, the pupil of the eye, with a groove-like opening ventral. This central cavity is the optic cup but ventral to it is the double-layered groove of the optic stalk, known as the **choroid fissure.**

The lens of the eye is formed from the superficial ectoderm by invagination of the deeper or nervous layer of ectoderm opposite the opening of the optic cup. This is brought about under the inductive influences emanating from the dorsal rim of the optic cup by the 4 mm. stage, some time before hatching. The lens originates as a **placode** or thickening in the inner or neural layer of the head ectoderm. This placode invaginates to form a (**lens**) **vesicle** by the 5 mm. stage. This vesicle pinches off from the head ectoderm and comes to lie within the ring of the optic cup and is supported by a suspensory ligament by the 6 mm. stage. The outer wall of the lens vesicle remains as cuboidal epithelial cells and the inner wall cells become elongated as lens fibers. The cavity is ultimately obliterated. The head ectoderm then closes over the lens to form a new covering which, in conjunction with the head mesenchyme, forms the double-layered cornea. This cornea is therefore derived from ectoderm and mesoderm and becomes a transparent covering of the lens by the 6 mm. stage.

After hatching, at about the 6 mm. stage, the outermost wall of the optic cup is seen as a pigmented layer which comes into contact with the thick inner retinal wall which thereupon begins to give rise to the **rods** and **cones** from its outer margin. These visually sensitive elements, the rods and cones, are fully developed by the 11 mm. stage. They point away from the light source, their posteriorly directed axons covering the exposed face of the retina. The inner margin of the retina, i.e., that toward the optic cup, is made up of neuroblasts and their fibers (axons) which pass over the surface of the retina to leave the optic cup together by way of the choroid fissure. They then pass along the walls of the optic stalk, which acts as a guiding path to the fibers, to reach the diencephalon of the brain as the second cranial or the **optic nerves.** There is a junction and crossing of the paired optic nerve fibers in the **optic chiasma** which is seen in the floor of the diencephalon. The choroid fissure will eventually close around the blood vessels and nerves which supply the optic cup. These latter nerves have no visual function. The ventral margins of the optic cup, where the choroid fissure originates, eventually fuse to form the **choroid knot** and it is from this cluster of cells that the cells of the **iris** arise. Pigment very soon disappears from the outer superficial layer of the original optic cup.

The large cavity of the eye between the lens and the retina, designated as the optic cup, becomes filled with a viscous fluid known as the **vitreous humor.** This is derived from the cells of the retinal wall and lens and is therefore of ectodermal origin. Head mesenchyme

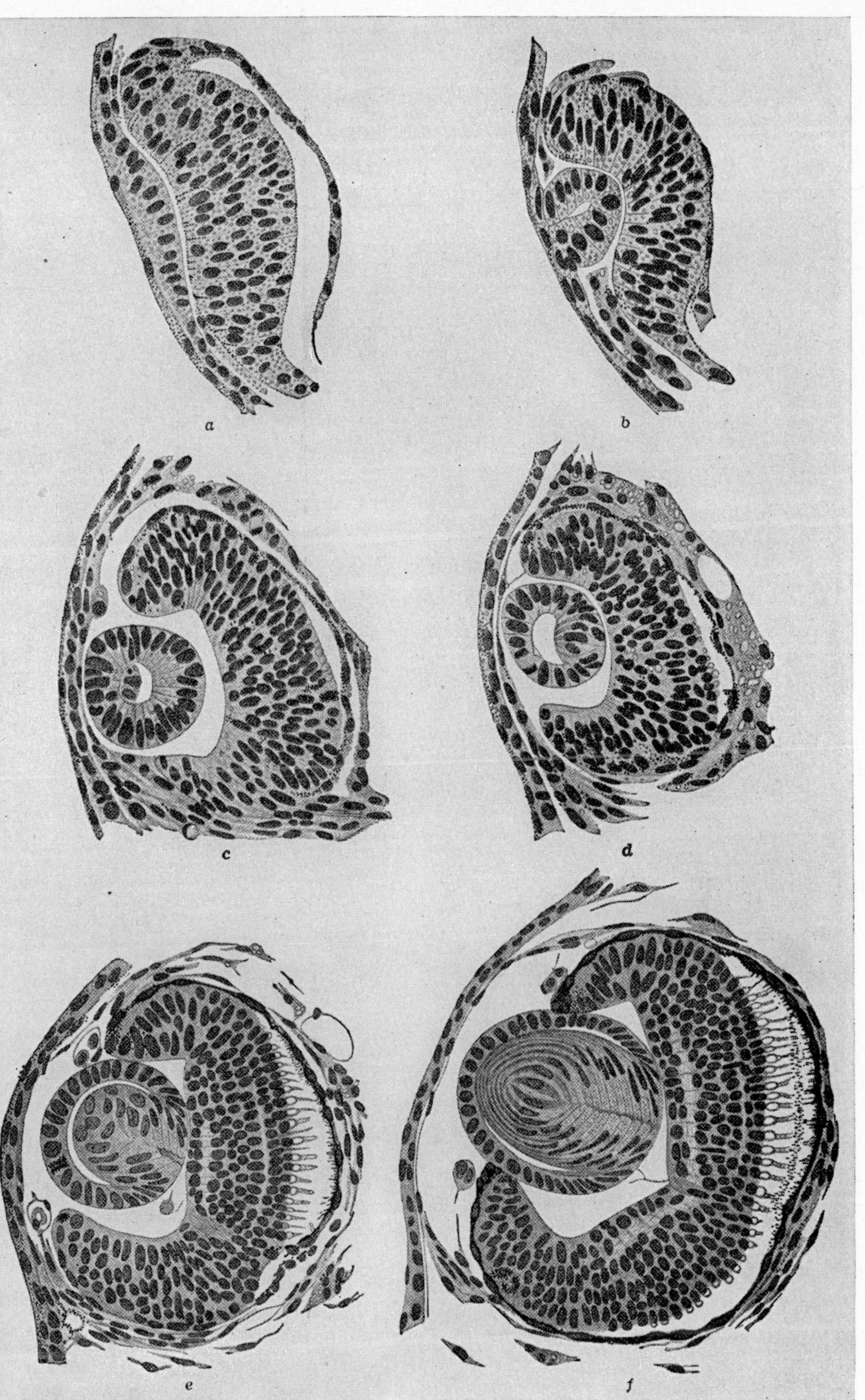

Development of the optic cup and lens in *Siredon pisciformis*. (After Rabl.)

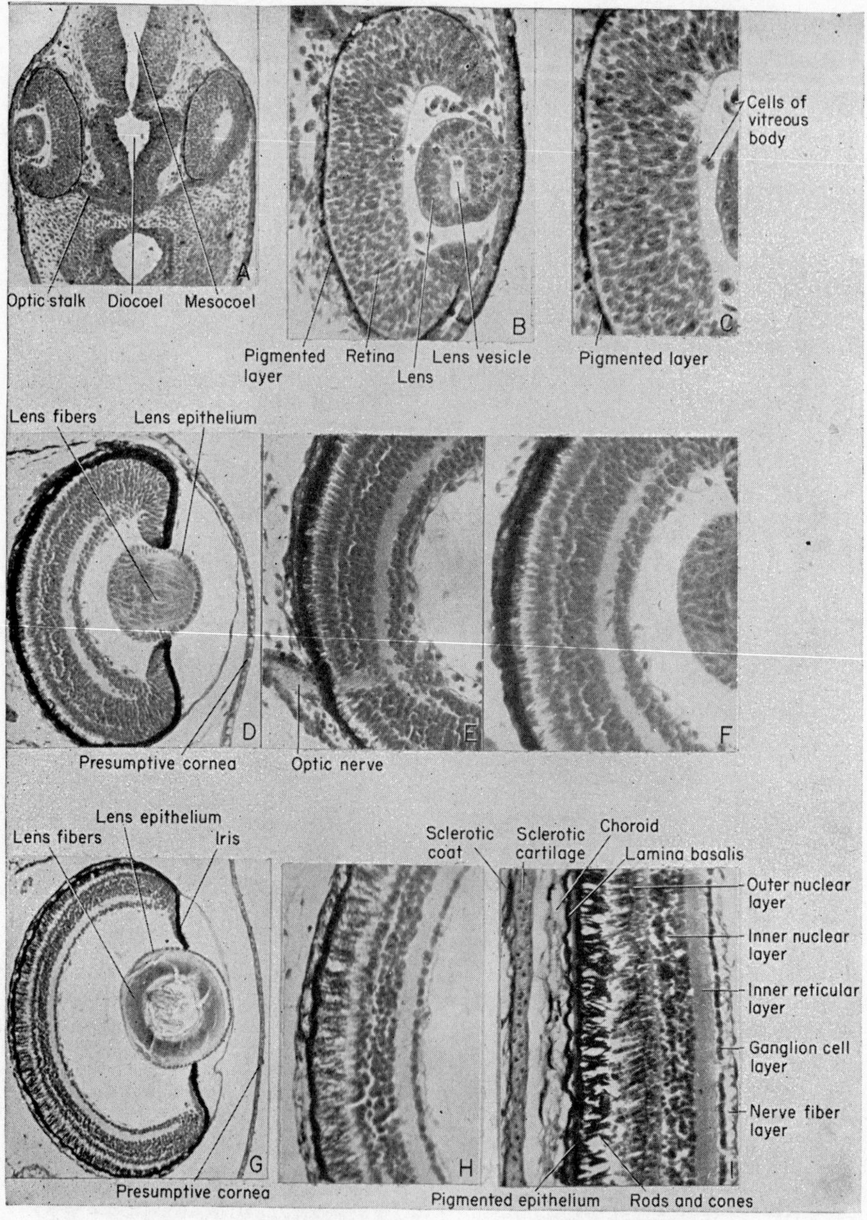

Development of the amphibian eye. (A,B,C) Progressive enlargements of the 5 mm. stage. (D,E,F) Progressive enlargements of the 11 mm. stage. (G,H,I) Progressive enlargements of the metamorphic stage.

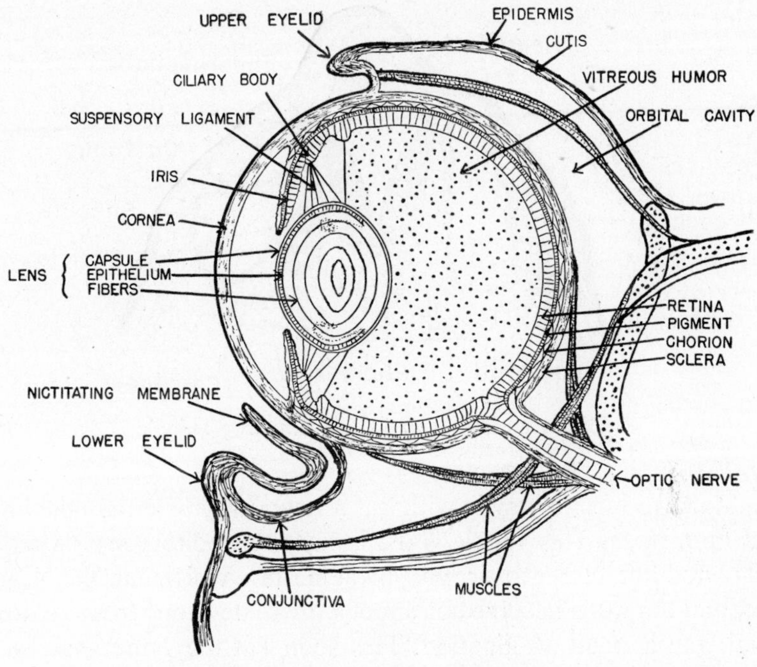

SCHEMATIC DIAGRAM THROUGH FROG'S EYE

(REDRAWN FROM MANGOLD '31)

gives rise to the connective tissue of the **choroid coat** that surrounds the pigmented layer of the eye. Outside of the choroid coat is the very tough **sclerotic coat,** also mesenchymal. The nervous (sensory) parts of the eye are therefore ectodermal in origin, but the blood vessels, connective tissues, cartilage, and parts of the cornea are all mesenchymal (mesoderm).

The Ear.

The frog has no outer ear. The inner and the middle ear are developed much in the manner of all vertebrate ears, but to a less efficient and complicated degree.

THE INNER EAR. The superficially placed **auditory placode** develops from nervous ectoderm on the side of the head at the level of the rhombencephalon, prior to the time of hatching (at about the 2.5 mm. stage). This occurs under the inductive influences of the medulla and archenteric roof. It moves inwardly toward the brain and

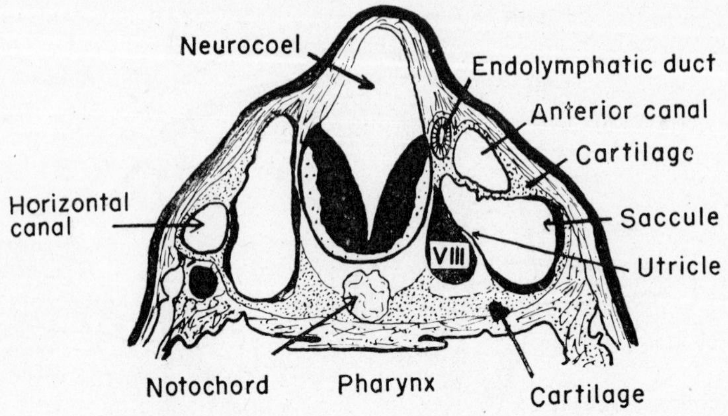

Auditory apparatus of an 11 mm. frog tadpole.

invaginates to form a vesicle with but a temporary external opening at the 3 mm. stage. This vesicle is the otocyst or **auditory sac.** After the head ectoderm closes over this invaginating vesicle at the 4 mm. stage, and the walls become continuous, there develops from its dorso-mesial wall a small evagination. This soon (at the 7 mm. stage) becomes tubular and is known as the **endolymphatic duct.** The duct on each side grows dorsally to fuse with the duct of the other side of the brain. It finally loses its cavity and forms a vascular membrane which covers the rhombencephalon, having no auditory function whatever. The duct remains as a vestige even in the adult frog, originating between the membranous labyrinth (inner ear) and the hindbrain.

At about the 11 to 12 mm. stage there develops a vertical fold which divides the main cavity of the otocyst into mesial and lateral chambers. The more dorsal and mesial portion is the **utricle** and the more ventral and lateral portion is the **saccule,** both being joined by a small pore.

The utricle, by the 15 mm. stage, becomes further subdivided by three folds or ridges. These develop on the inside of the utricular wall. One is vertical and anterior (**anterior semi-circular canal**), one is horizontal and lateral (**horizontal semi-circular canal**), and finally there will appear a third fold which is vertical and posterior (**posterior semi-circular canal**). These ridges fuse with one another to form three loop-like tubes, each of which opens at both ends into the utricular cavity with which it retains connection throughout the life of the frog. These are known collectively as the **semi-circular canals** which later become free from the utricular wall and continue to grow and

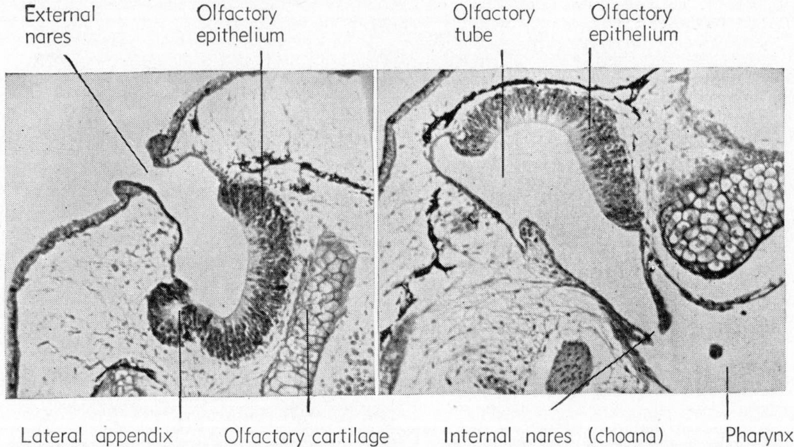

External and internal nares of the 11 mm. frog tadpole. (*Left*) External nares. (*Right*) Internal nares (choana) opening into the pharynx.

the 2.5 mm. body length stage, long before the time of hatching. The overlying superficial epithelial ectoderm disappears so that the nervous layer of the placode becomes the exposed lining of the olfactory pit.

After hatching (6 mm. stage) a solid rod of ectodermal cells grows ventro-laterally from the olfactory pit to become attached to the pharynx just dorsal to the oral plate (i.e., stomodeum). By the 11 mm. stage this core of cells acquires a lumen which is continuous from the external nares (**olfactory pits**) to the internal nares (**internal choanae**) which open into the pharynx. The major part of this olfactory tube is lined with non-sensory epithelium. It develops a dorsal and a ventral chamber (sacs), each of which acquires glandular masses which are known as the **organs of Jacobson.**

The neuroblasts of the olfactory placodes send extensions posteriorly and give rise to the fibers which form the **olfactory** or first cranial **nerve.** These grow toward the brain and are guided in their directional development by the outgrowth of the telencephalon known as the **olfactory lobes.**

The Lateral Line Organs.

The most posterior or fourth cranial placode (cranial nerve X) sends a growth posteriorly beneath the lateral body epidermis, on either side, beginning at about the 4 mm. stage. It grows posteriorly to the

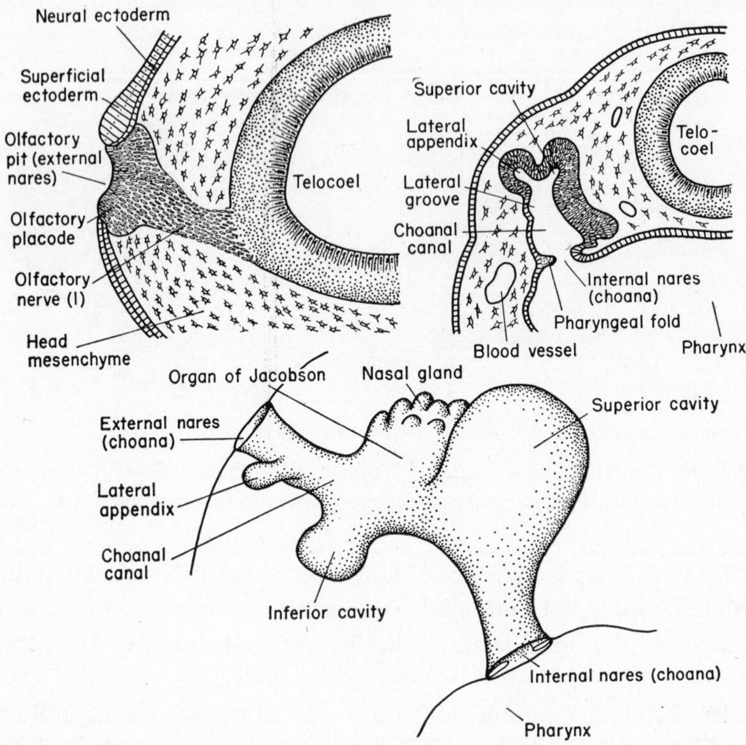

Development of the olfactory organ of the frog. (*Top, left*) Sagittal section through the olfactory placode and nerve. (*Top, right*) Posterior transverse section through the choanal canal. (*Bottom*) Schematic reconstruction of the embryonic olfactory organ.

tip of the tail. Along these cords arise groups of sensory cells which grow through the epidermis to become exposed along the sides of the body as the **lateral line system.** The exposed cells are ciliated, and are therefore sensitive to vibrations in the surrounding aquatic medium. They are protected by inner and outer sheath cells and a basement membrane and are connected functionally with branches of the lateral line nerve. At the head level the extensions of this system seem to be innervated by cranial nerves VII, IX, and X, principally the latter. This structure is no doubt a vestige of the aquatic ancestry of the Anura, for, as in lower forms, these organs are innervated by a branch of the vagus (X) ganglion, known as the **lateral line nerve** or ramus lateralis. In the Anura this system disappears by the time of metamorphosis.

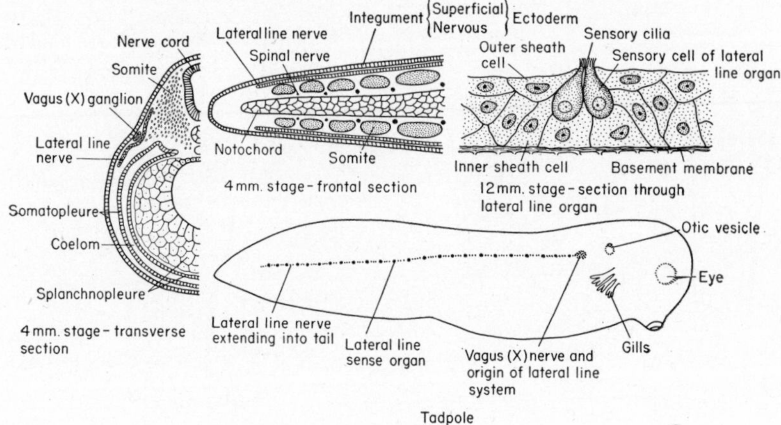

Origin of the lateral line sense organ system in the frog larva.

The Cranial Nerves

These nerves, as in the case of practically all nerves of the embryo, are developed in pairs. Many of them are both sensory (afferent) and motor (efferent). Each nerve will be dealt with as a separate entity.

As the neural folds close they leave a column of cells between the fold and the dorsal ectoderm. These are known as the **cranial** or **neural crests,** depending upon the level under consideration. The **cranial crests** of the brain level are different from the neural crests of the spinal cord level in that they become divided into four large pairs known as the **cranial placodes.** These consist of thickened patches of neural ectoderm of the head, one of which, the auditory placode, has been described already. The original cellular connection between each cranial crest segment and the brain remains as the sheath of the nerve fibers to be developed in that region. At the spinal cord level the segments are metameric and will be as abundant as the spinal nerves developed therefrom.

Four ganglionic masses are found in the development of the frog cranial nerves as early as the 6 mm. stage. These include the first or **semilunar ganglion** of the fifth nerve. The second is the **acusticofacialis** (VII–VIII) ganglion which becomes associated with the auditory placode. The third is the **glossopharyngeal** (IX) and the fourth is the **vagus** (X). The third and fourth arise together as the post-otic ganglionic masses and each becomes associated with an epibranchial placode.

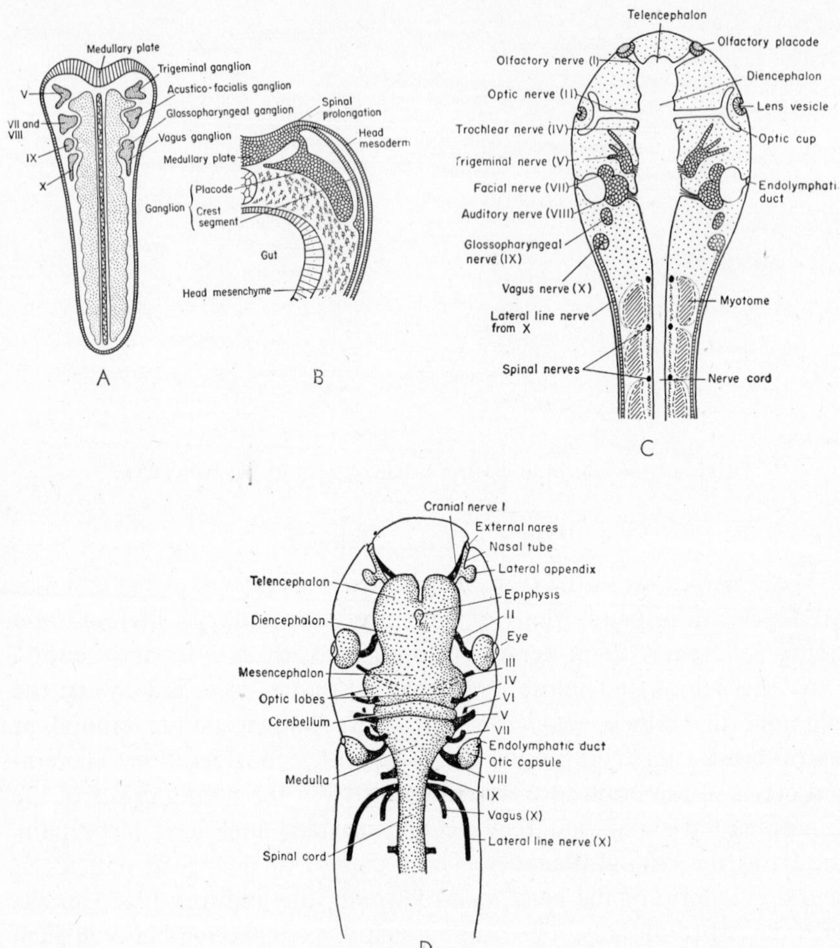

Origin and derivatives of the cranial ganglia. (A) Origin of the cranial ganglia: frontal section. (B) Relation of the crest segments and placodes: transverse section. (C) Relation of the sense organs to the cranial ganglia. (D) Brain, sense organs, and cranial nerves of the 12 mm. tadpole.

Embryologically the rudiments of all of the cranial nerves are more complex than are the rudiments of the spinal nerves. They are made up of cell masses from the neural crests, from ectodermal patches on the surface of the head, and from cell processes extending out from the ventro-lateral brain neuroblasts. The spinal nerves do not have the surface ectodermal constituent. Following is a summary of the cranial nerves of the frog embryo:

I. Olfactory: This is sensory, arising after hatching (11 mm.) from neuroblasts of the olfactory lobe (telencephalon) and growing to the **olfactory placode.**

II. Optic: This is sensory, arising at an early stage (6 mm.) from the neuroblasts of the **retinal layer** of the optic cup to grow along the ventral wall of the optic stalk to join the lateral wall of the diencephalon.

III. Oculomotor: This is motor, arising just before hatching from the ventro-lateral wall of the mesencephalon (crura cerebri) to innervate four muscles of the eye. These are the **rectus superior** and the ciliary ganglion, the **rectus inferior,** the **rectus medialis,** and the **obliquus inferior.**

IV. Trochlear: This is motor and remains very small. It arises late in development from near the roof of the mesencephalon between the optic lobes and the cerebellum just posterior to the valvula cerebelli and the posterior commissure. It innervates the **superior oblique muscles** of the eye.

V. Trigeminal: This is a mixed nerve, also known as the trifacial ganglion, which appears as early as the 5 mm. stage and has a complicated origin from the dorsal (superficial) ganglionic elements of the first cranial crest segment and the ganglionic

Segments of neural crest	I	II	III	IV	V	VI
Nerves derived from them	V ramus ophthalmicus	V main branch	VII and VIII	IX	X	dorsal root of 1st spinal

	Head Somites			Trunk Somites			
Mesodermal Somites	Premandibular	Mandibular	Hyoid	1st	2nd	3rd	4th
Ventral roots	I	II	III	IV	V	VI	
Nerves derived from them	III	IV	VI	disappears	disappears	ventral root of 1st spinal	

(Courtesy, Jenkinson: "Vertebrate Embryology," Oxford, The Clarendon Press.)

portion of the first cranial placode. It is well developed by the 9 mm. stage. The level is at the anterior end of the medulla. This is a very large and tri-radiate ganglion, including an **Ophthalmic** branch from the placode whose fibers pass to the skin and snout, and a forked **Gasserian ganglion** which arises from both the crest and placode elements and gives rise to the **maxillary** (upper) and **mandibular** (lower) branches of the fifth nerve. The entire mixed trigeminal nerve ganglion (V) joins the dorso-lateral wall of the medulla oblongata. The outer or non-nervous portion of the placode disappears and it is believed that the non-nervous portion of the crest segment may contribute some of the mesenchyme to the mandibular arch. It is certainly difficult to distinguish between them.

VI. Abducens: This is a motor nerve arising late (11 mm. stage) from the neuroblasts of the ventral side of the medulla and innervating the lateral or **external rectus** and **retractor bulbi muscles** of the eye.

VII. Facial: This is a mixed nerve, arising by the 5 mm. stage from the anterior ganglionic portion of the second or **acustico-facialis** (second cranial) **crest segment** and **placode** and is associated with neuroblasts coming from the medulla just posterior to cranial nerve V. The motor (efferent) fibers are divided between the **hyoid** and the **palatine** (mouth) branches, but a good portion of the crest segment, from which these fibers arise, is non-nervous and is presumed to give rise to **mesenchyme** of the hyoid arch.

VIII. Auditory: This is a sensory nerve arising by the 5 mm. stage from the posterior ganglionic portion of the second (**acustico-facialis**) **crest ganglion,** in close association with the auditory placode, and innervates only the inner ear.

IX. Glossopharyngeal: This is a mixed ganglion, arising by the 9 mm. stage from the ganglionic portion of the **third cranial crest segment** and **placode.** Fibers of the ninth and tenth cranial ganglia enter the sides of the medulla together, but peripherally the ninth or glossopharyngeal nerve supplies the **first branchial arch,** the **mouth,** the **tongue,** and the **pharynx.** This ganglion is incompletely separated from the vagus by the anterior cardinal vein.

X. Vagus or pneumogastric ganglion: This is mixed and arises by the 9 mm. stage from the fourth cranial crest segment and placode and becomes associated with the neuroblasts from the medulla. Peripherally the branches feed the **second** and **third branchial arches,** the **tympanum,** the **muscles of the shoulders,** the **viscera** (including larynx, oesophagus, stomach, lungs, and heart), and the **lateral line system.** The non-nervous portion of the crest segment forms mesenchyme and the superficial non-nervous elements of the placode then disappear.

SUMMARY OF DERIVATIVES OF THE CRANIAL NERVES IN TABULAR FORM

Cranial Crest Segment	*Cranial Nerves Derived Therefrom*
I	V ophthalmic branch V mandibular branch
II	VII and VIII
III	IX
IV	X

THE SPINAL NERVES

The **spinal nerves,** aside from their component parts, differ from the cranial nerves in that they are related to mesodermal somites rather than visceral clefts.

The spinal nerves arise from the pair of continuous **neural crests.** These are elongated strands of neural ectoderm left outside of the dorsal neural tube, between it and the dorsal ectoderm, at the time of closure of the neural tube. These crests become metamerically segmented and are paired as a result of the development of the somites. In frontal sections of the 7 mm. stage these crests will be seen as dorsal root ganglia of the spinal nerves. No placodes are developed in association with any part of the neural crests, as were described in association with some of the homologous cranial crests.

Each crest segment is made up of many neuroblasts which send fibers to the dorso-lateral wall of the spinal cord to form the **dorsal root** or ramus of the spinal nerve. This connects the **dorsal root ganglion** (original neural crest) with the spinal cord. Also, other fibers grow ventro-laterally from this ganglionic crest to become the afferent tracts from the skin and other sensory organs.

Within the spinal cord, as early as the 4 mm. stage, neuroblasts develop and send out bundles of efferent axons (fibers) which emerge from the ventro-lateral wall of the spinal cord and almost immedi-

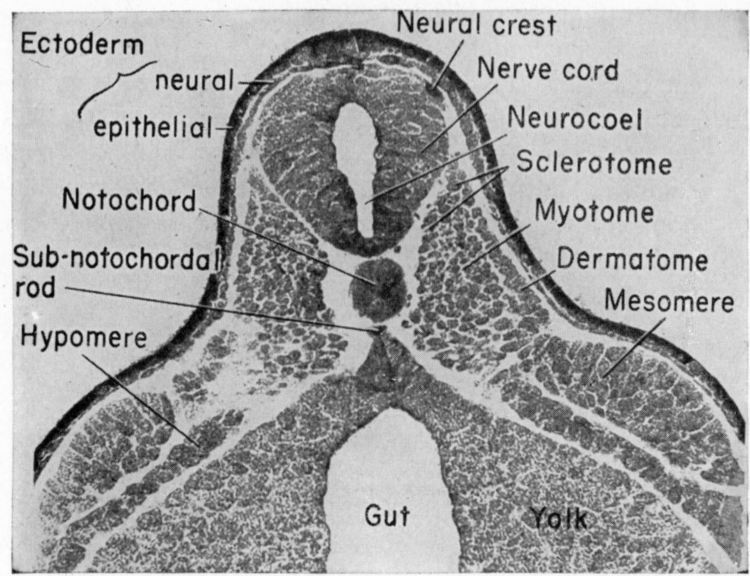

Early organogeny. The 5 mm. frog tadpole at mid-body level. Photograph of cross section.

ately co-mingle with the afferent fibers, already described. The **ventral nerve roots** or rami are entirely efferent, the **dorsal nerve roots** are entirely afferent, but the nerve trunks contain, within a common sheath, both the afferent and efferent fiber trunks. Many of these spinal nerve trunks fork to send both types of fibers dorsally to the sense organs and ventro-laterally to the muscles and to the limbs.

The tadpole may have a total of 40 or more pairs of spinal nerves, but only the anterior 10 pairs remain after the degeneration of the tail at metamorphosis. The first pair (**hypoglossal**) emerges from between the first and the second vertebrae, to innervate the tongue and some of the muscles of the hyoid arch. The second pair (**brachial**) emerges from between the second and the third vertebrae and are very large. They have connections with the first and third spinal nerves and thus form the large **brachial plexus,** innervating the forelimbs and the muscles of the back. The third pair has the aforementioned connection with the brachial but it then supplies the external oblique and transverse muscles and the skin. The fourth, fifth, and sixth spinal nerves supply the skin and muscles of the abdominal wall. The seventh, eighth, and ninth spinal nerves together form the **lumbosacral** or **sciatic plexus** which innervates the posterior abdominal region and

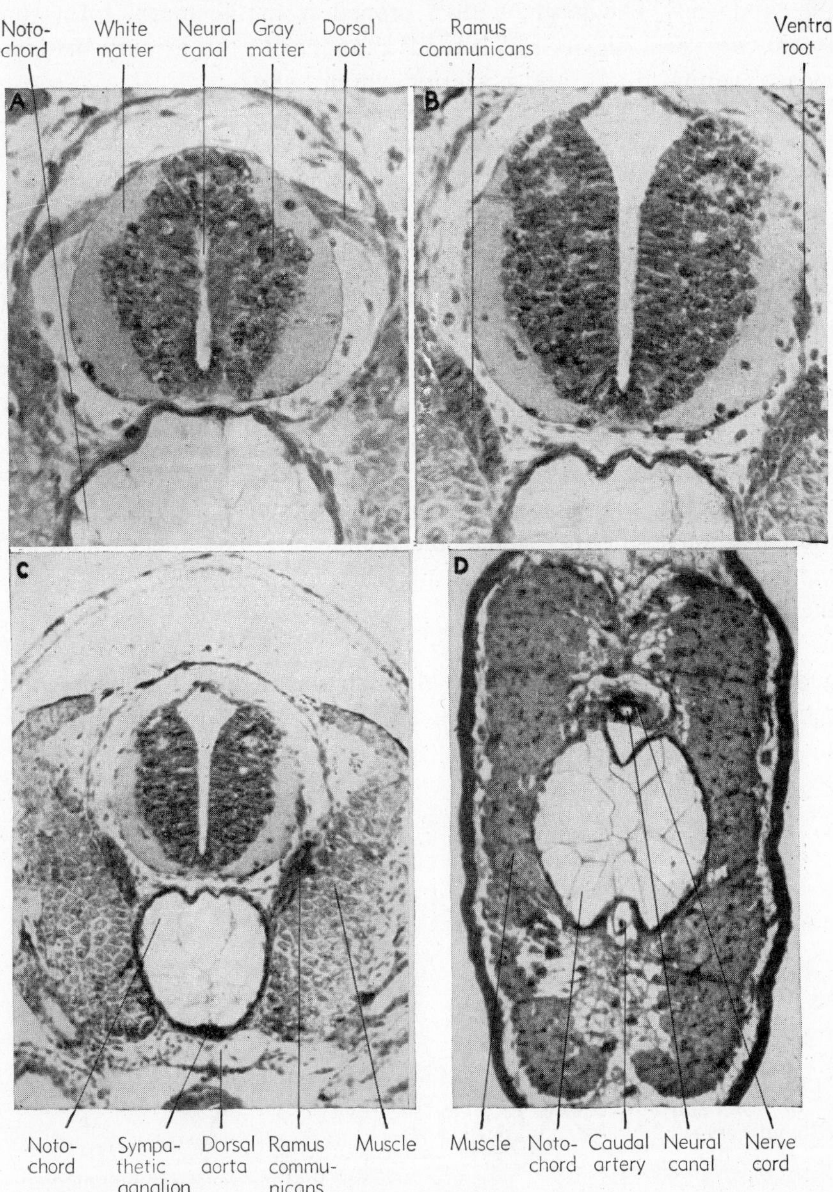

Development of the spinal cord and sympathetic nerves. (A) Showing the dorsal root (from neural crest). (B) Showing the ventral root (from cord neuroblasts). (C) Showing connection between the spinal nerve and the sympathetic ganglion, known as the ramus communicans. (D) A section in the tail region to show the relatively large notochord and reduced nerve cord.

the hind legs. The tenth, with a branch from the ninth, forms the **ischio-coccygeal plexus** which sends branches to the urinary bladder, cloaca, genital ducts, and posterior lymph hearts.

The Neural Crest Derivatives

The Sympathetic Nervous System.

The development of the sympathetic nervous system is not understood clearly but it is believed also to arise from the neural crests, by a downgrowth along the afferent trunk to the spinal nerve and thence to the dorsal aorta and the viscera beginning at about the 6 mm. stage. The sheath cells probably come from the neural tube itself. Just before hatching there may be seen clusters of cells around the junction of the dorsal and ventral nerve roots, and these clusters will give rise to the **sympathetic ganglia** which become associated with the **dorsal aorta** and the **viscera.** These ganglia are also interconnected by paired longitudinal strands on either side of the spinal cord. The fibers which join the sympathetic ganglia with the spinal nerve are known collectively as the **ramus communicans.**

The sympathetic system arises with the vagus (cranial nerve X), and its connecting fibers extend through the jugular foramen of the

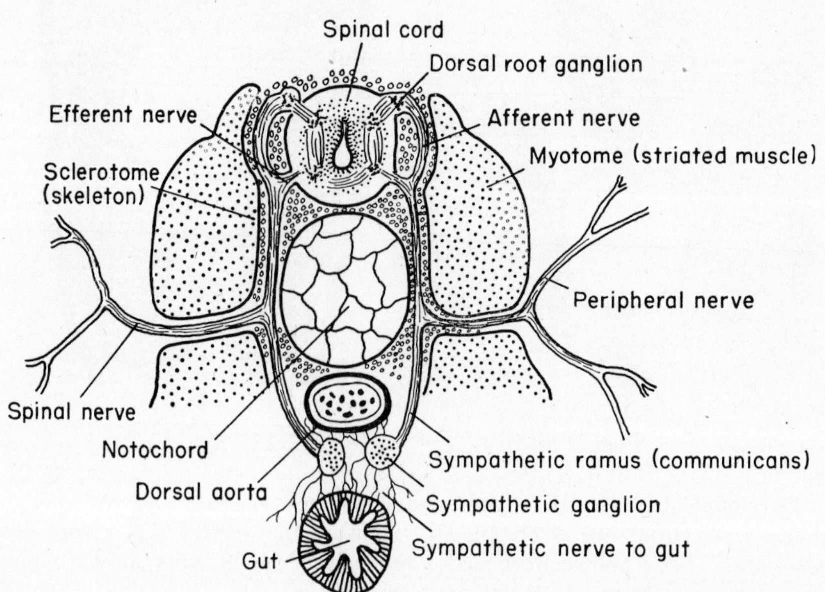

Relation of the spinal and the sympathetic nervous systems.

skull and along each side of the spinal cord to receive these connecting rami from the segmental spinal nerves. Both independent sympathetic nerves and plexi are developed and are found often quite removed from their source of origin.

The Adrenal Medulla.

The large brown cells of the inner portion of this endocrine organ arise some time before metamorphosis by migration from the sympathetic ganglia and hence are of ectodermal origin. They have lighter staining nuclei and are scattered among the more abundant cortical cells. These latter cells arise from the mesoderm and will be discussed subsequently.

The Stomodeum and Proctodeum

The **stomodeum** and **proctodeum** are also of ectodermal origin, each being represented by an invagination of ectoderm at either end of the digestive tract. The stomodeal ectoderm meets the oral endodermal evagination to form the oral plate which at the 6 mm. stage ruptures through to form the mouth. Therefore, a portion of the mouth (to the tongue) is lined with ectoderm. The proctodeum is a similar caudal invagination of ectoderm which meets the evagination of the anal endoderm resulting in the formation of a temporary anal plate. This shortly ruptures. The anus is thus partially lined with ectoderm.

SUMMARY OF EMBRYONIC DEVELOPMENT OF THE 11 MM. FROG TADPOLE: ECTODERMAL DERIVATIVES

Epidermis—thickened, ciliated on tail only.

Central Nervous System—differentiated into four brain vesicles and spinal cord.

Prosencephalon (Forebrain)

Telencephalon—anterior to optic recess; thin-roofed.

Cerebral hemispheres develop around each of lateral ventricles.

Anterior choroid plexus as median dorsal invagination into telocoel which becomes vascularized.

Olfactory (I) nerve from floor of cerebral hemisphere to mesial side of nasal tube.

Diencephalon—from epiphysis to dorsal thickening to tuberculum posterius.

Epiphysis as mid-dorsal evagination just posterior to choroid plexus.

Optic recess—just posterior to torus transversus or region of lamina terminalis (anterior fusion of neural folds) as median ventral evagination.

Optic chiasma—thickened floor where optic nerve enters (posterior to recess).

Optic (II) nerve—from chiasma to eyes, may be seen entering retina.

Infundibulum—bulbous evagination in floor of diencephalon between optic chiasma and tuberculum posterius, ventral to notochord.

Mesencephalon—bounded by dorsal thickening and tuberculum posterius.

Optic lobes from dorsal thickening, bi-lobed, become corpora bigemina.

Cavity—mesocoel, iter, or aqueduct of Sylvius.

Oculomotor (III) nerve—mesio-lateral, from floor.

Trochlear (IV) nerve—dorso-lateral, just posterior to optic lobes and difficult to find, being small.

Rhombencephalon—from dorsal thickening to spinal cord, metencephalon and myelencephalon not distinguishable in the frog.

Cerebellum—from thickened roof, anterior.

Posterior choroid plexus—from thin, vascular posterior roof.

Otic vesicles—found at level of cerebellum.

Cranial nerves V to X are associated with this portion of the brain.

Trigeminal (V) nerve—anterior to otocyst, large, sends branches to mandibular and maxillary processes of first visceral arch.

Abducens (VI) nerve—from floor of rhombencephalon, anterior and ventral to origin of trigeminal. Supplies eye muscles as do oculomotor and trochlear.

Facial (VII) and auditory (VIII) nerve—arises as a single ganglion, mesio-posterior to otocyst, supplying facial muscles and saccule and utricle of ear.

Glossopharyngeal (IX) nerve—arises posterior to otocyst, sending branches to first branchial arch. Ganglion.

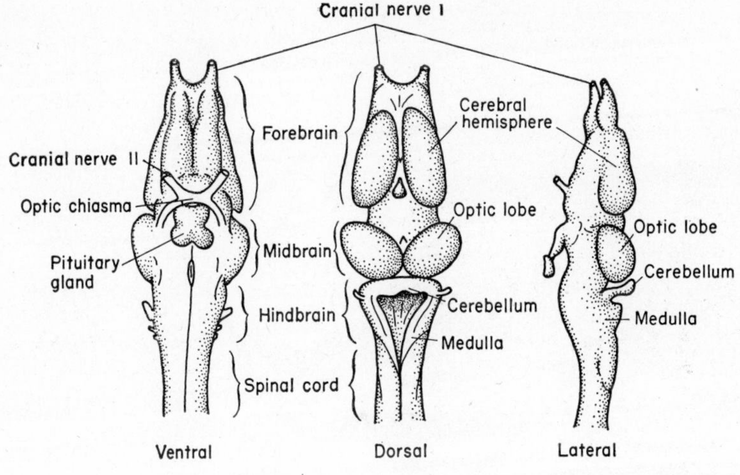

Brain of the adult frog.

Vagus (X) nerve—arises with IX, sending branches to second, third, and fourth branchial arches; to lateral line organs and to viscera.

Cranial Crest Segments—visceral cartilages, parts of the cranial cartilages from head mesenchyme originally derived from ectoderm.

Spinal Cord—from rhombencephalon into tail, with continuous cavity.

Neural (central) canal—original neurocoel, constricted centrally.

Ependymal layer—elongate, ciliated cells lining the canal.

Mantle layer—gray matter consisting of compact cell bodies, lateral.

Marginal layer—white matter, consisting of outermost axons.

Dorsal root—afferent fibers passing dorso-mesially to join dorsal root ganglion.

Dorsal root ganglion—paired thick bundle of neurons dorso-lateral to spinal cord, derived from neural crests.

Ventral root—efferent fibers passing ventro-laterally from spinal cord to spinal nerve trunk.

Spinal nerve—fusion of afferent and efferent fibers associated with distal organs (muscles, etc.).

Dorsal ramus—branch of spinal nerve to dorsal muscles.

Ventral ramus—branch of spinal nerve to ventral muscles.

Communicating ramus—fibers from spinal nerve to sympathetic ganglion.

Sympathetic ganglion—nerve cells lateral to dorsal aorta, derived from neural crest.

Special Sense Organs—found in the head region.

Eye—well developed in 11 mm. stage, some parts mesodermal.

Retinal layer—sensory portion consisting of rods and cones (inner and outer granular layers).

Pigmented layer—thinner layer outside of retinal layer.

Lens—arising as vesicle, now a solid ball lying in opening of optic cup.

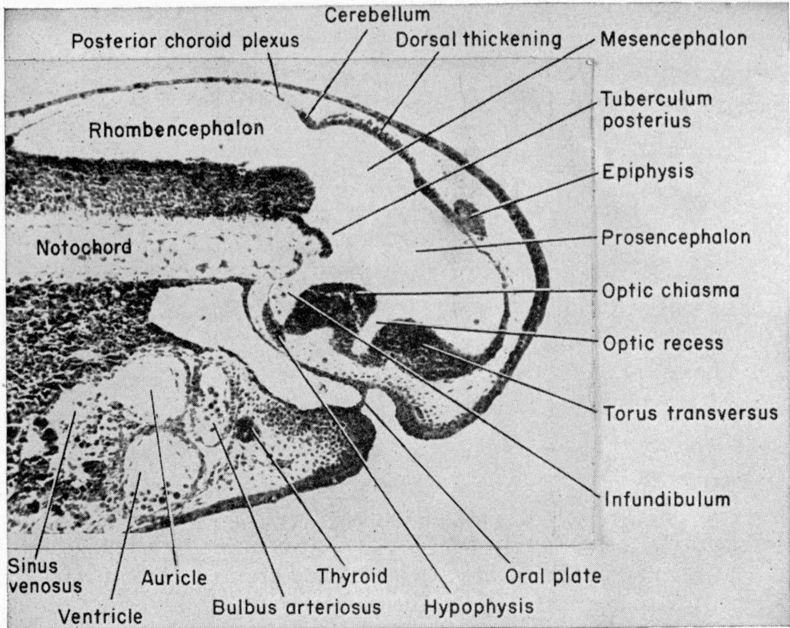

Sagittal section through the anterior end of the 8 mm. frog larva.

*Choroid coat—thin, vascular layer of mesenchyme immediately around the eye.

*Sclerotic coat—loose mesenchyme investing choroid layer.

*Cornea—extension of sclerotic layer and underlying the epidermis, therefore both ectoderm and mesoderm.

*Eye muscles—small bundles of muscles which control eye movements by way of cranial nerves III, IV, and VI.

Ear—arising from auditory placode, then otocyst.

Utricle—mesial and dorsal, giving rise to the three semi-circular canals, two of which have developed, i.e., anterior dorso-ventral and outer horizontal canals.

Saccule—outer and ventral portion of original otocyst.

Endolymphatic duct—between utricle and brain, joining saccule.

Cochlea—mesial portion of saccule, pigmented and ciliated.

Nose—arising from olfactory placodes.

External nares—glandular organ of Jacobson, opened to exterior.

Internal nares—extension of tubular opening from external nares into pharynx, called choana.

Stomodeum and Proctodeum—ectodermally lined openings into mouth and cloaca.

*Part or all of the starred structures are derived from mesoderm.

CHAPTER TWELVE

The Endodermal Derivatives

- The Mouth (Stomodeum, Jaws, Lips, Etc.)
- The Foregut
  - The Pharynx
  - The Thymus Gland
  - The Carotid Glands
  - The Parathyroid Glands
  - The Ultimobranchial Bodies
  - The Thyroid Gland
  - The Tongue
  - The Lungs
  - The Liver
  - The Pancreas
  - The Oesophagus and Stomach
- The Midgut
- The Hindgut

The endoderm gives rise to all structures associated with the original archenteron, from the mouth (**ectodermal stomodeum**) to the anus (**ectodermal proctodeum**), and all of its derivatives. It must be emphasized, however, that the endoderm contributes only the lining epithelium of these structures and that (since each of them is invested with blood, connective and nervous tissue, and often with muscle) ectoderm and mesoderm may also be involved. It is nevertheless convenient to describe in sequence from the anterior to the posterior (foregut, midgut, and hindgut) those structures whose linings are endodermal in origin.

The Mouth (Stomodeum, Jaws, Lips, Etc.)

The **lips** and anterior lining of the **mouth** are ectodermal and the margin between the ectoderm and endoderm can be determined in the larva by the extent of the invaginated and pigmented stomodeal ectoderm. This ectoderm plus the oral endoderm form the **oral plate,** or **oral membrane,** which generally ruptures through shortly after the time of hatching (6 mm. stage) to form the mouth opening. The lateral margins of the mouth (stomodeum) are the original **mandibular ridges** between which are the dorsal and the ventral (larval) **lips.** These are transitory but important feeding organs of the tadpole. The **dorsal lip** develops three medially placed rows of superficial **teeth** which are periodically sloughed off and replaced. The **ventral lip** of the larva develops four rows of somewhat more complete teeth, but all teeth are covered with stomodeal ectoderm. A cornified ectodermal

"jaw," consisting of a hardened ridge, develops at the base of both the dorsal and the ventral lips.

By the time of metamorphosis the horny **larval teeth** and jaws are lost and the mandibular arches give rise to the jaw elements of the adult. The upper larval teeth are replaced by **permanent teeth** which bear only superficial resemblance to the teeth of mammals.

The **tongue,** which is ultimately attached anteriorly and will be free posteriorly, begins to develop by the time of metamorphosis from a proliferation of cells from the endodermal floor of the pharynx. The bulk of the tongue will, of course, be of mesodermal origin but most of its covering and glandular elements come from the endoderm, the anterior portion being covered with stomodeal ectoderm.

The Foregut

This anterior portion of the original archenteron expands widely in front of the yolk mass and consists of all of the derivatives from the stomodeum to and including the pancreas and liver. The stomodeum, the anterior covering of the tongue, and the roof of the mouth anterior to the internal choanae are ectodermal and only the posterior covering of the tongue and mouth, beginning at about the level of the thyroid gland, is endodermal. This foregut portion of the archenteron therefore assumes a major role in the early development of the frog, where it gives rise to three successive sets of respiratory organs (i.e., external and internal gills, then the lungs) to most of the endocrine organs, and to a good portion of the digestive tract.

The Pharynx.

The **pharyngeal cavity** is widely expanded anterior and ventral to the yolk mass of the frog embryo. The earliest elongated and vertical evaginations of the pharyngeal endoderm are known as the **visceral** or branchial **pouches.** Those of the most anterior pair, which develop between the mandibular and the hyoid arches, are known as the **hyomandibular pouches.** The dorsal remnant of this first pair of pouches gives rise to the Eustachian tube of the adult and connects the pharynx with the middle ear chamber. The second and third pairs of visceral pouches are known as the first and second branchial pouches, because they give rise to gill clefts, and they develop between the succeeding visceral arches. Eventually, six pairs of endodermal evaginations develop in this manner, but those of the last (most

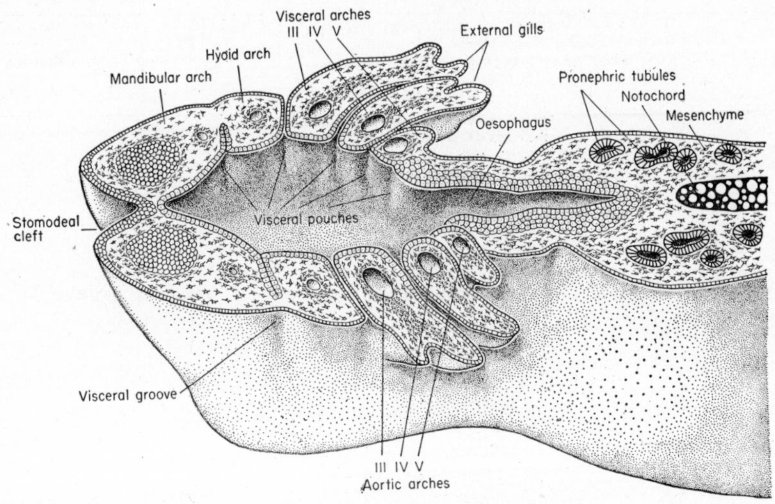

Frontal (horizontal) reconstruction of the external gill stage of the frog larva. (Redrawn and modified after Huettner.)

posterior) pair rarely open as pouches, remaining as mere cords of endoderm. By definition we use the term **"pouch"** for the endodermal evagination, **"groove"** for the ectodermal invagination, and **"cleft"** for the combination of ectoderm and endoderm which meet when these grooves and pouches break through. **Visceral pouches** I to V inclusive appear in this order and grow laterally toward the head ectoderm, all but the first and fifth, meeting a corresponding groove and breaking through to form clefts. Occasionally a sixth visceral pouch is developed, but it is generally vestigial.

These clefts can be classified in tabular form as follows:

Pouch (Endoderm)	Arch (Mesoderm) Cleft (Ectoderm and Endoderm)	Groove (Ectoderm)
	Visceral arch I—mandibular (Aortic arch I)	
Visceral pouch I	***Visceral cleft I** (Hyomandibular—Eustachian tube. Ectodermal plate—tympanic membrane)	**Visceral groove I**

*Does not perforate.

Pouch (Endoderm)	Arch (Mesoderm) Cleft (Ectoderm and Endoderm)	Groove (Ectoderm)
	Visceral arch II—hyoid (Aortic arch II) (Opercular fold arises at 9 mm. stage, covers gills at 10 mm. stage)	
Visceral pouch II (Branchial pouch I)	**Visceral cleft II** (Branchial cleft I)	**Visceral groove II** (Branchial groove I)
	Visceral arch III (Branchial arch I) (Aortic arch III—carotid) (External gill at 5 mm. stage)	
Visceral pouch III (Branchial pouch II)	**Visceral cleft III** (Branchial cleft II)	**Visceral groove III** (Branchial groove II)
	Visceral arch IV (Branchial arch II) (Aortic arch IV—systemic) (External gill II at 5 mm. stage)	
Visceral pouch IV (Branchial pouch III)	**Visceral cleft IV** (Branchial cleft III)	**Visceral groove IV** (Branchial groove III)
	Visceral arch V (Branchial arch III) (Aortic arch V) (External gill III at 6 mm. stage)	
Visceral pouch V (Branchial pouch IV)	**Visceral cleft V** (Branchial cleft IV)	**Visceral groove V** (Branchial groove IV)
	Visceral arch VI (Branchial arch IV) (Aortic arch VI—pulmonary)	

The first four pairs of branchial clefts constitute channels or gill slits from the pharynx to the exterior, and are lined with both ectoderm and endoderm. The first visceral (hyomandibular) cleft and the sixth visceral cleft are rudimentary in that they rarely open through to the outside.

The finger-like and branched **external gills** arise as outgrowths of the lateral wall of the third, fourth, and fifth visceral (branchial I, II, III) arches shortly after the gill clefts are perforated. The first and second external gills arise at the 5 mm. stage and the third at the 6 mm. stage of development. The arches carry with them the covering ectoderm and the capillary loop of blood vessels and the nerves that are always found within the arches themselves. The ectodermal covering is very thin so that the relatively large capillaries in each gill can readily exchange CO_2 and O_2 in the surrounding aqueous medium. These external gills constitute the respiratory organs of the larva from about the fifth to the tenth days, and then the gills begin to atrophy. This process of degeneration is assisted by the development of a posterior growth from the hyoid arch, known as the **operculum.** This is a membrane which covers the gills and forms, along with a similar membrane of the other side, a ventral and ventro-lateral **opercular chamber.** While the external covering of the operculum is ectodermal it contains mesoderm. Water taken in through the mouth continues to pass over the external gills, within the opercular chamber, but escapes through the **spiracle** at the posterior margin of the left opercular fold.

In the meantime the **internal gills** must develop in order to take over the respiratory functions that gradually are being relinquished by the external gills. These internal gills develop a double row of filaments, ventral to the branchial arches and arising doubly from the postero-external (anterior and posterior) faces of the same first three pairs of branchial arches. These are visceral arches III, IV, and V. The fourth pair of branchial (sixth visceral) arches may also give rise to reduced single internal gills from their anterior faces only. These gills are termed internal because of their position on the arches and also because of the fact that they are covered by a body flap, the operculum, and are therefore truly within the body. The entire opercular (branchial) chamber is lined with ectoderm, however, and this includes the covering of all of the external and internal gills. The internal position of this new set of gill filaments is therefore secondary.

The ventro-lateral position of the external gills, plus the development of the operculum, tends to move them to a position beneath rather than lateral to the pharynx, within the spacious **opercular cavity** or **chamber.** The original endodermal branchial pouches, lateral to the pharynx, become partially separated off by lateral projections of the pharyngeal floor and also by longitudinal folds in the lateral aspects

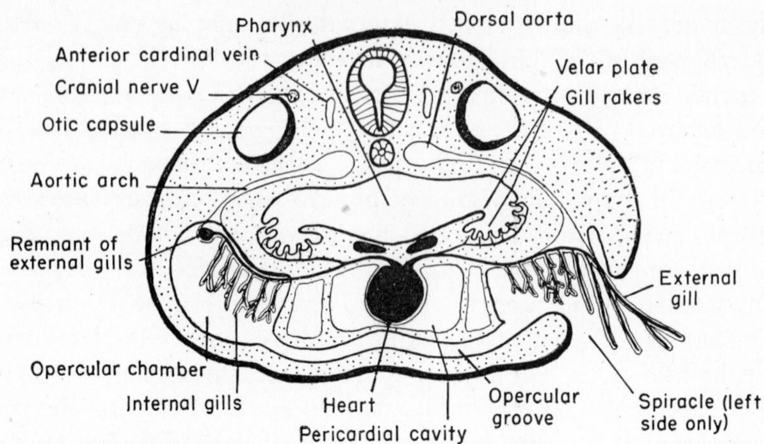

Relation of the pharynx to the internal and external gills of the frog, transverse section.

of the roof. This provides a lengthwise pair of pockets between the pharynx and the latero-ventral gill chambers. From the floor of each of these pockets develop finger-like, endodermally covered, frilled organs known as the **gill rakers.** These tend to filter the water as it passes from pharynx to gill chamber, removing any relatively large particles of matter and retaining them within the pharynx to be carried into the oesophagus with the food. In addition, the shelf-like projection or flap of tissue from the floor of the pharynx and also from the lateral wall of the pharynx likewise aid in the mechanical sifting or filtering of the water. These shelves are known as the **velar plates.** During subsequent metamorphosis both the gill chamber and the related opercular chamber become filled with rapidly multiplying cells which ultimately become incorporated into the body wall.

The Thymus Gland.

The glandular derivatives of the various branchial pouches may be classified as **epithelioid bodies,** since they are all lined with endodermal epithelium. The most anterior derivatives are the paired **thymus glands** which arise by the proliferation of cells from the dorsal ends of the hyomandibular and the first branchial (second visceral) pouches. The bulk of the gland of the adult comes from the cells of the first branchial pouch, rather than from the hyomandibular (first visceral) pouch, as a solid internal proliferation of cells from the upper lining. At about the 12 mm. stage the sac-like outgrowths separate from the pouches, become invested with mesenchyme, and move to the final position just posterior to the tympanic membrane and ventral to the depressor mandibulae muscle. This gland is larger in the younger frogs, attaining its maximum size in frogs of about 20 mm. body length. It is a lymphoid gland, presumably a source of some blood corpuscles, and apparently is essential to the early development of the frog.

The Carotid Glands.

From the ventral ends of the first branchial (second visceral) pouch there arise cell proliferations, at about the time the internal gills appear (9 mm. stage) which develop into the **carotid glands.** These glands develop and move to the junction of the internal and external carotid arteries. Their function is to regulate the flow of blood, particularly that entering the internal carotid artery. This is accomplished by means of its final spongy consistency. They may aid also in achieving adequate aeration of the blood.

The Parathyroid Glands (Pseudo-thyroid or "ventraler Krimenust").

From the ventral ends of the second and the third branchial (third and fourth visceral) pouches are derived the **parathyroid bodies,** otherwise known as the pseudo-thyroid bodies. In the adult these are small, rounded, vascular glands which come to lie on either side of the posterior portion of the hyoid cartilage.

The Ultimobranchial Bodies (Supra-pericardial or Post-branchial Bodies).

The fourth pair of branchial (fifth visceral) pouches have no glandular derivatives, but a pair of **ultimobranchial** (post-branchial) **bodies** arise by cellular proliferations from the rudimentary fifth branchial (sixth visceral) pouches. These organs arise as solid proliferations of the pharyngeal wall and come to lie beneath the mucous membrane of the pharynx lateral to the glottis. They shortly separate from the pharynx and acquire cavities. The structure in the adult is somewhat like that of the thyroid gland but the function has not yet been determined.

The Thyroid Gland.

The thyroid is an endocrine gland which arises as a single median thickening and evagination from the floor of the pharynx between the base of the second pair of visceral arches, just before the time of hatching and at about the 5 mm. stage. It later becomes a bi-lobed and solid organ, far removed from its site of origin. Only its original lining is endodermal, the bulk of the gland being mesodermal in origin. At about the 10 mm. stage, however, it becomes separated from the pharyngeal floor as a closed sac. This divides into two lobular and vesicular masses, and moves to a position on either side of the hyoid cartilage apparatus. The thyroid gland of the 15 mm. stage is divided but retains a connection at its anterior ends by a short isthmus, so that it takes the shape of an inverted "Y," with a short base. The wings move posteriorly, along the ventral face of the hyoid cartilage, and these changes are correlated with gradual changes in the hyoid apparatus. The glands enlarge, the surround-

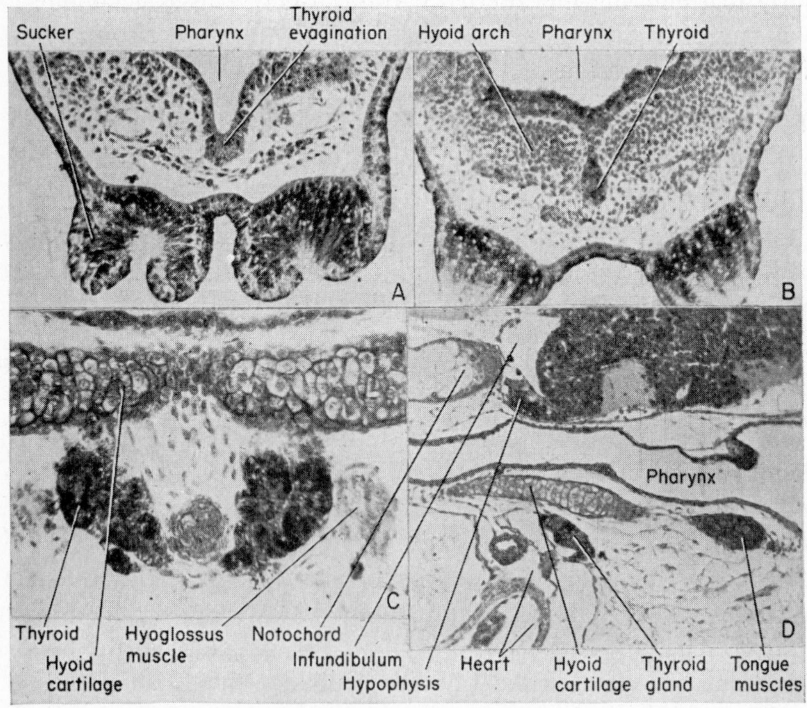

Early development of the thyroid gland of the frog. (A,B) Separation of the thyroid anlage from the pharynx. (C) Division of the thyroid anlage into lobes at the 9 mm. stage. (D) Sagittal section of the 11 mm. stage showing the position of the thyroid anlage in relation to the pharynx.

(*Continued on facing page.*)

ing cartilaginous elements expand, the major blood vessels become enmeshed in them, and eventually they come to lie close to the heart. At the forelimb emergence stage of metamorphosis there is a marked distension of the follicles, and by the tail resorption stage there is high

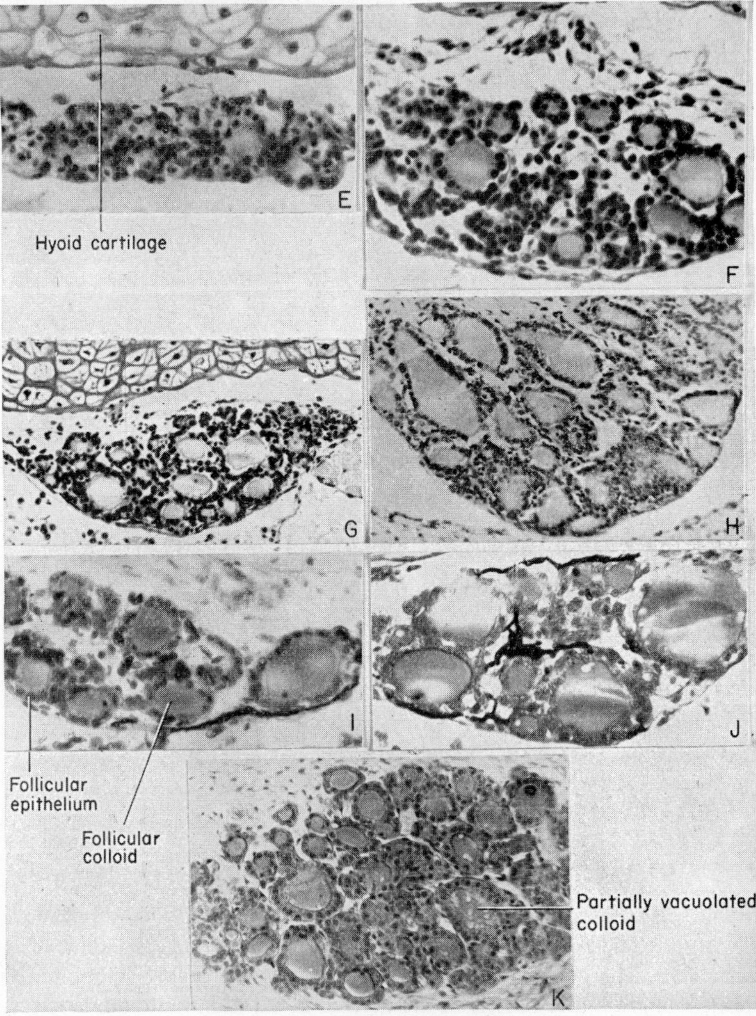

Early development of the thyroid gland of the frog—(*Continued*). (E) Earliest differentiation of the thyroid follicles. (F) Thyroid gland of the hindlimb bud stage. (G) Same as "F" but entire gland at low power. (H) Thyroid gland of the forelimb emergence stage. (I, J) Active follicular secretion of the thyroid of the metamorphosing frog. (K) Thyroid gland of the frog immediately after metamorphosis.

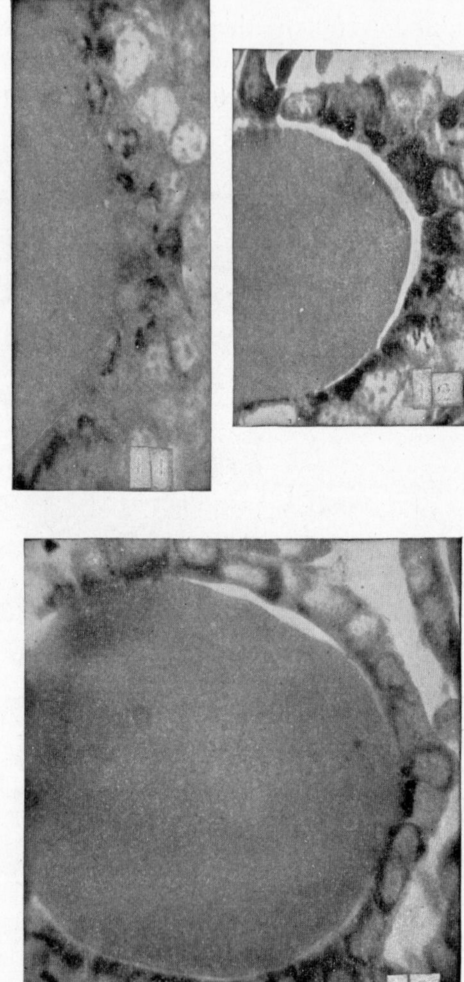

Thyroid gland at the time of metamorphosis. (*Top, left*) A portion of a follicle at the tail resorption stage. Note the considerable number of parafollicular cells. The cells adjoining the colloid show the highly elaborated Golgi network. (*Top, right*) A follicle of the thyroid in a 3 mm. hindlimb length stage. Note the homogeneous dense colloid and the heavy, compact Golgi material. (*Bottom*) A large follicle of the thyroid of the forelimb emergence stage. Colloid shows areas of various densities. Higher epithelium contains material showing definite network and extensive ramification. (From S. A. D'Angelo & H. A. Charipper, *J. Morphol.*, **64**:355.)

epithelium liquefaction while erosion of the colloid and follicular collapse occur. At this time the genio-hyoid, hypoglossus, and sterno-hyoid muscles are in close proximity to the thyroid, a situation which does not persist to the adult. The gland shows hyperactivity during metamorphosis with relative inactivity at the completion of the metamorphic process. Its activity during these phases of development is closely correlated with the development and function of the pituitary gland, particularly of the basophilic cells in the pituitary gland.

In later stages it may be seen attached to the ventral aspect of the hypoglossus muscle. The fully formed thyroid gland consists of separate follicles, each made up of a single circular layer of cuboidal (endodermal) epithelial cells, in the center of which is a lumen filled with a colloidal mass.

The Tongue.

The **tongue** appears just before metamorphosis and is indicated as an elevation in the anterior floor of the pharynx, just posterior to the site of origin of the thyroid gland. Anterior to this the pharyngeal floor is depressed and glandular, but during metamorphosis this glandular area becomes the free anterior tip of the tongue.

The Lungs.

Shortly after the time of hatching, when the larva measures about 6 mm. in length, there appear bifurcating but solid cell proliferations from the pharyngeal endoderm just behind the developing heart. These soon develop into paired saccular evaginations, directed posteriorly. These **lung buds** arise from the median ventral floor of the pharynx at about the level of the rudimentary sixth visceral (fifth branchial) pouch. The single short tubular connection of the lung buds opens into the foregut through the **glottis.** The connecting column of cells which has acquired a lumen, from which the lung buds arise, will become the **trachea.** At the level of the glottis there is a short transverse chamber known as the **laryngeal chamber.** The more posterior bi-lobed mass eventually will open up as the **primary bronchi** or lung buds. In the 11 mm. stage each lung bud will be surrounded by peritoneal epithelium and will be invested with splanchnic mesenchyme. Later, each lung will become an ovoid, thin-walled, and slightly alveolated sac, lined with endodermal squamous epithelium. Outside of this epithelium, and constituting the substance of the lung, are connective tissue, blood, and lymph vessels, all of mesodermal origin.

The Liver.

The **liver** originates very early as a single median ventral endodermal diverticulum which is directed posteriorly between the heart rudiment and the yolk mass. The diverticulum enlarges slowly and its anterior wall will thicken, become folded, and finally branched, to form the liver proper. The ultimate lobes of the liver will retain their tubular connection with the original diverticulum as the **hepatic duct.** The original diverticulum will elongate as the **bile duct** leading to a terminal vesicle, the **gallbladder,** which becomes very large in the tadpole. All of these derivatives become invested with connective tissue and blood from the splanchnic mesoderm, but some of the adjoining yolk cells become the true hepatic cells.

The Pancreas.

The pancreas arises as three rudiments at about the 9 mm. stage in a manner somewhat similar to the liver. The first rudiment appears as a single posteriorly directed ventral diverticulum of the bile duct at its point of entrance into the foregut. This diverticulum soon divides into two and the cellular elements grow around the bile duct to fuse into a single mass of spongy tissue anterior to the bile duct. Subsequently a third mass of similar tissue arises from the dorsal wall of the gut, and attains junction with the original masses, all three to form the much-lobulated pancreas. These three pancreatic rudiments then use the single **pancreatic duct** which retains its original connection with the gut, just posterior to the liver or hepatic duct. It marks the boundary between the foregut and the midgut. The cells of the islet of Langerhans arise early from endoderm.

The Oesophagus and Stomach.

After hatching, the undifferentiated portion of the foregut between the glottis and the bile duct elongates to become the **oesophagus.** During early larval development this part of the gut becomes temporarily occluded by an **oesophageal plug** of cells whose origin is unknown. Its function during its brief appearance may be to help direct any water and food from the mouth out over the gills. These early larvae require no external source of food as they are supplied with abundant yolk. The oesophageal plug disappears by the 9 to 10 mm. stage of development.

Beginning at about the 11 mm. stage, the oesophagus develops into the very distensible organ of the adult while the **stomach** becomes differentiated simply by a dilation of the next adjacent part of the foregut. By the time of metamorphosis the stomach is somewhat more distended than the oesophagus but it is otherwise indistinguishable

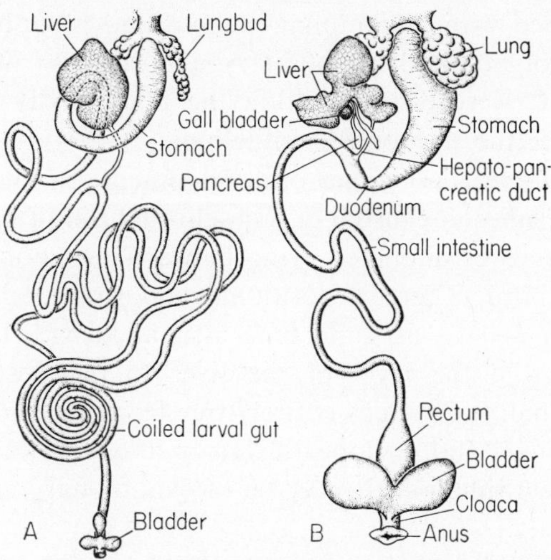

Digestive system and derivatives. (A) Before metamorphosis. (B) After metamorphosis. (Modified and redrawn from the Leuckart wall chart.)

from it. In the newly metamorphosed frog, however, it assumes a transverse position, shifting from the earlier longitudinal position, and has all the characteristic layers of any vertebrate gut. This includes an inner and glandular layer of mucosa, intermediate layers of connective and muscular tissue, and an outer covering of serosa.

The Midgut

The midgut is that portion of the original archenteron which is found dorsal to the yolk mass as long as this mass exists, having a roof and sides one cell in thickness. The floor is the thick yolk endoderm. After the time of hatching the yolk is rapidly absorbed. Before the time of metamorphosis the heretofore undifferentiated tubular midgut becomes very much elongated into a doubly-coiled tube which may be nine to ten times as long as the body of the tadpole. During metamorphosis, and while the tadpole changes from an herbivorous (of the tadpole) to an omnivorous (of the frog) diet, this midgut (potential **small intestine**) shortens to about three times the length of the body, and its histology changes correspondingly. That portion of the midgut directly posterior to the stomach becomes the bent **duodenum** or duodenal loop. The small intestine, like the stomach, is lined with a glandular mucosa and is supplied with both circular and longitudinal (involuntary and smooth) muscles and an outer serosa. It is suspended within the body cavity by a thin but double layer of the peritoneal epithelium.

During the the earliest stages of development (2.5 mm. stage) there may be seen a **sub-notochordal** or **hypochordal rod** of pigmented cells, two or three cells in diameter, lying between the roof of the midgut and the notochord. There is positional and structural evidence that this column of cells is at some time associated with the roof of the archenteron, from the level of the liver to the posteriorly placed neurenteric canal. It becomes entirely free from gut and notochord by the 4.5 mm. stage and disappears shortly after the time of hatching. It has no known function. It may be of evolutionary and ontogenetic significance only.

The Hindgut

This is the smallest portion of the original archenteron which lies posterior to the yolk mass, between it and the posterior body wall. The endoderm ventral to the closed blastopore evaginates to fuse with the invaginating proctodeal ectoderm to form the **anal plate.** This plate finally ruptures at about the 4 mm. stage to form the **anus,** only the inner portion of which is lined with endoderm. The **rectum** is the enlarged posterior end of the archenteron, and is therefore endodermally lined. This does not develop until the time of metamorphosis.

Dorsal to the rectum are a temporary extension of the archenteron, developed in consequence of the presence of the **neurenteric canal,** and the posterior growth of the notochord. This is the **post-anal gut.** At the 5 mm. stage only a remnant of the **neurenteric canal** can be identified as parallel rows of pigmented cells extending ventro-posteriorly from the hindgut. This is the region of the disappearing post-anal gut. It represents the enteric portion of the temporary neurenteric canal connecting the posterior ends of the neurocoel and archenteron. It has no derivative in the adult, but has homologues in the development of most of the vertebrates.

That portion of the hindgut between the rectum and the anus forms an ectodermally lined chamber known as the cloaca. Into this chamber empty the paired urogenital ducts, to be developed later. Before metamorphosis there appears a ventral evagination of the cloaca which gives rise to the bladder. This ultimately bi-lobed and elastic organ has no direct connection with the excretory ducts as do the bladders of higher forms. However, it is considered to be a reservoir, by way of the cloaca, for excretory fluids. In the closely related toads, which live in hot sand, it also may be a reservoir for water storage and an aid in respiration.

Summary of Embryonic Development of the 11 mm. Frog Tadpole: Endodermal Derivatives

The derivatives of the primary digestive tube, from anterior to posterior, are:

Mouth—with the exception of that part from oral aperture to point of the internal nares (choanae).

Pharynx—dorso-ventrally flattened cavity into which mouth leads.

Visceral clefts—junction of endodermal lining of visceral pouch with ectodermal invagination from side of head to form clefts associated with visceral pouches II, III, IV, and V. Pouch VI never forms a cleft. By the time the clefts are open they are covered by the operculum so that they lead into the opercular chamber ventro-laterally. External gills degenerating.

Thyroid gland—now separated from floor of pharynx, dividing posteriorly into two lobes. Found just anterior to heart as paired pigmented masses.

Thymus gland—derived from dorsal part of first and second visceral pouches (first degenerating) and migrating posteriorly to position near the ear.

Parathyroid glands (epithelioid bodies)—from ventral portions of third and fourth visceral pouches. Difficult to locate.

Ultimobranchial bodies—small pigmented masses at level of trachea ventral to sixth visceral pouches. Difficult to locate.

Trachea and lungs—laryngo-tracheal groove from median ventral floor of pharynx near visceral clefts leads into tubular trachea which bifurcates into two primary bronchi. These expand posteriorly into lungs.

Oesophagus—gut from laryngo-tracheal groove to stomach, bending behind liver.

Stomach—identified by folded lining and thick muscular walls.

Duodenum—from pyloric end of stomach to coiled intestine.

Liver—highly vascularized and enlarged organ which incorporates vitelline veins. Original liver diverticulum becomes gallbladder with common bile duct (ductus choledochus) leading into dorsal wall of duodenum.

Pancreas—within curvature of stomach, duct joining common bile duct.

Intestine—two complete spiral coils posterior to duodenum. Cloaca as yet unformed but pronephric ducts open into posterior end of hindgut.

CHAPTER THIRTEEN

The Mesodermal Derivatives

The Epimere (Segmental or Vertebral Plate)

The Somites.

These dorsally located blocks of metamerically arranged mesoderm are differentiated from the anterior to the posterior. The first ones to be completed are located just posterior to the auditory capsule. A total of 13 pairs is formed from the head to the base of the tail. In the tail of the 6 mm. tadpole there may develop as many as 32 pairs of these transient somites, making a total of 45 pairs by the 6 mm. stage. The two most anterior or occipital pairs of somites become indistinguishable and the larval tail somites are lost during the process of metamorphosis. This leaves a total of 11 pairs of somites from which develop most of the striated muscles and the primary skeleton of the body. In the head and pharyngeal region the mesoderm is in the form of loose mesenchyme.

Each somite develops in a characteristic manner, having an outer thin layer of cells known as the **dermatome** or **cutis plate** and a mesial mass of cells known as the **myotome** or **muscle segment.** Between these is a cavity, the **myocoel,** which becomes elongated dorso-ventrally as the cutis plate extends to the body wall and appendages. Originally this myocoel is continuous with the splanchnocoel or body cavity. The myocoel eventually becomes obliterated. From the

TABLE OF SOMITES, VERTEBRAE, AND RELATED NERVES OF THE TADPOLE (ELLIOTT)

Cartilaginous Elements in Sclerotome	*Somites*		*Nerves*
	Embryo	*Adult*	*Adult*
Occipital region of skull	1	Absent (disappears at time of limb formation)	Root of vagus nerve
	2	Absent (disappears at time of vertebrae formation)	No nerve. Ganglion in embryo only
1 vertebra	3	1	Ganglion and nerve in embryo. Absent in adult
2	4	2	1 spinal nerve hypoglossal
3	5	3	2 brachial plexus
4	6	4	3 brachial plexus
5	7	5	4 to body wall
6	8	6	5 to body wall
7	9	7	6 to body wall
8	10	8	7 sciatic plexus
9	11	9	8 sciatic plexus
Part of urostyle	12	10	9 sciatic plexus
	13	11	10 to pelvic region

mesial margin of the somite, **sclerotomal cells** are proliferated off to take up their positions as a continuous skeletogenous sheath around the spinal cord and notochord, and between the segmental myotomes. This embryonic sheath gives rise to the cartilage and finally the bone of the axial skeleton. A total of nine anterior well-formed vertebrae develop in this manner, alternating with the myotomes. A tenth vertebra is modified into a **urostyle** or posteriorly elongated bony projection. The sclerotome of the two potential posterior vertebrae fuses to form the cartilage and then the bony urostyle which encloses the posterior end of the notochord.

The dermatome or cutis plate gives rise to the dermal layer of the dorsal and lateral skin, to connective tissue between the myotomes, and to the musculature of the limbs. The dermal layer of the ventral body wall arises from the somatopleure, so that while the dermis becomes continuous it originates from two sources.

The myotomes or muscle segments of the early larva arise as rather solid aggregations of cells, concentrated at the level of the spinal cord and notochord. They enlarge at the expense of the contained myocoels. Before the time of hatching, these myotomal cells become elongated and their muscle fibrillae orient their axes in the longitudinal direction of the embryo. This indicates a shift in the axes from the original direction in the early myotomes. The myotomes become separated from each other by septa or myocommata (connective tissue sheets). These are derived from the cutis plate, and assume a "V" shape with the apex of the "V" pointing posteriorly. These myotomes become the layer of striated or voluntary (voluntarily controlled) muscles of the back, limbs, and dorsal body wall. The fibers of many of these muscles are arranged ultimately in a variety of directions to provide for complete body control.

The muscles of the heart, blood vessels, and viscera arise from the hypomeric splanchnopleure and are known as smooth or involuntary muscles.

Limb buds develop from the accumulation of loose mesenchyme of adjacent somites surrounded by ectoderm. Within this blastema of somatic mesoderm there arise muscle and bone, developing from the body outwardly. The forelimb muscles develop before those of the

RELATION OF THE ANTERIOR SOMITES TO NERVES

Head Somite	*Ventral Roots*	*Nerves Derived*
Pre-mandibular.	I	III
Mandibular.	II	IV
Hyoid.	III	VI
Trunk somite I.	IV	Disappears
Trunk somite II.	V	Disappears
Trunk somite III.	VI	Ventral root of first spinal

hindlimbs, although the hindlimbs are the first to emerge during the process of metamorphosis.

The sclerotome arises at loose cells which are proliferated off from the ventro-medial portion of the myotome of the somite. They will give rise to the entire axial skeleton, as described below. By this time (5 mm. stage) the somites are entirely separate from the lateral plate mesoderm.

The Vertebral Column.

The development of the **notochord** has been described already. Its origin cannot be attributed exclusively to any of the three germ layers. Its cells remain few in number, become flattened antero-posteriorly, and are highly vacuolated. The notochord then becomes surrounded by (1) the primary or **elastic sheath** derived from the notochordal cells, (2) the secondary or **fibrous sheath,** and (3) eventually an outer **skeletogenous sheath** which is of mesodermal origin. This latter connective tissue sheath encapsulates the nerve cord and also extends laterally between the myotomes by the 15 mm. stage. The notochord finally disappears in the frog. It is partially replaced by and partially converted into material of the centrum of each vertebra. Neural arches and transverse processes develop outwardly from the cartilaginized skeletogenous sheath.

The **vertebral column** of the frog consists of ten vertebrae of which the last is modified into an elongated rod-like bone known as the urostyle, mentioned above. The first vertebra is the cervical **atlas,** followed by seven abdominal vertebrae and finally the ninth or **sacral** vertebrae. The **urostyle** takes the place of the caudal vertebra. The skeletogenous sheath from the sclerotome encloses the spinal cord and notochord by the time of hatching, and by the 15 mm. stage some of this sheath has given rise to cartilage. It is within this cartilage that the vertebrae develop. The formation of this cartilage, due to the accumulation of the sclerotomal cells between the myotomes, is segmented in a manner which alternates with the developing muscle segments. However, at all levels the spinal cord and notochord will be enclosed in this double ring of connective tissue which is being transformed progressively into cartilage and finally into bone. Around the notochord it is known as the **perichondrium** and around the spinal cord as the **vertebral cartilaginous** arch.

Ossification begins, and the cartilage gradually is displaced by an inward growth of true bony cells known as **osteoblasts.** Eventually the notochord itself becomes invaded by these bone-forming cells and is transformed into the bony **centrum** of the vertebra. Each centrum becomes concave anteriorly, for the reception of the convex projection of the more anterior centrum. At the level of the lateral myotomal mass, connective tissue invades the notochord to form the **intervertebral discs** or **ligaments** of hyaline cartilage. Each disc splits into an anterior and posterior part, and each becomes ossified and later fuses with the corresponding part of the adjacent centrum. There are connecting ligaments which arise from the original sclerotome along both the dorsal and the ventral faces of the centra. They alternate in position with the myotomal segments.

The ossified cartilage which surrounds the spinal cord is known as the **neural arch.** Both the anterior and the posterior margins of each neural arch bear a pair of short zygapophyses which are processes that articulate and tend to join successive vertebrae. Spinal nerves emerge from the spinal cord through intervertebral foramina, between the sides of the succeeding neural arches.

Dorsal to each potential vertebra surrounding the spinal cord is a single median cone of ossification which becomes the spinous or neural process of the vertebra. The successive neural spines are connected by ligaments. The **paired transverse** and **bony processes** arise laterally, at right angles, from the cartilage of the centrum and become continuous with the minute bony ribs. No transverse processes or anterior zygapophyses are developed on the most anterior vertebra, the atlas. This vertebra is modified to articulate with the occipital condyles of the skull. The transverse processes of the ninth vertebra are elongated and are directed obliquely posterior to provide attachment for the ilium of the pelvic girdle. The tenth vertebra is greatly modified into the single tubular urostyle and is derived from the sclerotome (skeletogenous material) of the last two somites of the body.

The Skull (Neurocranium of the Adult).

The **skull** of the adult frog, defined as that part of the skeleton which surrounds and supports the brain and special sense organs, is composed of relatively more cartilage than is the skull of most higher vertebrates. The cranial cartilages are an exception to the general rule as to origin, and are derived from ectodermal neural crests.

The frog skull represents a type intermediate between the skulls of lower fishes and higher reptiles. It is made up of the **cranium,** which arises from the cartilage and is therefore known as the **chondrocranium;** the *sense capsules;* a portion of the *notochord;* and a **visceral skeleton,** which includes the jaws and the hyoid apparatus and membrane and dermal bones. There are **cartilage** (endochondral) **bones**

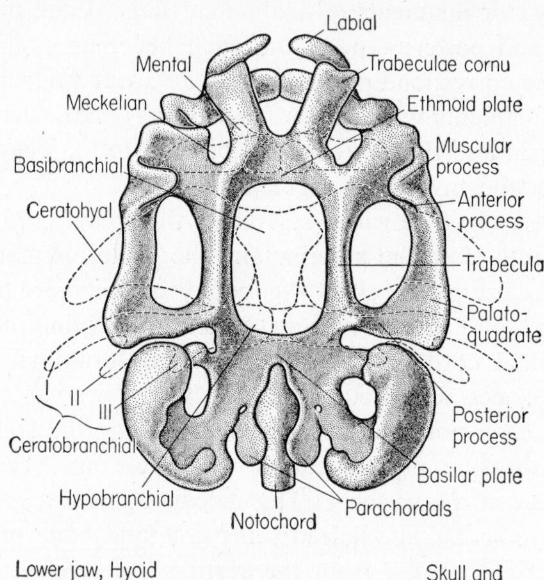

Rana pipiens embryonic chondrocranium. Dorsal view of the 11 mm. stage. Neurocranium is solid, labeled to the right. Splanchnocranium is in outline, labeled to the left. (After Gaup, from Ziegler.)

which arise by the ossification of cartilage and there are **membrane** (dermal) **bones** which develop from (dermis) superficial membranes without the intervention of a cartilage phase. These latter bones are sheet-like and can be stripped from the cartilage of the true cranium.

The bony floor of the cranium arises largely from the notochord in conjunction with a pair of cartilaginous (sclerotomal) rods known as the **parachordals** at about the 7 mm. stage. These are arranged longitudinally on either side of the notochord with which they become fused to form the **parachordal plate** or floor of the cranium. The **basilar plate** is immediately articulated with the notochord and is

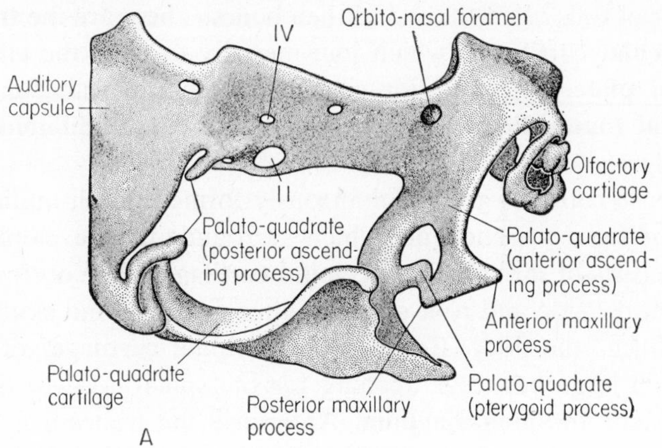

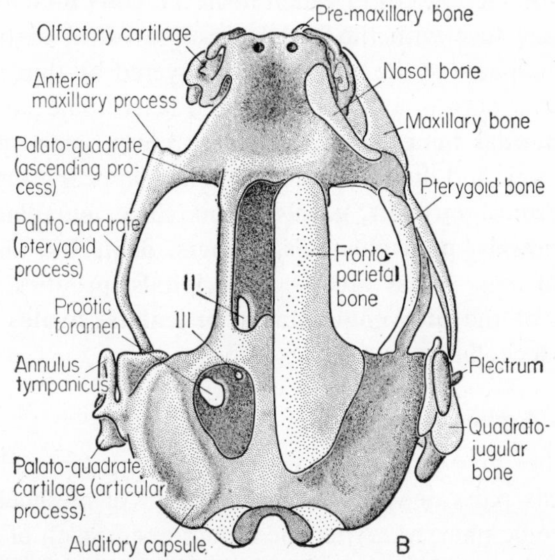

Skull of *Rana* during metamorphosis. (A) Chondrocranium of *R. fusca* during metamorphosis, lateral view. (B) Skull of *R. fusca* after metamorphosis, dorsal view. The membrane bones are shown removed from the left side. (After Gaup, from Ziegler.)

united with the parachordals on either side. The cartilaginous elements of the skull appear by the time of hatching and form what is known as the **chondrocranium.** These elements are not displaced by bone until about the 30 mm. body length stage.

Anterior to the parachordal plate, and continuous with it, is another pair of rods of cartilage and then bones. These are the **trabeculae** (or **trabecular cartilages**) which join mesially to form the **ethmoid** or **intranasal plate.** The anterior space between the trabeculae is the **basicranial fontanelle** within whose cavity the **infundibulum** temporarily lodges.

The sense capsules are simultaneously formed. Each **auditory capsule** forms from mesenchyme which surrounds the developing inner ear. It consists of **mesotic** and **occipital cartilages.** The occipital cartilages form the side and roof of the auditory capsule and skull and the mesotic forms the floor. Between the occipital cartilages of the two sides is the large posterior opening for the spinal cord to the brain, known as the **foramen magnum.** Anteriorly the trabeculae form the **orbital bones** around the eyes. The anterior extremity of these cartilages are the trabecular cornu which form the bony **olfactory capsules.** Anteriorly they fuse with the labial or suprarostral cartilages.

Some of the parts of the cranium are covered by thin plates which originate in the dermis and not from the sclerotome and are therefore called **dermal bones.** Many of these cover open spaces of the chondrocranium and line the mouth. They appear very early and include the **fronto-parietals, nasals, premaxillae, maxillae, quadratojugals, squamosals, parasphenoids, vomers, dentaries,** and **palatines.** The main cartilage bones are the **exoccipitals, proötics, stapes, ethmoids,** parts of the **pterygoquadrates, articulars, hyoids, branchials,** and **mento-Meckelians.**

The Visceral Arches.

These arches give rise to the **visceral skeleton** (splanchnocranium) but arise as six pairs of vertical condensations of mesenchyme lateral to the embryonic pharynx. After the mouth opens each of these arches develops cartilage. The most anterior pair, the mandibular arches, give rise to the dorsal **palatoquadrate bone** and to the ventral **Meckel's cartilage.** The **palatoquadrate** (pterygoquadrate) **cartilage** arises from the **maxillary** (dorsal) portion of this first visceral arch and joins the posterior end of the **trabeculae.** The palato portion gives rise to the bulk of the **upper jaw** and the quadrate portion to the **annulus tympanicus** of the middle ear. The **Meckel's cartilage** gives rise to the core of the lower jaw or the **dentary bone.** The large **ceratohyal** cartilages appear posterior to the Meckelian cartilage in the hyomandibular arch. The **basicranial** (copula) is an unpaired cartilage found between

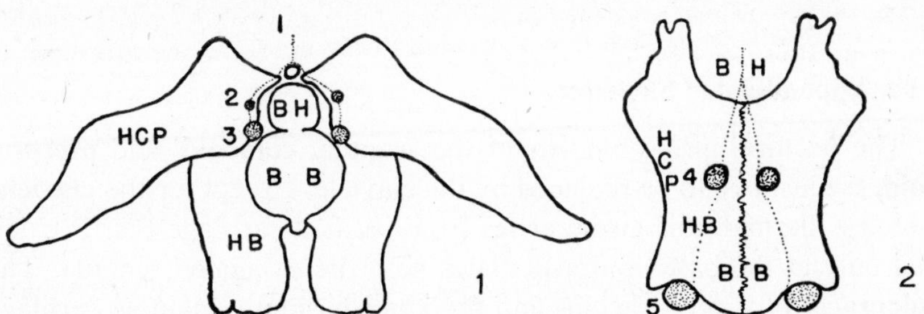

Development of the thyroid gland and related hyoid cartilages. (1) Diagrammatic representation of the developing thyroid of the frog in relation to the hyoid cartilages in early metamorphosis; (HCP) hyoid cartilage proper, (BH) basihyoid cartilage, (BB) basibranchial cartilage, (HB) hyobranchial cartilage, (1) approximate initial site of the thyroid anlage, (2) approximate position of the thyroid at the hindlimb bud stage, (3) approximate position of the thyroid at the fully differentiated hindlimb bud stage.

(2) Same as "1" except at later stages of metamorphosis; (4) Approximate position of the thyroid at forelimb emergence, (5) approximate position of the thyroid at the tail resorption stage. (D'Angelo and Charipper: 1939.)

the two large ceratohyals. The more anterior **basihyal** is slow to develop cartilage but can be identified by the U-shaped thyroid gland which appears directly ventral to it. The jaws are suspended to the skull by a cartilaginous bone which develops from membranes.

Portions of the second visceral (hyoid) arch give rise to the **hyoid cornu.** Parts of the third and fourth visceral arches (first and second branchials) give rise (at the 9 mm. stage) to the plate-like **hypobranchial** cartilage apparatus of the adult. The four pairs of slender **ceratobranchials** extend posteriorly from the hypobranchials. None of the arches remain as such by the time of metamorphosis, the only remnants being the derivatives just listed. The frog tadpole does not possess true teeth, but does have ectodermally covered horny "jaws" and so-called teeth. Oral papillae, appearing as teeth, constantly are wearing away and bear no relation to the bones with which the more functional teeth of the post-metamorphic frog will be associated. At metamorphosis dermal papillae appear on the upper jaw, associated with the vomers, and are known as tooth germs. The overlying epidermis is then involved in transforming the papillae into pseudoteeth, with a minute amount of dentin and enamel. The teeth are for holding rather than for macerating living food, and never are developed as highly as in reptiles or mammals.

The Appendicular Skeleton.

The pectoral girdle consists of the **scapula, coracoid,** and **precoracoid,** the last two to be replaced by the clavicle. Except for the **clavicle,** which is dermal, this girdle arises from ossified cartilage that is calcified only at the base, and articulates with the elongated scapula. The **epicoracoid** (or precoracoid) and the **xiphisternum** remain as cartilage while the single **sternum,** paired coracoids, and single **episternum** become ossified. The sternum arises from the fusion of a longitudinal pair of cartilages which never join the ribs but remain both anterior and posterior to the pectoral girdle. The **humerus,** or upper portion of the forelimb, articulates with the **glenoid cavity** of the **pectoral girdle.**

The **pelvic girdle** is a V-shaped fused mass of bone which supports the hindlimbs and is associated with the urostyle. The paired anterior ends of the pelvic girdle (**ilium**) are united with the enlarged transverse process of the ninth or sacral vertebra. Other bones of this girdle, arising from cartilage, are the **ischium** and **pubis.** The pubis alone does not ossify. The ilium forms a cup, the **acetabulum,** which receives the head of the **femur** of the hindlimb. The bones of both anterior and posterior girdles and limbs arise by the ossification of preformed cartilage (i.e., endochondral in origin). There is evidence that appendicular muscles of some amphibia may develop in situ from somatic mesoderm.

The Mesomere (Intermediate Cell Mass)

Early in embryonic development the upper level of the lateral plate mesoderm becomes separated off from the ventral sheets of mesoderm, to give rise to the excretory and parts of the reproductive systems. This is known as the **intermediate cell mass** or **mesomere** because of its position relative to the other masses of mesoderm. It is also known as the **nephrotome** because it gives rise to excretory units, both the larval pronephros and the functional mesonephros of the frog. The derivatives of this mesoderm will now be described; the description of the development of the hypomere and its derivatives, the coelom and circulatory system, will be deferred until later in the book.

The Pronephros or Head Kidney.

The somatic wall of the nephrotomal region at the level of the second, third, and fourth somites thickens and projects laterally between the hypomere and the body ectoderm. This longitudinal bulge is known as the **pronephric shelf,** because it is due to the development of the **pronephros** or head kidney and can be seen readily from the exterior. This is noticed first from the external view at the tail bud stage (2.5 mm. body length) as the pronephric ridge or bulge just posterior to the gill plate. Within the lateral extensions of these nephrotomal masses there appear cavities, the **nephrocoels,** which run together longitudinally to form a common tube. This tube and its lumen grow posteriorly along the lateral border of the nephrotomes, to join the cloaca and be known as the paired **pronephric** or **segmental ducts.** Actually the duct is not in any way segmented, but it will receive segmental kidney tubules. Posterior to the fourth somite this duct develops independently of the nephrotomal tissue and becomes joined to the cloaca at the 4.5 mm. stage.

Three pairs of **pronephric tubules,** one at the level of each of the somites II, III, IV, appear between the segmental duct and the coelom. The original connection of the nephrotomes with the somites is lost in favor of a nephrogenic cord. Finally each tubule acquires an opening, the **nephrostome,** into the adjacent coelom. This opening shortly acquires cilia and becomes funnel-shaped, by the time it reaches the 5 mm. body length stage. The pronephric tubules lengthen and become coiled (convoluted) and at the 6 mm. stage are embedded in the mesenchyme and sinuses of the developing posterior cardinal

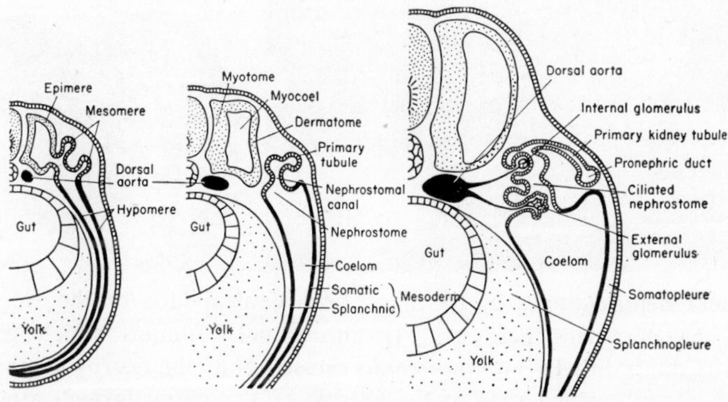

Development of the pronephric tubule. (Schematized after Felix.)

vein. The entire pronephric mass is surrounded by the connective tissue of the **pronephric capsule,** derived from the adjacent somatic mesoderm and myotome.

Between each nephrotome and the dorsal aorta, suspended into the body cavity and surrounded by splanchnic mesoderm, a very rudimentary capillary network known as the **glomus** arises from the dorsal aorta. This appears to be an abortive attempt to develop a glomerulus characteristic of the adult mesonephric kidney, and occurs in response to inductive influences from the non-functioning pronephric tubules.

The **pronephros** is structurally much like the functional kidney of the frog, except that it is much less complex. It acquires a rich vascular supply, both arterial and venous, but has no outlet. It is doubt-

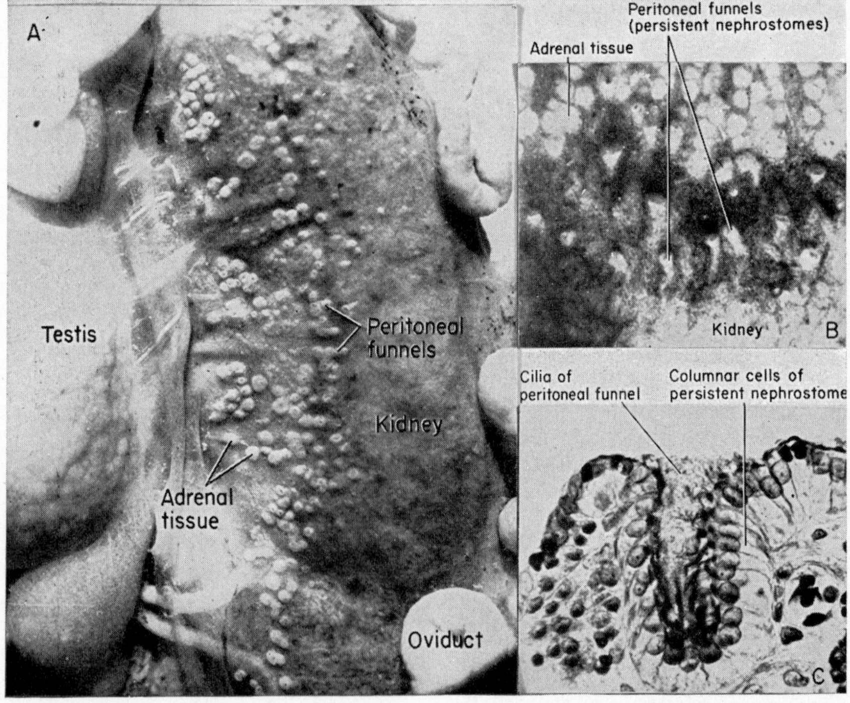

Persistent nephrostomes of the frog. (A) Ventral face of the frog kidney showing the persistent peritoneal (nephrostomal) funnels which drain the body cavity fluids directly into the venous sinuses. Note the nearby adrenal tissue. (B) High power surface view of the kidney. (C) Section through a peritoneal (nephrostomal) funnel.

ful that it ever functions as an excretory organ, but it attains its maximum development at about the 12 mm. stage. Along with the glomus the elongated and coiled tubes of the pronephros constitute a formidable mass of tissue which projects into the dorsal body cavity and is surrounded largely by peritoneal epithelium. As the pronephric mass expands, it fills the posterior cardinal sinus and is bathed in venous blood. As the lungs enlarge and grow against the pronephros, the splanchnic mesoderm covering the lungs and the pronephros is brought together to form a trap or pocket which is merely a reduced coelomic chamber into which the temporary nephrocoels open. This is the **pronephric chamber.** It remains open both anteriorly and posteriorly into the lung chamber. A **pronephric capsule** is formed by an overgrowth of myotomic mesenchyme and an upfolding of somatic mesoderm from the lateral plate. Thus a connective tissue sheath is formed around the embryonic head kidney.

By the 11 mm. body length stage the pronephroi are large and conspicuous bodies with blind tubular outgrowths; but by the 20 mm. stage they have begun to degenerate and neither the tubules at this level nor the related glomi remain. The mesonephric kidney develops rapidly and takes over the increasingly important excretory functions.

The Mesonephros or Wolffian Body.

The nephrotomal mass posterior to the pronephros and mesial to the segmental duct gives rise to the **mesonephros** or **Wolffian body** which is the functional kidney of the adult frog. It extends from the level of somites VII through XII and begins to develop at the 8 to 10 mm. stage.

In this region, as in the more anterior regions, there are segmental nephrotomes which merge to form a pair of continuous **nephrotomal masses** from the seventh to the twelfth somites. The mesonephros is therefore of both somatic and splanchnic mesodermal origin. At the level of each of these somites there develop several **nephrotomes,** each with a separate **nephrocoel.** The nephrocoels at this level are known as the **mesonephric vesicles** which become convoluted and constricted so as to give rise to primary, secondary, and tertiary units, in that consecutive order. It is obvious, therefore, that the kidney units of the mesonephros are more complicated than those of the pronephros, from the very beginning of their formation. They are not actually metameric.

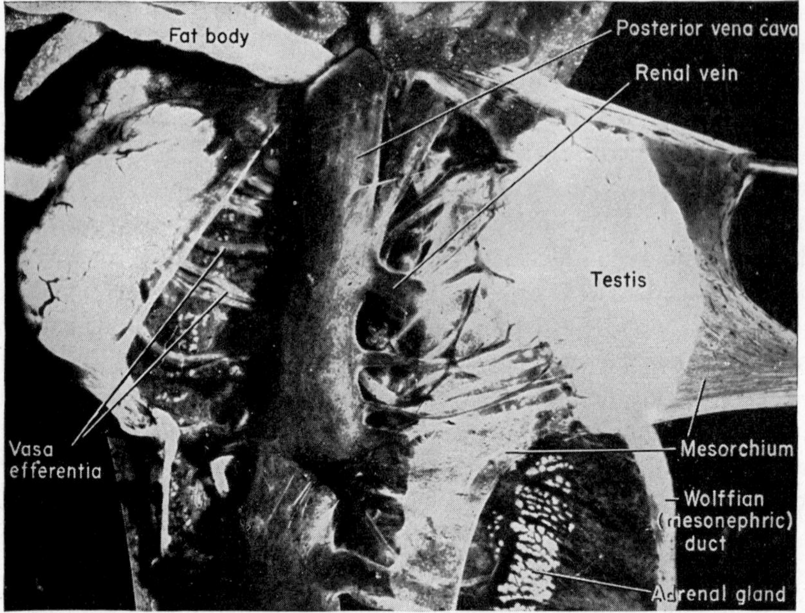

Urogenital system of the male frog during amplexus, showing vasa efferentia white with spermatozoa. Note the mesorchium and huge posterior vena cava.

The **primary mesonephric vesicle** gives rise to a dorsal evagination which becomes the **secondary** unit of the **mesonephric vesicle.** Following this there is another evagination from the ventro-lateral side of the primary vesicle, toward the segmental duct with which it becomes continuous. This is known as the **inner** tubule of the **tertiary mesonephric vesicle.** It becomes greatly coiled and encroaches upon the developing and adjacent cardinal vein. The inner tubules become the tubular portion of the adult kidney. The **segmental duct** from this level posteriorly is known as the **Wolffian** or **mesonephric duct,** and this will remain as the excretory duct or ureter.

A third evagination, the **outer tubule,** develops ventrally from the mesonephric unit. The cavity of this tubule joins the coelom by way of the nephrostome. However, by the 20 mm. stage this unit has broken away from the rest of the mesonephric unit and has changed its connection from the mesonephros to the lateral division of the **cardinal vein.** This vessel becomes the **renal portal vein.** This connection can be demonstrated very easily in the recently metamorphosed adult frog where persistent ciliated nephrostomes can be seen on the ventral face of the kidneys and which can be shown to maintain direct connections with venous capillaries of the kidneys. The outer tubule aids in forming **Bowman's capsule** around each glomerulus. The ciliated **nephrostome** then arises along with the mesonephric unit, develops a normal coelomic connection, and then shifts its relationship to become associated with blood sinuses of the **posterior cardinal vein.** This occurs within the kidney, at about the 15 mm. stage. The original nephrostomes remain in the adult frog on the ventral face of the kidney as ciliated **peritoneal funnels** which are readily seen. These convey coelomic fluids directly into the blood sinuses of the kidney. They might still be regarded as accessory excretory structures. More nephrostomes appear than can be accounted for in the above manner and it is not known whether the extra ones arise by splitting of the original ones or by additional peritoneal invaginations to the mesonephric tubules.

The mesonephric tubules which remain to give rise to the **uriniferous tubules** of the functional and adult mesonephric kidney are elongated considerably. They form spherical masses around developing blood capillaries emanating from both the renal artery (from the dorsal aorta) and from the renal portal vein. These form capillary networks which are both arterial and venous and constitute true **glomeruli,** having no connection with the coelom as do the glomi of the pronephric level. Each glomerulus is surrounded by the thin-walled **Bowman's capsule** of the fully formed **Malpighian body** (renal corpuscle) within the mesonephric kidney. By the time of metamorphosis this mesonephric kidney is fully formed and functional, ready to assume the increased excretory load of a terrestrial organism.

The Adrenal Glands.

Most of the endocrine glands are derived from the pharyngeal endoderm or brain ectoderm, but the **adrenals** are derived from both ectoderm and mesoderm. They are a complex of two endocrine glands and are not related functionally to the excretory system but can be described conveniently at this time because of their proximity of origin and their final position in the adult. In the adult frog this composite gland appears as a thin layer of yellowish brown granular material on the ventral face and closely adherent to each kidney. It is composed of both a medullary (suprarenal) substance and a cortical (interrenal) substance, so called because of their positional relationship in the higher forms rather than in the frog.

The Adrenal Cortex (Interrenal Gland). The cortical cells of the adrenal gland may be seen as early as the 10 mm. body length stage, and probably arise from the coelomic mesothelium. They are aggregated into round or elliptical bodies lying on the dorsal surface of the coelomic cavity, just ventral to the dorsal aorta. The original mass measures about 0.8 mm. in length. It contains a number of nuclei embedded in a syncytial mass of acidophilic tissue. The contained granules may be pink, yellow, or black. By the 12 mm. stage

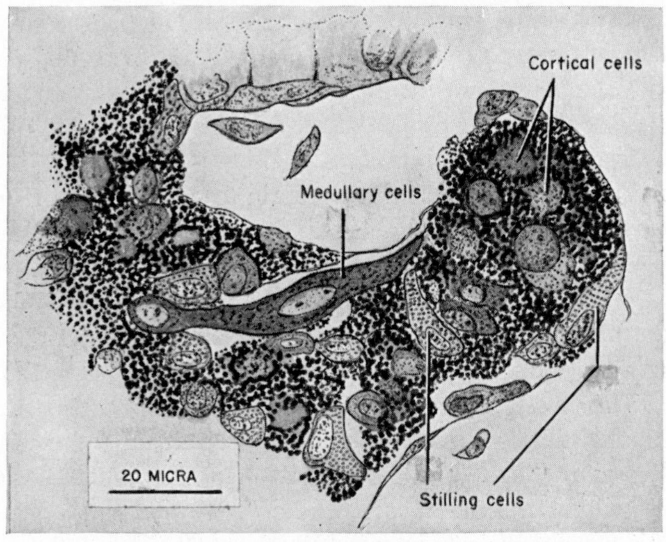

Adrenal gland of the recently metamorphosed frog. Camera lucida drawing illustrating the detailed nature of an islet from the interrenal region. (From Stenger and Charipper: 1946.)

paired gonad primordia may be seen, also in the dorsal coelomic epithelium but in a more lateral position. By the 13 mm. stage the cortical masses have doubled. They form a cap around the base of the upper four-fifths on either side of the dorsal aorta, just posterior to the site of formation of a single aorta. At this stage the cortical material may be seen intermingled with, or in close proximity to, the gonad anlage.

By the 37 mm. body length stage the adrenal cortex consists of lobed masses of cells surrounded by the notochord, the body wall, and the Wolffian duct below. Groups of cortical cells are, by this time, encapsulated and come into intimate association with the mesonephros. By metamorphosis these groups of cortical cells are interspersed with strands of medullary cords. The groups migrate from the dorso-mesial side of the mesonephros to its ventral surface where they are found in the adult, extending almost the full length of the kidney. It now consists of clear-cut areas of medullary tissue associated with circumscribed lobes of cortical tissue. This cortical tissue characteristically contains distinct Stilling cells, never to be found in the medullary tissue. We must conclude, therefore, that since the

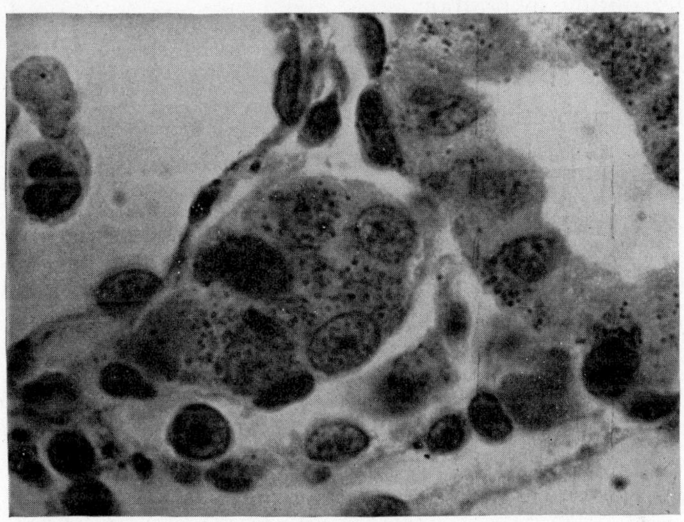

Adrenal cortical anlage at the 10 mm. stage of the frog tadpole, showing the syncytial nature of the mass and the presence of pigment granules. (From Stenger and Charipper: 1946.)

frog adrenal contains both cortical and medullary material its origin is from both mesoderm and ectoderm.

The Reproductive System.

THE GONODUCTS: *The Male.* In the male the **mesonephric** or **Wolffian duct** acts as both an excretory organ (i.e., ureter) and a reproductive duct (i.e., **vas deferens**) since all spermatozoa pass from the testis into the **uriniferous tubule** of the mesonephric kidney by way of the **vasa efferentia.** These tubules are modified anterior mesonephric tubules which convey spermatozoa into the **Malpighian corpuscle** by way of a permanent opening into the **Bowman's capsule.** The sperm then continue to the cloaca by way of the uriniferous tubule and the mesonephric duct. There is therefore no separate **vas deferens,** this mesonephric or Wolffian duct acting in the normal capacity of a vas deferens. In the male frog, then, it is a true **urogenital** duct from the beginning.

As the mesonephric (Wolffian duct or vas deferens) duct reaches the cloaca it enlarges and becomes somewhat glandular, and is known as the **seminal vesicle.** It is within this vesicle that the sperm masses are retained during amplexus and from which they are ejected into the water during oviposition.

The **Müllerian duct,** which is the male homologue of the oviduct, develops late in embryogenesis from a longitudinal ridge of cells which project into the coelomic cavity just ventral and lateral to the pronephric region and the Wolffian duct. This ridge sometimes develops a tube and extends from the cloaca to a point near the junction of the lungs, anterior liver lobes, and heart. It is covered with and suspended by a thin layer of peritoneal epithelium. Originally this Müllerian duct was described as originating from a longitudinal splitting of the segmental duct, but this has been doubted recently. The duct often degenerates in the male adult but there may be vestiges in higher vertebrates such as the appendix, testis, and prostatic utricle. Its homology to the female oviduct can be demonstrated by treating the male with estrogens which cause it to hypertrophy, and to have the appearance of an oviduct.

The Female. The **mesonephric** or **Wolffian duct** of the female functions exclusively as a **ureter.** The **oviducts** arise in a manner similar to the Müllerian ducts of the male but they acquire a lumen which is surrounded by ciliated and glandular epithelium and muscular walls. It is suspended to the dorsal body wall by a double fold of peritoneum. The anterior end of each oviduct consists of a persistent group of nephrostomes which become the fimbriated and highly elastic **infundibulum** or **ostium tuba.** The oviduct shows slight differential gland development and convolutions from the anterior to the posterior, where it becomes the very distensible **uterus.** The two uteri open separately into the **cloaca.**

The body cavity of the female develops an abundant supply of cilia, in response to the appearance of an ovarian hormone. These cilia may therefore be regarded as secondary sexual characters of the female, appearing shortly after the time of metamorphosis.

THE GONADS. The paired gonads arise as a single median sex cell ridge dorsal to the midgut at about the time of hatching (6 mm. stage). These cells presumably arise from the **yolk sac splanchnopleure,** or from the gut endoderm. Some evidence in favor of this theory is the fact that the primordial germ cells are heavily laden with yolk. As the two lateral mesodermal plates converge above the gut, this group of cells migrates to a position directly dorsal to the dorsal mesentery, between the posterior cardinal veins at the 8 to 9 mm. stage. Since this ridge of primitive gonadal material is rather long, it is now called the **sex cell cord.** This shortly divides longitudinally into two, and each part moves ventro-laterally to a position between the developing Wolffian body and the dorsal mesentery projecting into the body cavity as the **genital ridges.** Each mass will enlarge and project ventrally into the coelomic cavity, carrying with it a covering of peritoneal epithelium. This membrane becomes double and suspends the gonad to the body wall as the gonad grows into the coelom.

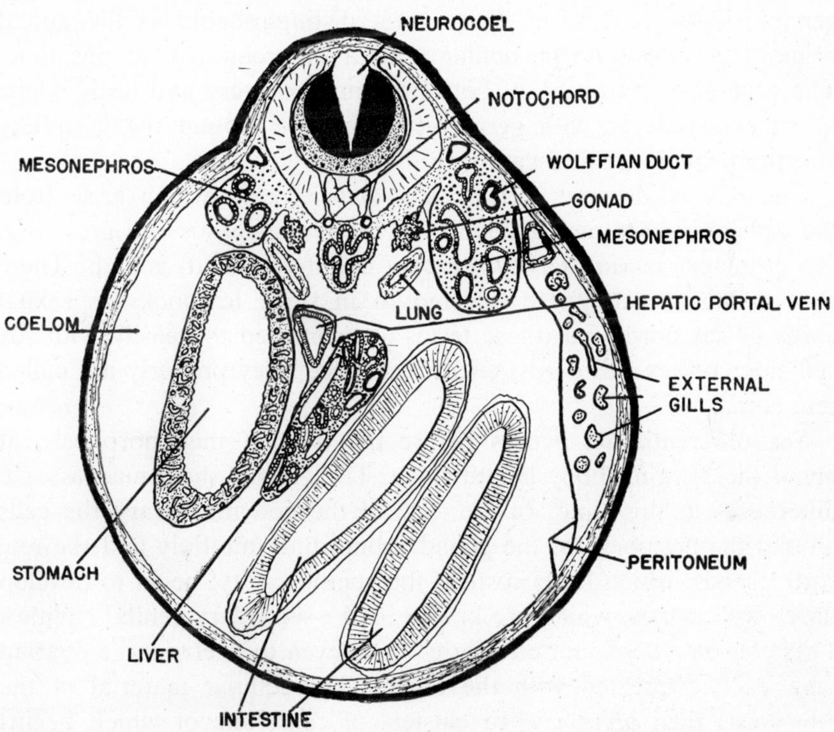

Schematized diagram through the level of the gonad primordium of the 11 mm. frog tadpole.

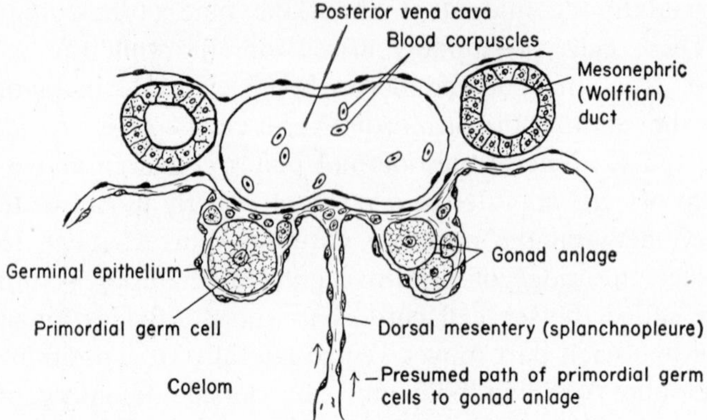

Gonad primordia of the 11 mm. frog tadpole.

This double membrane is known as the **mesorchium** in the male and the **mesovarium** in the female.

These coelomic projections of pre-gonad material are known as **genital ridges.** Sex is, of course, not distinguishable as the gonad primordium shows no particular cellular differentiation at this time. The general organization of both presumptive ovary and testis is one of an enlarged sac with **germ cell primordia** around the periphery and the **primary genital cavity** in the center.

The **rete cords** now appear as strands of cells which arise from the developing Malpighian bodies of the mesonephros and grow into the primary genital cavity of the undifferentiated gonad. These strands unfortunately are referred to in some textbooks as sexual cords or sex cords, but these terms are confused too easily with sex cell ridge or sex cell cords, terms just used. They properly are called rete cords.

Sex differentiation occurs before the time of metamorphosis, at about the 30 mm. body length stage. The gonads show macroscopic differences at this time. In the case of the potential ovary the cells around the periphery of the gonad primordium multiply and the rete cord strands, which have invaded the genital cavity, begin to develop their own cavities, which are known as the **secondary genital** cavities. These become confluent and form from seven to twelve large ovarian sacs, each connected with the others. The cellular material of the rete cords then gives rise to clusters of cells, one of which begins to grow toward the primary oöcyte stage. The others (primordial germ cells) become the surrounding nurse or follicle cells. All these

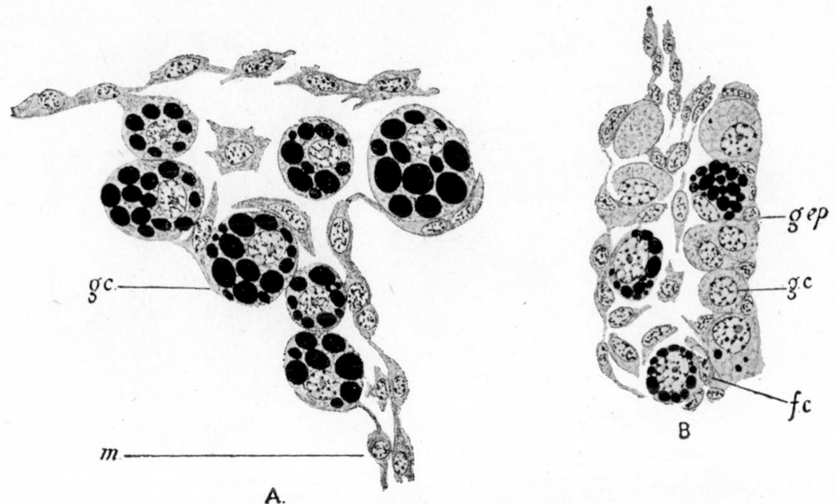

Primordial germ cells (*g.c.*) in the tadpole of the common frog (*Rana temporaria*). (A) In the mesentery (*m.*). (B) In the genital ridge; (*g.ep.*) germinal epithelium; (*f.c.*) follicle-cell. (Courtesy, Jenkinson: "Vertebrate Embryology," Oxford, The Clarendon Press.)

cells probably are derived from the outer germinal epithelium. They are found at all times as clusters of potential ovarian follicles, both nurse cells and ova. Many primordial germ cells are expelled from the forming follicles and disintegrate within the peritoneal cavity.

In the testes the rete cord material remains condensed to give rise to germ cells which migrate from the periphery to the gonad primordium, to form cysts. These cysts give rise to the **seminiferous tubules** of the newly metamorphosed male frog in which all stages of spermatogenesis will develop. Each seminiferous tubule is connected with a **collecting tubule** and **vasa efferentia,** all within the rete cord material. Some of the rete cord cells give rise to the **interstitial** (endocrine) and **connective** (stroma) **tissue** of the testis.

Fat bodies develop from one-third to one-half of the anterior ends of either of the genital ridges. These are storage masses built up during the summer feeding periods in anticipation of hibernation and the subsequent active spring breeding period. In closely related toads of certain species the anterior end of the testis often may develop a rudimentary ovary, with oöcytes, which will respond to hormonal treatment much in the manner of a normal ovary. This is known as **Bidder's organ.** Isolated oöcytes have been found in the seminiferous

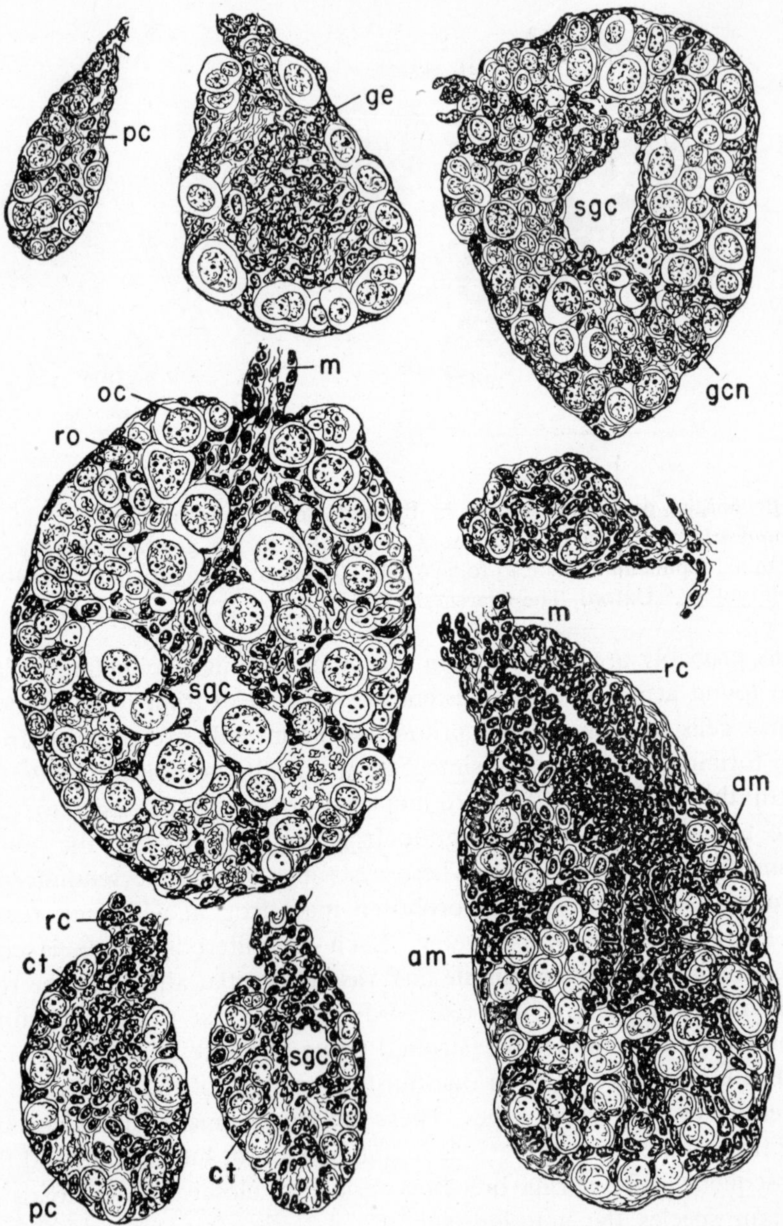

Sections through the gonads of Anurans before and after differentiation. (*Top left*) Section through the gonad of a 30 mm. tadpole. Note the migration of sex cord elements into the gonad, and the appearance of the primary genital

(*Continued on facing page.*)

tubules of the otherwise normal male frog, and hermaphrodites have been described. These facts simply emphasize the fundamental similarity of the frog ovary and testis, both in origin and in early development.

The Hypomere (Lateral Plate Mesoderm)

The Coelom (Splanchnocoel).

This **splanchnocoelic cavity** arises as irregular spaces in the lateral plate mesoderm, ventral to the mesomere. These spaces become confluent to form a continuous split, the **coelom.** The cavity therefore develops between an outer **somatic** and an inner **splanchnic** layer of mesoderm. The earliest appearance of any coelomic space is in the tail bud stage, and in the anterior heart mesenchymal area. There shortly develop three continuous divisions of the coelom, the muscle coelom (**myocoel** of the somite), kidney coelom (**nephrocoel** of the intermediate cell mass), and gut coelom (**splanchnocoel** of the lateral plate). In addition, there is the heart coelom or **pericardial** cavity.

By the time of hatching, the coelomic space (splanchnocoel) on

---

(*Continued from opposite page.*)

cavity, pc, filled with embryonic connective tissue. (*Top center*) The gonad of a 40 mm. larvae, showing the maximum development of the morphologically undifferentiated germ gland. The solid sex cords completely fill the gonad. (*Top right*) Section through a young ovary. The secondary genital cavity, sgc, is small. The germ cell nests, gcn, are disappearing. The germ cells are in early stages of pseudoreduction. (*Center left*) The ovary of a 70 mm. larvae, showing the obliteration of the egg nests and secondary genital cavity. A few residual oögonia persist at the periphery of the gland, ro. (*Center right*) The germ cells have passed from the peritoneum into the sex cords in this gonad and are surrounded by a follicular covering of peritoneal and sex cord elements. (*Bottom left*) Section through a gonad, showing the first signs of differentiating into a testis. Large irregular primary genital spaces filled with embryonic connective tissue are present. At ct are cords of cells passing out to germ cells in the epithelium. (*Bottom center*) Young testis, showing the secondary genital cavity at sgc and two germ cells enclosed within a cross tubule from the sex cords at ct. Note the formation of other cross cords growing out to the germinal epithelium. (*Bottom right*) Testis showing the nests of germ cells—anlagen of testis ampullae. Note that the sex cord cells have become organized into vasa efferentia at the hilus and short tubules pass out to enter the ampullae. (From "The Germ Cells of Anurans," by W. W. Swingle. Reprinted from *J. Morphol. Physiol.,* **41,** No. 2, March 1926.)

one side merges ventrally with that on the other side (except at the extremities of the embryo) to form a horseshoe-shaped cavity surrounding the yolk and enteron. The only region where the coelom does not become continuous is the area dorsal to the enteron (gut) or ventral to the notochord. At this region the splanchnic mesoderm comes together to form the **dorsal mesentery.** This double sheet of splanchnic mesoderm then acts as a suspensory mesentery for the gut, and it continues around to enclose the enteron and the yolk. This lining of the visceral cavity and covering of the gut will become the **peritoneal epithelium.**

Just posterior to the pharynx the coelomic space extends into the heart mesenchyme as the pericardial cavity, to be described below. During the tail bud stage, for instance, one could inject a colored dye into the coelom at the yolk level and this would be carried anteriorly to fill the forming pericardial cavity. The frog develops lung respiration by the time of metamorphosis but it does not develop a diaphragm to separate the coelom further into a pleural and peritoneal cavity as in the case of higher vertebrates. These cavities remain continuous, in the frog, as the **pleuro-peritoneal cavity,** but the pericardial cavity becomes cut off entirely from the embryonic coelom. This is accomplished by the aid of the developing **ductus Cuvieri** which helps to form the **septum transversum** at about the time of metamorphosis.

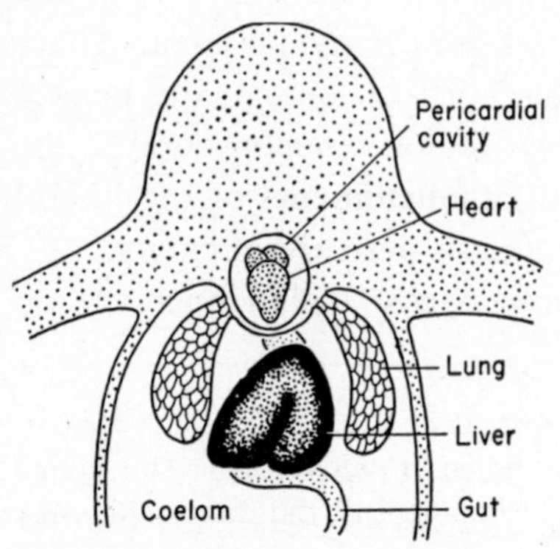

The coelom and its derivatives in the frog.

The Heart.

The heart rudiment develops early from splanchnic mesenchymal cells which grow ventrally toward the mid-line below the pharynx. There they aggregate to form paired spaces (anterior coelomic spaces) at about the tail bud stage. This seems to occur under the inductive influence of the archenteric floor. In the meantime there appear scattered and possibly endodermal cells dorsal to the point of junction of the converging mesodermal masses and ventral to the pharynx. These are known as **endothelial cells** which become endocardial cells.

It will be remembered that the mesoderm of the ventral lip of the blastopore is at first continuous with the floor endoderm of the gut by way of the yolk. It may be suggested that the separation of the heart endothelial cells may be a later (hence more anterior) phase of the same separation of endoderm and mesoderm. It is purely an academic consideration whether the endocardium is endodermal or mesodermal in origin, for it arises from original endoderm in a manner similar to most mesoderm. The converging sheets of mesoderm then fuse above and below, enclosing these endothelial cells. The wall of the inner tube thus formed becomes greatly thickened during this convergence and is known as the **myocardium.** It will begin to give rise to the striated, syncytial, and involuntary muscles of the heart by the 5 mm. body length stage of development. The enclosed endothelial cells will form the lining of the heart known as the **endocardium.** The cavity surrounding the myocardium is the **pericardial** cavity which itself is enclosed by an outer (splanchnic) **pericardium.** The pericardial portion of the embryonic coelom is separated from the peritoneal cavity by growth of the common cardinal veins, the liver, and peritoneal folds, all of which comprise the **septum transversum.** This process is completed during metamorphosis.

As in the gut region there will develop a double-layered suspensory membrane of the heart known as the **dorsal mesocardium**. This remains attached to the heart at the anterior and posterior extremities of that organ, but ruptures at the level of the elongating and expanding heart itself. There is also a temporary **ventral mesocardium,** which arises before the dorsal mesocardium. It soon ruptures through to provide a single continuous enclosing pericardial cavity completely surrounding the heart except for the previously described dorsal mesentery.

The mesocardium then disappears both dorsally and ventrally at the level of the heart, and this is accomplished in part by the rapid growth and expansion of the heart itself. The heart arises by the bilateral downgrowth of mesenchyme which becomes a single short tube. This tube finally lengthens and becomes divided to form the coiled, folded, and three-chambered heart of the adult.

The early differentiated heart consists of a simple tube which becomes divided into three chambers. The fused pair of vitelline veins becomes the **meatus venosus** which empties into the first division of the heart, the sinus venosus. Then follows (more anteriorly) the thin-walled **atrium,** the thick-walled **ventricle,** and finally the **bulbus arteriosus** (bulbus aortae) which leads to the **ventral aorta** or **truncus arteriosus.**

The development of the heart is accomplished within the limited space provided by the surrounding body tissues and organs, so that this organ becomes a reversed "S" coiled tube. With the embryo facing to the right, and looking at it from the right side, the shape of the heart would be something like this:

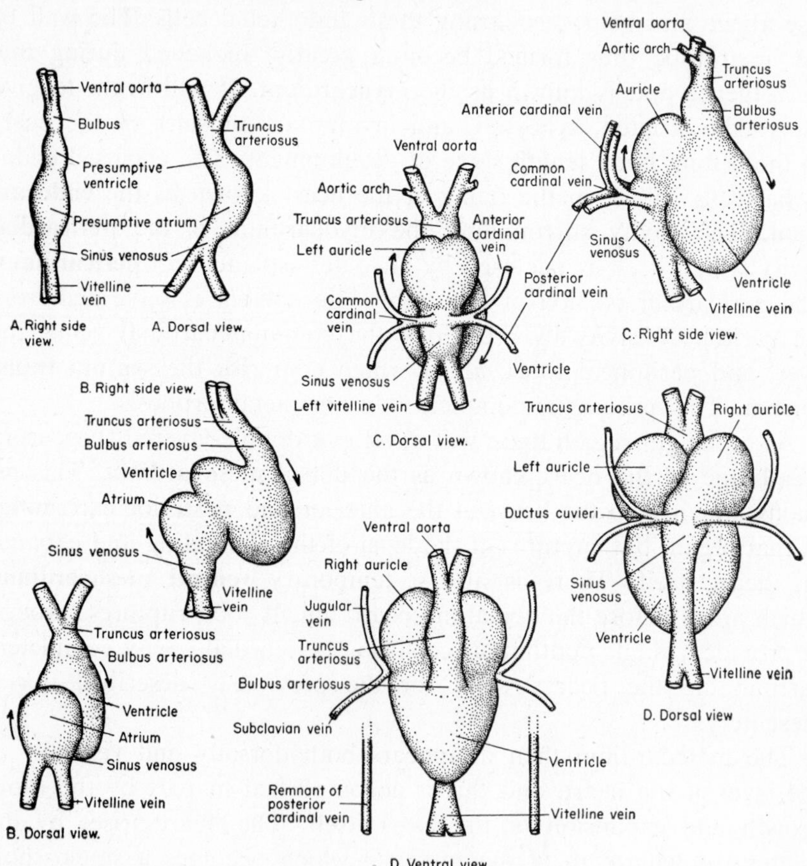

Development of the amphibian heart.

The posterior part of the original tube becomes folded dorsally and anteriorly to the more anterior part of the original tube. Conversely, the anterior part (which is destined to become the muscular ventricle) is folded ventrally and posteriorly to the other parts of the heart. There is thus a reversal in the original anterior-posterior relations of the heart in respect to the embryo. The extremities of the heart, those parts which are held in place by the dorsal mesocardium, are the posterior sinus venosus and the anterior truncus or bulbus arteriosus. Anteriorly the bulbus arteriosus gives rise to three pairs of arteries (aortic arches) to each of the three pairs of external gills. Later a fourth pair is added. In the frog there are no aortic (arterial) arches in either the mandibular or hyoid (first or second visceral) arches.

Before the development of the heart has progressed this far (i.e., the 4 mm. stage) there appears a pair of blood vessels in the ventrolateral splanchnic mesoderm known as the **vitelline veins.** These are associated closely with the yolk mass, hence the name "vitelline" from the vitellus (yolk). They probably are derived, as is the heart, by a separation of yolk endoderm and ventral mesoderm. They grow anteriorly by the merging of blood islands or lacunae until the veins merge, anterior to the yolk and liver mass, and become the fused **vitelline veins.** This point of fusion of the vitelline veins is called the **sinus venosus** from the very beginning. It represents the most posterior limit of the heart. The part of the heart into which the sinus venosus empties is the **atrium** or the undivided embryonic auricles. The atrium and subsequent auricles remain thin-walled and become very elastic. Shortly (i.e., at the 7 mm. body length stage) there grows down from the roof of the atrial chamber a longitudinal sheet of endocardium which is known as the **interatrial septum.** This divides the atrium into a **right** and **left** auricle, and the sinus venosus now leads into the right auricle. Eventually the left auricle will receive blood from the pulmonary veins.

The **ventricle** or anterior portion of the original heart tube becomes very thick-walled and muscular and is never divided longitudinally into two as it is among mammals. There is a transverse division groove between the atrium and the ventricle at the folds in the inverted "S" coil just described. The ventricle is therefore folded caudally and ventrally to the atrium and leads into the truncus arteriosus which is suspended to the dorsal body wall by the permanent **dorsal mesocardium** at this level. The truncus arteriosus becomes partially subdivided by a vertical and longitudinal septum (the spiral valve) and gives rise to the paired ventral aortae which are connected with the various aortic arches.

The Circulatory System.

The blood vessels arise from the fusion or confluence of **blood islands** which develop first in the splanchnic mesoderm and later in scattered mesenchyme. These are isolated groups of yolk-laden cells which form endothelial pockets containing blood-forming cells. These **lacunae** ("little lakes") merge to form the blood vessels, and eventually the embryo acquires a complete and closed blood vascular system, continuous with the heart. This occurs even before there is any rhythmic pulsation of the blood or the heart. The blood islands give rise to the early embryonic blood, but this blood is later derived from the spleen and bone marrow and possibly the liver.

THE ARTERIAL SYSTEM. The dorsal aorta arises in splanchnic mesoderm dorsal to the enteron. Above the pharynx it is double and the vessels are known as the supra-branchial aortae or **dorsal aortae.** Aortic arches develop within the mesenchyme of the visceral arches (III to VI). They arise first as **blood islands** which merge to form blood vessels. The afferent branchial portion of each arch joins the **ventral aortae,** while the efferent branchial portion joins the dorsal aortae. This junction does not occur in either the mandibular or the hyoid arches, but it does occur in all the others. A closed circuit is established, therefore, between the ventral heart and the dorsal aortae by way of the viscerally located aortic arches.

The third, fourth, and fifth visceral arches (branchial arches I, II, and III) now give rise to secondary blood vessels or **capillary loops.** These connect dorsally (efferent branchial artery) and ventrally (afferent branchial artery) with the corresponding aortic arch. The intermediate section of each new vessel then grows out into the developing external gill. That portion arising from the ventral part of the aortic arch, and therefore nearest the heart, is then known as the **afferent branchial loop.** The returning portion from the gill which is connected with the dorsal part of the aortic arch is the **efferent branchial loop.** These loops coil through the filaments of the developing external gills, but the original portion of the aortic arch in each of the visceral arches remains for a brief time. The blood may therefore flow through either of two courses (i.e., the arch or the branchial loop), during the early functioning of the external gills. Usually no external gill grows outward from the sixth visceral arch and as a result an external branchial vessel never develops. The aortic arches

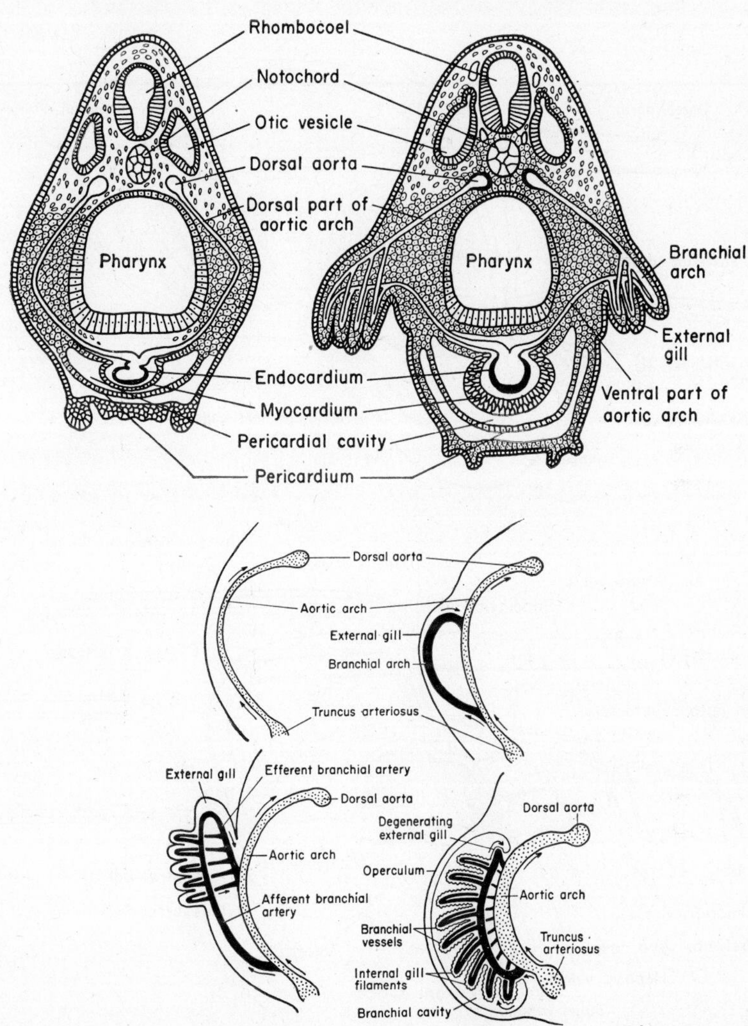

Larval respiration in the frog. (*Top*) Development of the external gills. (*Bottom*) Changes from internal to external gill circulation.

tend to disappear or become relatively non-functional, as the external gills handle the major volume of the blood flow in this region.

As the external gills degenerate there develops a short-circuited connection between the afferent (ventral) and the efferent (also ventral) ends of the branchial vessels. This probably is aided by the remnant of the original aortic arches. This short circuit supplies the newly forming internal gills. All of the blood from the ventral aorta

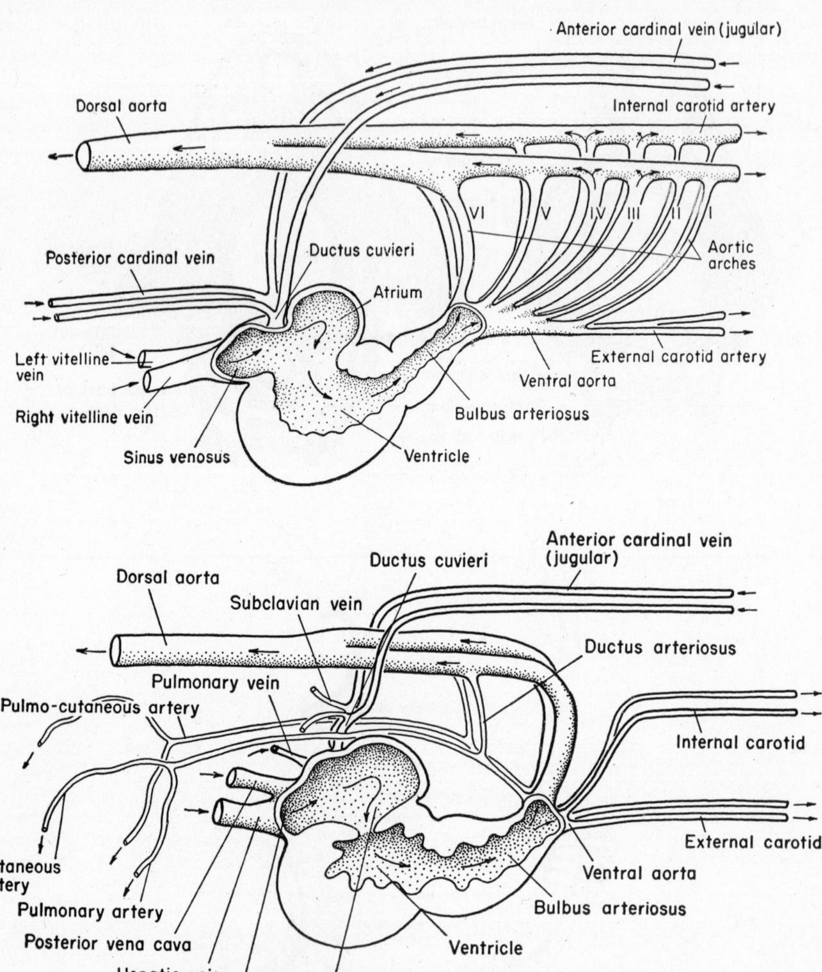

Blood vascular system of the developing frog embryo. (*Top*) Early embryo, from the right side. (*Bottom*) Late frog embryo, from the right side.

then must pass through the filaments of the internal gills until the lung circulation develops. These gills degenerate at the time of metamorphosis.

The paired dorsal aortae extend into the head and the aortic arches of the first pair of branchial arches (visceral arch III), after the loss of branchial respiration, remain to carry blood into the head from the heart. These become the large **anterior** or **internal carotids,** originally the anterior extensions of the dorsal aortae. They proceed to the base of the skull and give rise to the **palatine** (to the roof of the mouth), the **cerebral** (to the brain), and the **ophthalmic** (to the eyes) arteries. The original paired ventral aortae proceed into the head as the smaller **external carotids** and join the blood islands and sinuses of the floor of the mouth and the tongue as the **lingual arteries.** The **carotid glands,** derived from the third visceral arch and having the

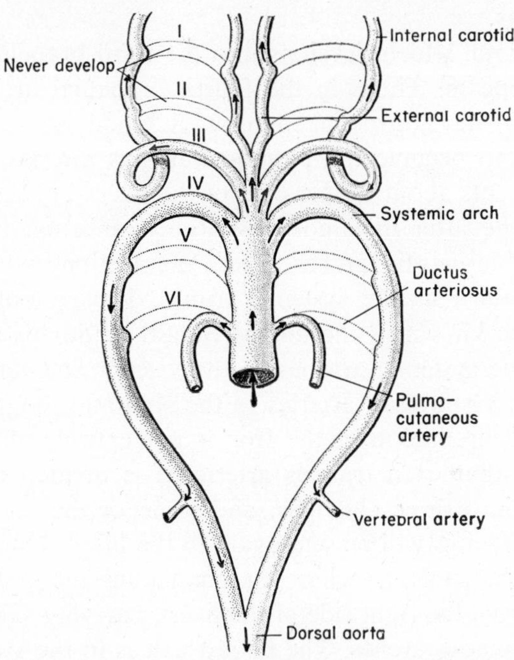

Fate of the aortic arches of the frog embryo.

function of filtering carotid blood, are located at the bifurcation of the internal and the external carotids. This is at the original ventral origin of the first branchial arch.

The aortic arches which pass through the second branchial (fourth visceral) arch become greatly enlarged and retain their connection with the dorsal aortae on both sides, to become the main **systemic trunk.** That portion of the dorsal aorta anterior to the second branchial arch then degenerates, so that all of the arterial blood of the first branchial arch must pass anteriorly and all of the blood of the second branchial arch must pass posteriorly. The systemic trunk on each side gives rise to the **laryngeal artery** (to the larynx and muscles of the hyoid apparatus) and the **oesophageal arteries** (to the shoulder and brachial arteries of the limb). The paired systemic arteries join within the body to form the single **dorsal aorta,** sometimes called the descending aorta, which in turn gives rise to many branches. These include the **renals** to the glomi of the pronephros and glomeruli of the mesonephros; the large **coeliac artery** to the stomach, liver, pancreas, and intestine; the **gonadals;** the **lumbars;** and finally the **iliacs** to the hind legs.

The aortic arch which develops into the third branchial arch (fifth visceral) disappears. Those in the fourth branchial arches, however (sixth visceral), develop connections with blood islands in the skin and the lungs to become the **pulmo-cutaneous arteries.** In the frog, the skin represents about 60 per cent of the necessary respiratory surface. Some time after metamorphosis the connection of this fourth pair of branchial aortic arches severs connections with the dorsal aorta (now known as the systemic trunk), leaving only a vestigial strand of tissue known as the **ductus Botalli** or **ductus arteriosus.** In this manner the systemic arteries to the viscera and limbs are separated from the respiratory arteries to the skin and lungs.

The arterial circulation of the frog is not entirely efficient for the simple reason that each truncus arteriosus is divided only partially by two septa into three channels, and some of the recently aerated blood from the lungs will be sent again to the lungs. One of the channels leads to the carotid arches; a second joins the systemic arches; a third leads from the right side of the heart, carrying venous blood to the pulmo-cutaneous arches. The largest exit is to the systemic trunk, and, until the time of metamorphosis, the two main anterior arteries must pass through the gill circulation where the blood can adequately exchange its carbon dioxide for oxygen. The systemic trunks give rise to the pharyngeal arteries, which supply the mandibular arches, and to the subclavians, which supply the forelimbs, and then they join to form the single dorsal aorta. This large vessel then gives off several thoracic and lumbar arteries to the back, a large coeliac artery and smaller mesenteric arteries to the viscera, iliac arteries to the limbs, and a caudal artery to the tail.

THE VENOUS SYSTEM. The **vitelline veins** are the first blood vessels to develop and they appear as **blood islands** ventro-lateral to the yolk mass. The fused anterior vitelline veins comprise the **meatus venosus,** later to become the **hepatic vein** emptying into the sinus venosus. The right posterior vitelline vein shortly disappears and the left one remains as the **hepatic portal vein,** bringing blood from the viscera to the liver. Shortly after hatching, a **hepatic vein** arises from the liver substance to pass directly to the sinus venosus via the path of the original anterior vitelline vein. After the development of the posterior vena cava the two main liver lobes direct their separate hepatic veins into the sinus venosus.

The paired **common cardinals** grow obliquely in a dorso-lateral direction from the sinus venosus toward the body wall and then divide to send branches anteriorly and posteriorly. The paired outgrowths of the sinus venosus are known as the **ducts of Cuvieri** or Cuvierian sinuses. The anteriorly growing extension of the common cardinal vein is the **anterior cardinal vein.** This receives blood from the tongue, hyoid, thyroid, parathyroid, and the floor of the mouth by a branch known as the **external (inferior) jugular vein.** It also receives blood from the brain, shoulder, and forelimb by way of another branch, the **internal (superior) jugular vein.** A third contributing vessel is the **subclavian vein** which brings blood from the **brachial** vessel of the forelimb and the **cutaneous vein** of the skin. All of these vessels contribute to the original anterior cardinal vein and at their point of junction are known as the **anterior** or **superior** vena cava. Since the posterior cardinal veins fuse mesially and become separated from the common cardinal, the anterior vena cava becomes the only remnant of the embryonic ductus Cuvieri.

The **posterior cardinal veins** are directed posteriorly from the paired common cardinals (ductus Cuvieri). Each of these forms a sinus around the temporary pronephric tubules and then grows posteriorly as the single median cardinal vein between the mesonephroi and into the tail. During its course it receives vessels from the dorsal body wall.

The posterior cardinals go through considerable change during the pre-metamorphic development of the frog. There is degeneration of the entire left cardinal and most of the right cardinal veins. The sections posterior to the pronephric sinuses tend to fuse mesially to form the single **posterior vena cava (post-caval vein or inferior vena cava)** which empties directly into the sinus venosus, having moved posteriorly from the ductus Cuvieri. The paired **hepatic veins,** from the liver lobes, are now incorporated into the enlarged posterior vena cava as it enters the sinus venosus. These changes leave the ductus Cuvieri connected with only the **anterior** or **superior vena cava,** which may now be called the **pre-caval vein.**

Posteriorly the vessel produced by fusion of the posterior cardinal veins, now considered as the **median cardinal vein,** is enlarged as

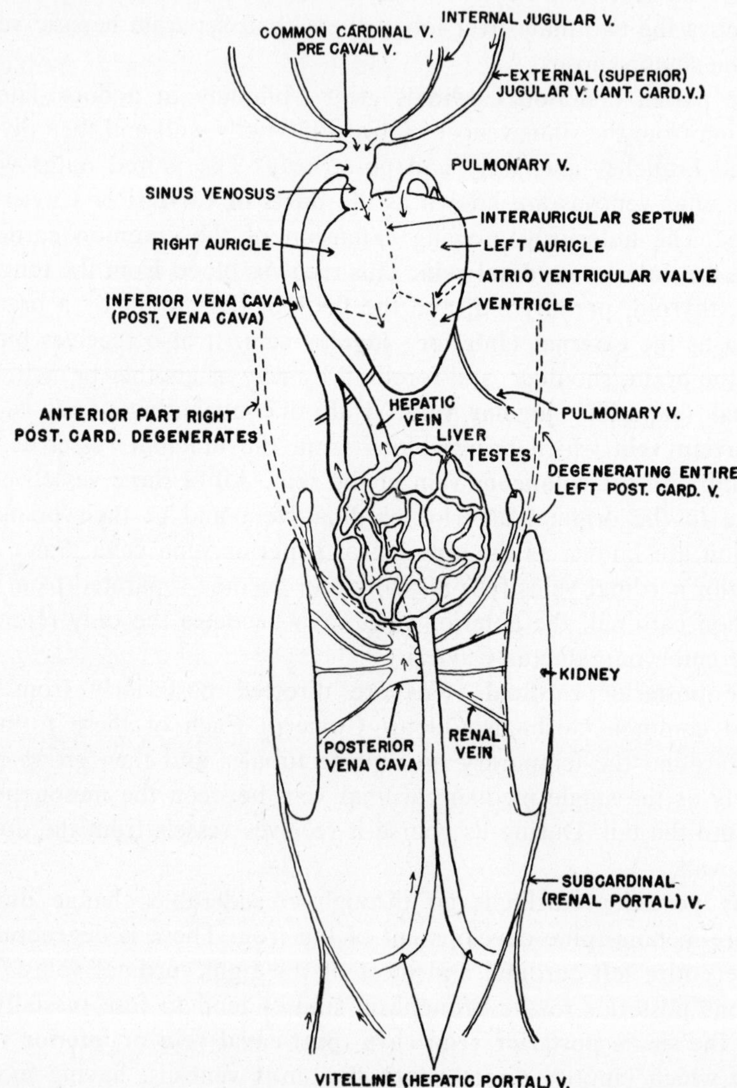

Blood vascular system of the frog tadpole. Venous system, ventral view.

(*Continued on facing page.*)

sinuses which shortly become organized into a vessel. This vessel connects with the hepatic vein through a new junction anterior to the liver. The median vein remains as the posterior vena cava to receive blood from the tail, which degenerates at metamorphosis, and from the kidneys (several short renal veins). After metamorphosis there is no remnant of this vessel posterior to the kidneys, since the tail disappears. Thus the post-caval vein is composed of several elements: a hepatic vein derived from the original left vitelline vein; a short portion of the right posterior cardinal vein; the median channel derived from the fused right and left posterior cardinal veins; and a short new section just posterior to the hepatic section, which grows posteriorly.

The lateral pair of vessels on the outer margin of the mesonephros brings blood from the hindlimbs (**sciatic** and **femoral**) by way of the **common iliac,** and from the dorsal body wall (**lumbar**). These are known as the **renal portal veins** and terminate in the mesonephroi.

The **pulmonary veins** arise at about the 6 mm. body length stage as posterior dorsal outgrowths of the sinus venosus to the **lung buds.**

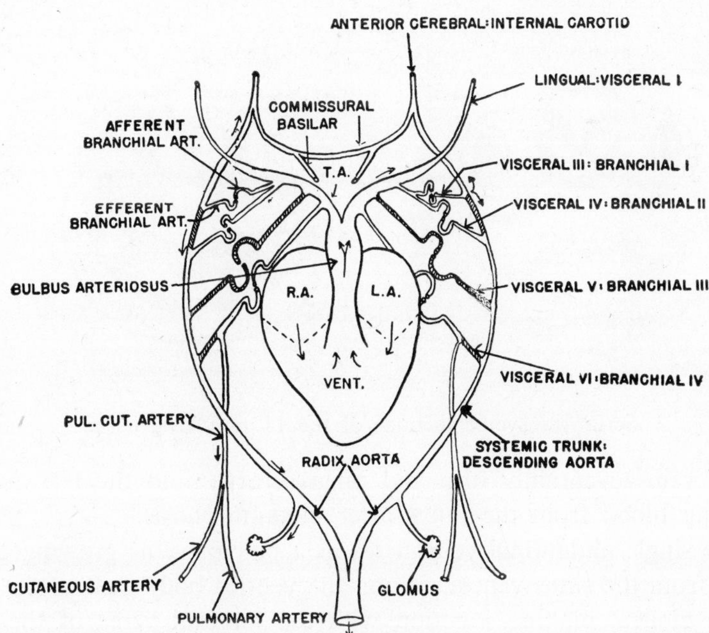

Blood vascular system of the frog tadpole—(*Continued*). Arterial system, ventral view.

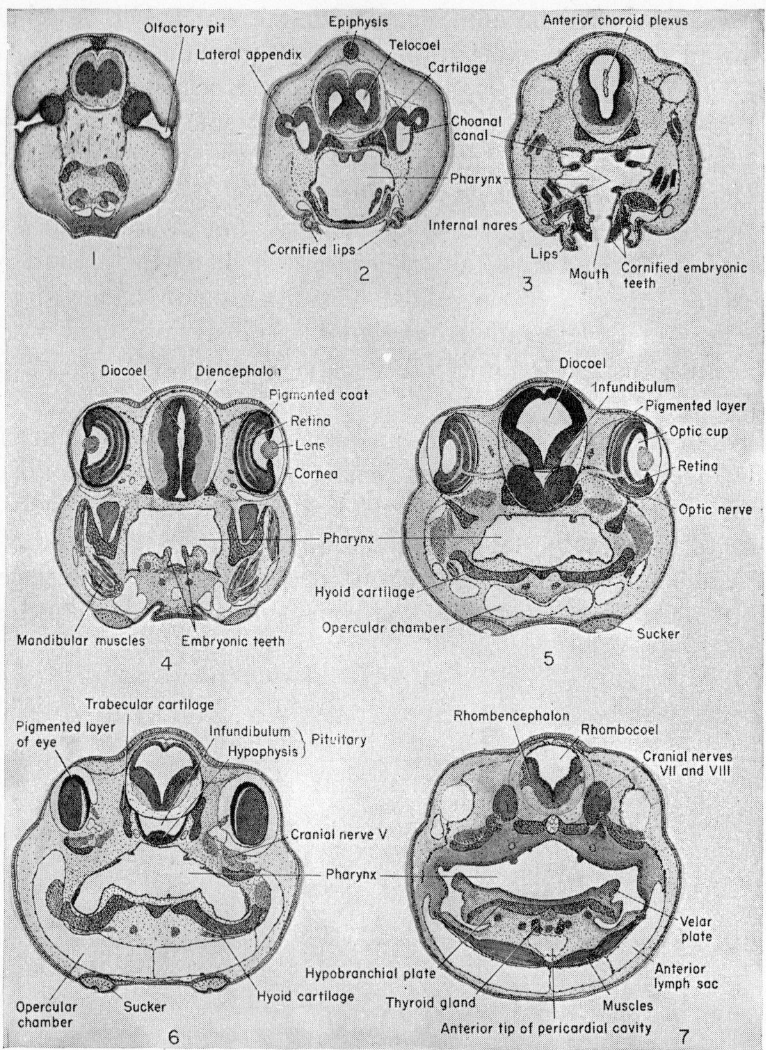

Serial transverse sections of the 11 mm. frog larva.

These veins eventually fuse and open directly into the left auricle, bringing blood from the lungs after metamorphosis.

The single **abdominal vein** arises as a pair of veins growing posteriorly from the sinus venosus along the ventral body wall to the level of the cloaca, making junction with the femoral veins of the hind legs. These paired vessels then fuse, anterior to the cloaca, into a single median ventral abdominal vein. It then loses its connection

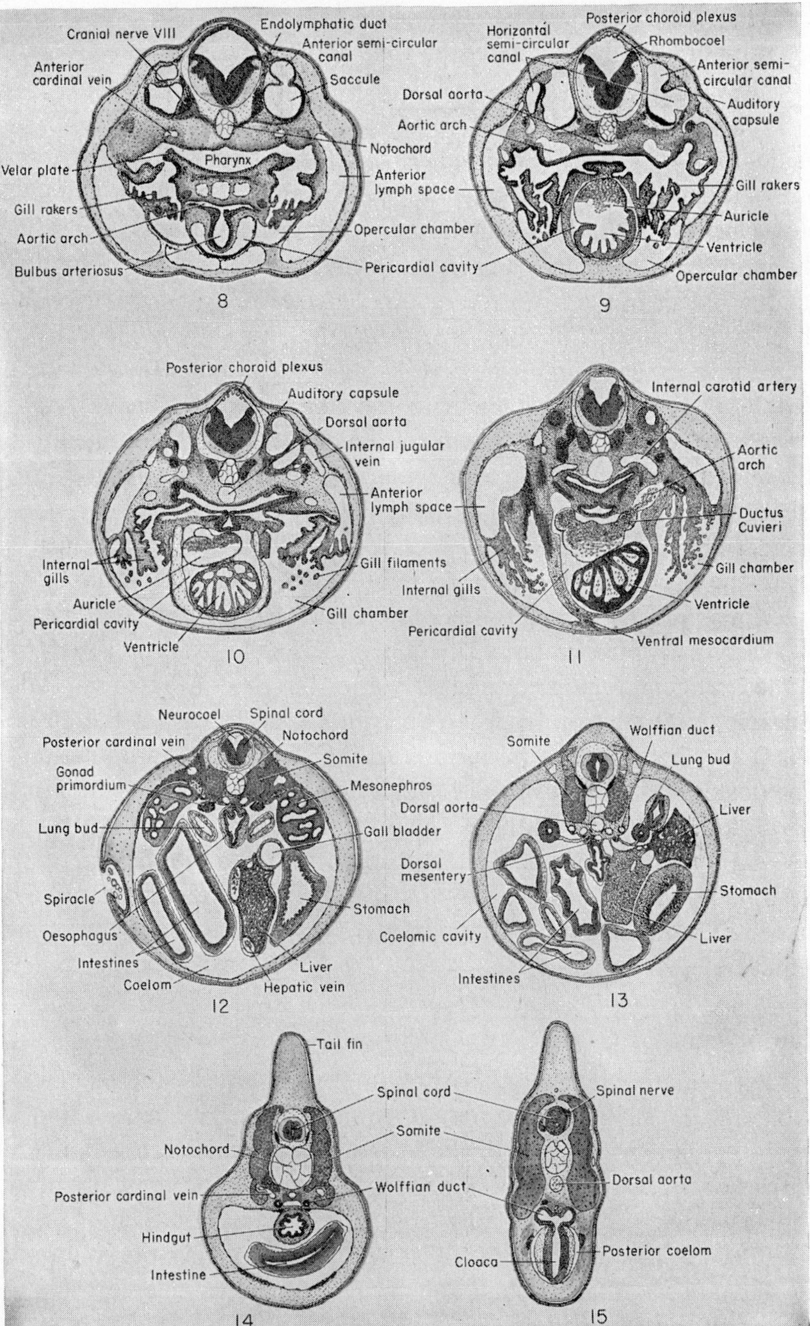

Serial transverse sections of the 11 mm. frog larva.

with the sinus venosus and establishes a new connection with the hepatic portal vein, originally the right vitelline vein, which enters the liver lobes.

THE LYMPHATIC SYSTEM. The lymphatic system of the frog is made up of very large **lymph spaces** in various parts of the body, without well-defined connecting lymph vessels such as occur in mammals. However, all of the four lymph hearts are protected by valves so that the lymph always passes from a lymph heart to a lymph or blood vessel, and never in the reverse direction. There are no muscular coats to the lymph spaces, but they are lined with flat endothelial cells and connective tissue. The connective tissue forms septa which divide the lymph spaces and attach them to the underlying muscle.

Between the third and fourth somites between the peritoneum and the integument, at the time of hatching (6 mm. body length), there are developed crude anterior **lymph hearts,** surrounded by muscle fibers. These are connected by an ill-defined pair of vessels just beneath the skin, the **subcutaneous lymph spaces,** one of which extends anteriorly and the other posteriorly, each to merge with the venous plexuses. The anterior paired lymph vessels send extensions ventrally to the branchial region considerably after the time of hatching. Paired **thoracic ducts** develop from the anterior lymph hearts (at the 26 mm. stage) just between the posterior cardinal vein and the dorsal aorta. The posterior vessels give rise to both dorsal and ventral vessels in the larval tail. After metamorphosis **posterior lymph hearts** appear in association with the intersegmental veins near the hindlimbs. As previously described, there is flow of lymph from the peritoneal cavity into the venous sinuses of the kidney by way of the ciliated peritoneal funnels of that organ.

The Spleen.

This hematopoietic organ arises in the vicinity of the stomach at about the 10 mm. body length stage as a cluster of cells within the dorsal mesentery. By the 15 mm. stage the spleen is seen as a definite projection from the mesentery, covered by coelomic epithelium. Apparently some wandering cells from the intestinal epithelium invade the spleen at this time. By the 30 mm. stage these cells become reticular and are vascularized and can be recognized as splenic cells, and the organ as the ovoid spleen of the adult.

Summary of Embryonic Development of the 11 mm. Frog Tadpole: Mesodermal Derivatives

Mesenchyme—loose, primitive mesoderm found scattered throughout tadpole. There are condensations in head region where cartilage-forming centers are developing, later to give rise to neurocranium except dura and pia mater, which come from neural crest. Connective and blood vascular tissues are also to be derived from mesenchyme. Around mesodermal notochord are sclerotomal (mesenchyme) cells which will form axial skeleton.

Epimere—most dorsal mesodermal masses appearing as metameric somites, the most anterior of which are being transformed. About 12 somites in trunk and 32 in tail remain.

Dermatome—distinct band of mesenchymatous cells lying dorso-laterally just beneath ectoderm, to form dermis (cutis).

Myotome—central portion of somite which is being organized into muscle bundles, divided in tail region into dorsal and ventral bundles.

Sclerotome—thin layer of mesenchyme cells surrounding nerve cord and notochord from which will develop axial skeleton.

Mesomere—intermediate mesodermal mass from which urogenital system is derived.

Pronephros—primary, embryonic kidney made up of a few coiled tubules and ciliated nephrostomes.

Pronephric ducts—lateral to dorsal aorta and dorsal to posterior cardinals, these ducts lead from pronephros posteriorly to join each other just before they fuse with cloaca.

Mesonephros—large mass of nephrogenic tubules, without nephrostomes, forming permanent frog kidney.

Gonads—cell masses hanging into coelom from dorsal peritoneum between mesonephros and gut, in vicinity of lung buds.

Hypomere—lateral plate mesoderm, ventral to mesomere, and consisting of somatic and splanchnic layers with intermediate coelomic cavity.

Pericardial cavity—surrounds heart, not yet separated from true peritoneal cavity.

Peritoneal cavity—body cavity, surrounding viscera.

Mesenteries—double-layered dorsal mesentery supports viscera. A remnant of ventral mesentery (gastrohepatic omentum) is found between stomach and liver.

Spleen—accumulation of cells lateral to mesenteric artery in dorsal mesentery.

Circulatory System—differentiated as heart, arteries, veins, lymphatics, and contained corpuscles.

Heart—already a three-chambered structure as in the adult.

Sinus venosus—junction of post-caval and common cardinals, leading to right atrium.

Atria—thin-walled, paired heart chambers, at least partially separated from each other by interatrial septum. Right atrium receives systemic veins while left atrium receives pulmonary vein from lung buds.

Ventricle—thick-walled, muscular, and generally ventral to atria. Leads into truncus and bulbus arteriosus.

Bulbus arteriosus—tubular extension of early embryonic heart which leads directly into aortic arches.

Truncus arteriosus—short, ventrally directed vessel leading into bulbus arteriosus. (Syn., ventral aorta.)

Arteries—major arteries only.

Afferent branchial arteries.

Lingual (external carotid)—extensions of ventral aorta into lower jaw. First branchial within third visceral arch.

Second branchial—forked portion of first branchial found within fourth visceral arch.

Third branchial—temporarily found within fifth visceral arch; degenerates.

Fourth branchial—within sixth visceral arch.

Efferent branchial arteries.

Anterior cerebral (internal carotid)—gives rise to basilar artery and commissural artery passing beneath infundibulum to other side of head (see diagram). Extensions of first branchial artery from within first visceral arch.

Second branchial—within fourth visceral arch, enlarges and grows posteriorly as descending aorta to join corresponding vessel of other side to form systemic trunk. Junction about level of liver.

Third branchial—within fifth visceral arch; degenerates.

Fourth branchial—within sixth visceral arch, loses its connection (ductus arteriosus) with descending aorta and grows posteriorly to form pulmonary and cutaneous arteries (see diagram).

Dorsal aorta—single large artery formed by junction of two descending aortae (radices aortae) and extending posteriorly into tail, giving off various smaller arteries en route.

Intersegmental arteries—paired and metameric arteries which grow from dorsal aorta dorso-laterally between myotomes.

Glomi—short branches from radices aortae which grow toward pronephric chambers. Really undeveloped glomeruli.

Mesenteric artery—single large vessel growing ventrad from dorsal aorta to supply viscera. Later becomes coeliac artery.

Caudal artery—extension of dorsal aorta into tail.

Veins—major veins only. Generally walls are thinner than arterial walls.

Cardinal system.

Anterior cardinals (superior jugulars)—irregular in cross section, found in head, closely associated with internal carotid arteries.

Inferior jugulars—bring blood from lower jaw, accompanying external carotid arteries, and join common cardinals.

Posterior cardinals—ventro-lateral to dorsal aorta, dorsal to nephrogenic tissue. Carry blood to common cardinals.

Subcardinals—smaller veins, ventral to mesonephric tissue, and bringing blood from caudal vein. Become renal portals.

Common cardinals—ducts of Cuvier which receive blood from anterior and posterior cardinal vessels, and pronephric sinus, and convey it to sinus venosus at its postero-lateral margin.

Post-caval vein—posterior vena cava or inferior vena cava. This vessel has grown posteriorly from hepatic vein and incorporates mesonephric level of right posterior cardinal vein. It therefore passes through liver into sinus venosus ventral to entrance of right common cardinal vein (see diagram).

Hepatic system—derivatives of original vitelline veins.

Hepatic vein—fused vitelline veins carrying blood from liver sinuses to the sinus venosus. Short and difficult to distinguish from post-caval vein to which it gives rise.

Portal vein—common vessel receiving blood from pancreas, stomach, intestine, etc., representing original vitelline veins.

Lymphatic system—not well developed at this stage.

Chondrocranium—cartilage centers may be found, within which bone will develop in formation of the embryonic skull.

Neurocranium—skeleton around brain and primary sense organs.

Anterior to posterior.

*Labial (supra-ostral) cartilages—paired, short, within upper lip and lateral to mouth.

*Cornua trabecularum (trabecular horns)—paired cartilage bars which accompany olfactory tubes.

Ethmoid (internasal) plate—fused trabeculae within median line, anterior to ascending process of pterygoquadrate.

*Pterygoquadrate (palatoquadrate)—derived from maxillary portion of first visceral arch and joins posterior end of trabecula by its posterior ascending process. At its anterior end joins anterior ascending process.

Basicranial fontanelle—skeletal cavity for pituitary gland.

Trabeculae—paired cartilage bars on either side of basicranial fontanelle, converging slightly anteriorly.

Basilar plate—single, fused cartilage mass immediately anterior to notochord. Joins parachordals and trabeculae.

Parachordals—lateral to notochord, at its anterior end.

Splanchnocranium—derived from the visceral arches. Anterior to posterior.

Mental (infra-rostral) cartilages—paired, but meet in mid-line of lower lip.

***Meckelian cartilages**—laterally projecting flanges to which muscles will be attached joining pterygoquadrate.

***Ceratohyals**—large cartilages arising within hyomandibular arches, posterior to Meckelian cartilages.

*May be ectodermal.

***Basibranchial (copula)**—single cartilage between ceratohyals.

***Hypobranchials**—paired, posterior to ceratohyals, and derived from third visceral arches. Articulates also with basibranchial.

***Ceratobranchials**—three or possibly four slender processes within third to sixth visceral arches, extending from hypobranchial on each side.

*May be ectodermal.

APPENDIX

Chronological Summary of Organ Anlagen

Appearance of *Rana pipiens*

Stage 17: 3 mm. total body length.

Blastopore closes, neurenteric canal transient, neural tube closed but no differentiation of central nervous system, body elongated with back curve changing from convex to concave, myotomes evident but movement by surface ciliation. Internally most of major organ systems begin to appear including heart mesenchyme, visceral arches, and lateral plate mesoderm, pronephros, hypochordal rod, sense and gill plates, optic vesicles, and both auditory and olfactory placodes.

Stage 18: 4 mm. total body length.

First evidence of muscular movement, primary brain differentiations, infundibulum and hypophysis still separate, lateral line nerve develops from vagus placode, auditory placode becomes separated from head ectoderm, lens placode formed, ventral roots develop from spinal cord, hypochordal rod separated from gut, notochord becomes vacuolated and acquires an elastic and a fibrous coating from sclerotome, oesophageal plug formed, dorsal aorta paired anteriorly and single posteriorly, vitelline veins prominent and functional.

Stage 19: 5 mm. total body length.

Epiphysis well developed as evagination of prosencephalon, infundibulum, and hypophysis are approximated in position, thyroid evagination develops, trigeminal nerve from first cranial crest and placode, facial and auditory nerves from second cranial crest and placode, lens vesicle separated from head ectoderm, 45 pairs of somites developed (by 5.5 mm. stage), 32 of which are in tail, muscles with fibrillae, sclerotome abundant, heart differentiated and beating.

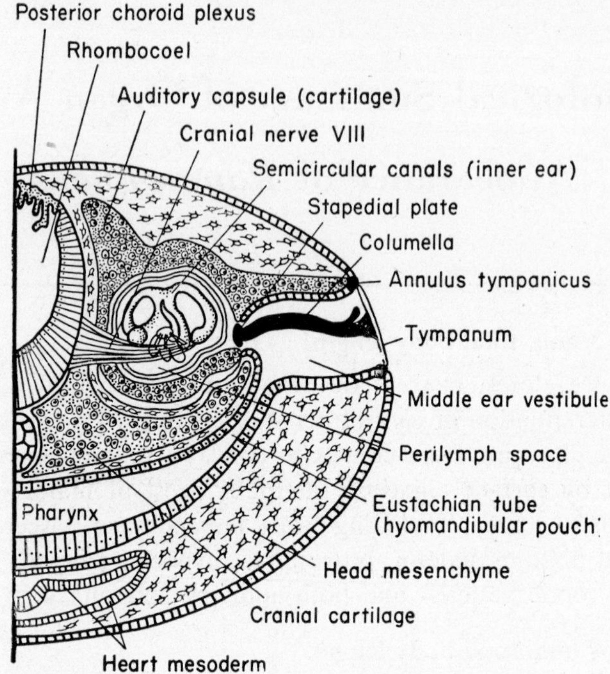

Parts of the middle and inner ear of the frog, schematized drawing.

Stage 20: 6 mm. total body length.

Hatches, oral suckers at maximum development, blood system well developed, including endocardium, myocardium, and pericardium of the heart, pulmonary veins develop but do not function, gill circulation abundant, blood islands numerous, lymph hearts first appear at level of somites III and IV, pronephros with glomi and segmental duct become partially embedded in posterior cardinal veins, a solid rod of ectoderm cells extend from olfactory pit to pharynx, four cranial ganglionic masses appear, optic nerve develops from neuroblasts of retina, and sympathetic nervous system arises from neural crests.

Stage 21: 7 mm. total body length.

Transition from larva to tadpole, mouth open, cornea transparent, cerebral hemispheres and vesicles differentiated, endolymphatic duct open to surface, heart folding upon itself, paired and metameric dorsal root ganglia, interatrial septum separates auricles, sex cell (genital) ridge appears.

Stage 22: 8 mm. total body length.

Heart partitions completed and heart differentiated, circulation reaches tail fin, lung buds develop, sub-notochordal rod disappears and mesonephros begins to form.

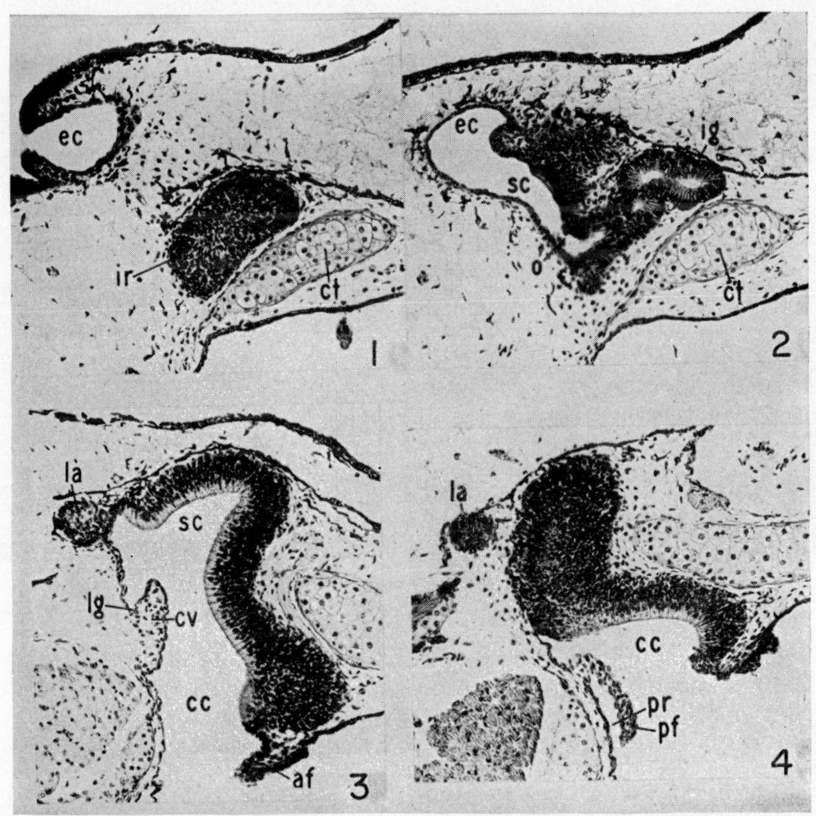

Olfactory organs of *Rana pipiens* tadpoles at 20 mm. total body length.

(af) Anterior choanal fold.
(cc) Choanal canal.
(ct) Cornu trabeculae.
(cv) Christa ventralis.
(ec) Entrance canal.
(ig) Inferior canal.
(ir) Inferior recess.
(la) Lateral appendix.
(lg) Lateral groove.
(pf) Posterior pharyngeal fold.
(pr) Posterior recess.
(sc) Superior cavity.

(Courtesy, Ruth Cooper, *J. Exper. Zoöl.*, **93**:415.)

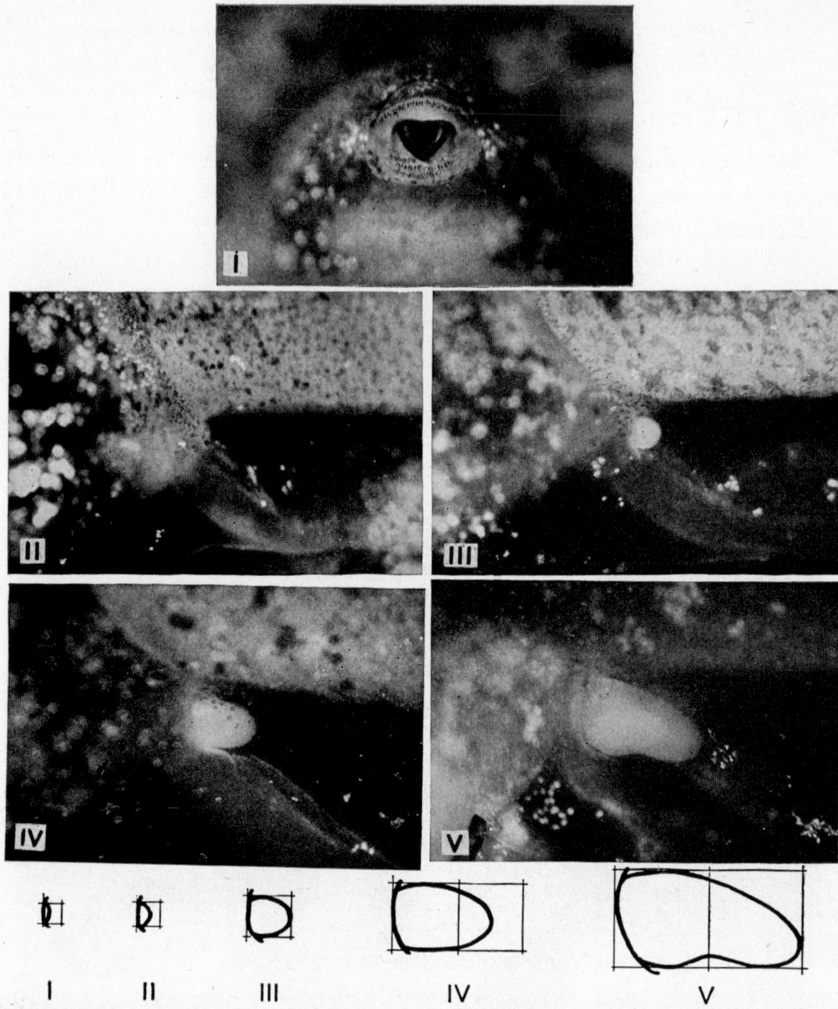

I II III IV V

Stages in the metamorphosis of *Rana pipiens*. (*Stage I*) The oral sucker elevations have completely disappeared. Four rows of labial teeth are present, one pre-oral and three post-oral. Chromatophores have appeared and become numerous on the dorsal and lateral surfaces, and extend progressively ventrad. The limb bud is visible as a faintly circumscribed elevation in the groove between the base of the tail and the belly wall. The height of the elevation is less than half the diameter of the disk. (*Stage II*) The height of the limb bud elevation (i.e., the length of the bud) is equal to half of its diameter. The first row of post-oral labial teeth is usually at the middle to form a pair of crescents. On the dorsal surface of the head the lateral line system is becoming conspicuous as pigment-free lines, especially in darkly pigmented individuals. The melanophore patches covering the gill region on either side usually meet in a narrow band ventral to the heart. (*Stage III*) The length of the limb bud is equal to its diameter, and it continues to grow both in length and diameter at an approximately equal rate. This stage is relatively long in duration. (*Stage IV*) The length of the limb bud is equal to one and a half times its diameter. (*Stage V*) The length of the limb bud is twice its diameter. The distal half of the bud is bent ventrad. There is no flattening of the tip.

(*Continued on facing page.*)

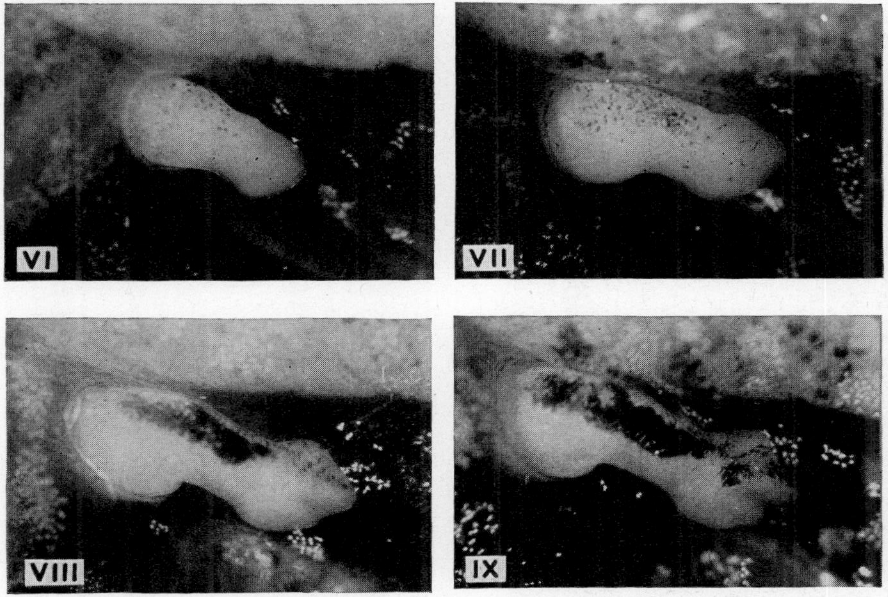

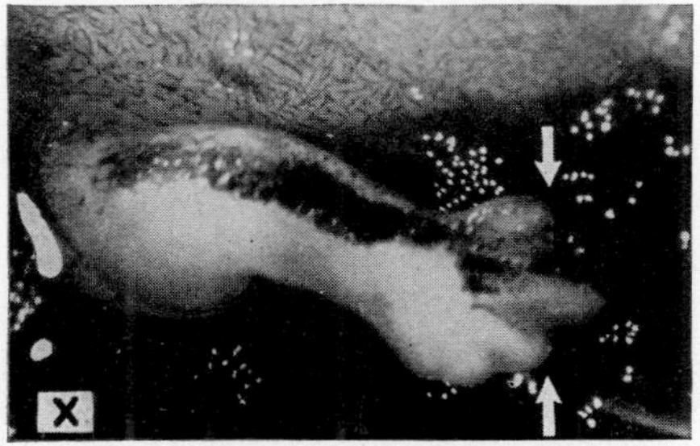

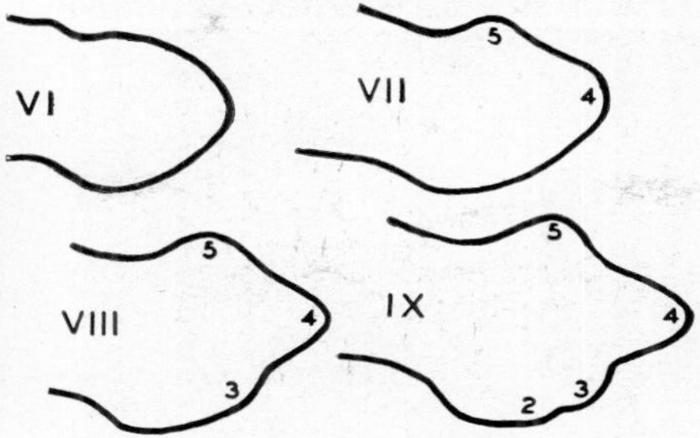

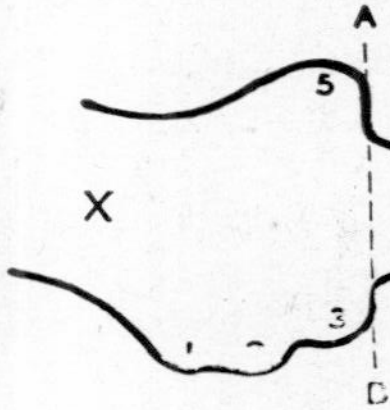

Stages in the metamorphosis of *Rana pipiens*—(*Continued*). (*Stage VI*) The distal end of the limb bud is flattened mediolaterally to form the foot paddle. There are no interdigital indentations of the paddle margin. (*Stage VII*) The fourth and fifth toe prominences are separated by a slight indentation of the margin of the foot paddle. Melanophores usually appear scattered over the bud and tend to form a distinct patch on the lateral surface. Guanophores appear sporadically on the limb bud. (*Stage VIII*) The margin of the foot paddle is indented between toes 5–4 and 4–3. The patch of melanophores on the limb lengthens into a streak extending from above the knee bend to the foot. (*Stage IX*) The margin of the foot paddle is indented between toes 5–4, 4–3, and 3–2. Usually spontaneous movements of the limb proper (flexion of knee and ankle) can be seen under binocular microscopes. These movements may not appear until the following stage. Shortly after such movements appear similar movements may be elicited by stroking the limb or tail base with a hair. The melanophore streak extends onto toes 4 and 5. (*Stage X*) The margin of the foot paddle is indented between all five toes. The margin of the fifth web is directed toward the tip of the third toe. As toes 4 and 5 lengthen, the angle of the interdigital notch formed by the margin of the web becomes more acute. The half of the web adjacent to the fifth toe is referred to as the fifth toe web. If a line coinciding with its margin be extended, it will be seen to pass successively through the tips of toes 3, 2, and 1 and the prehallux.

(*Continued on next page.*)

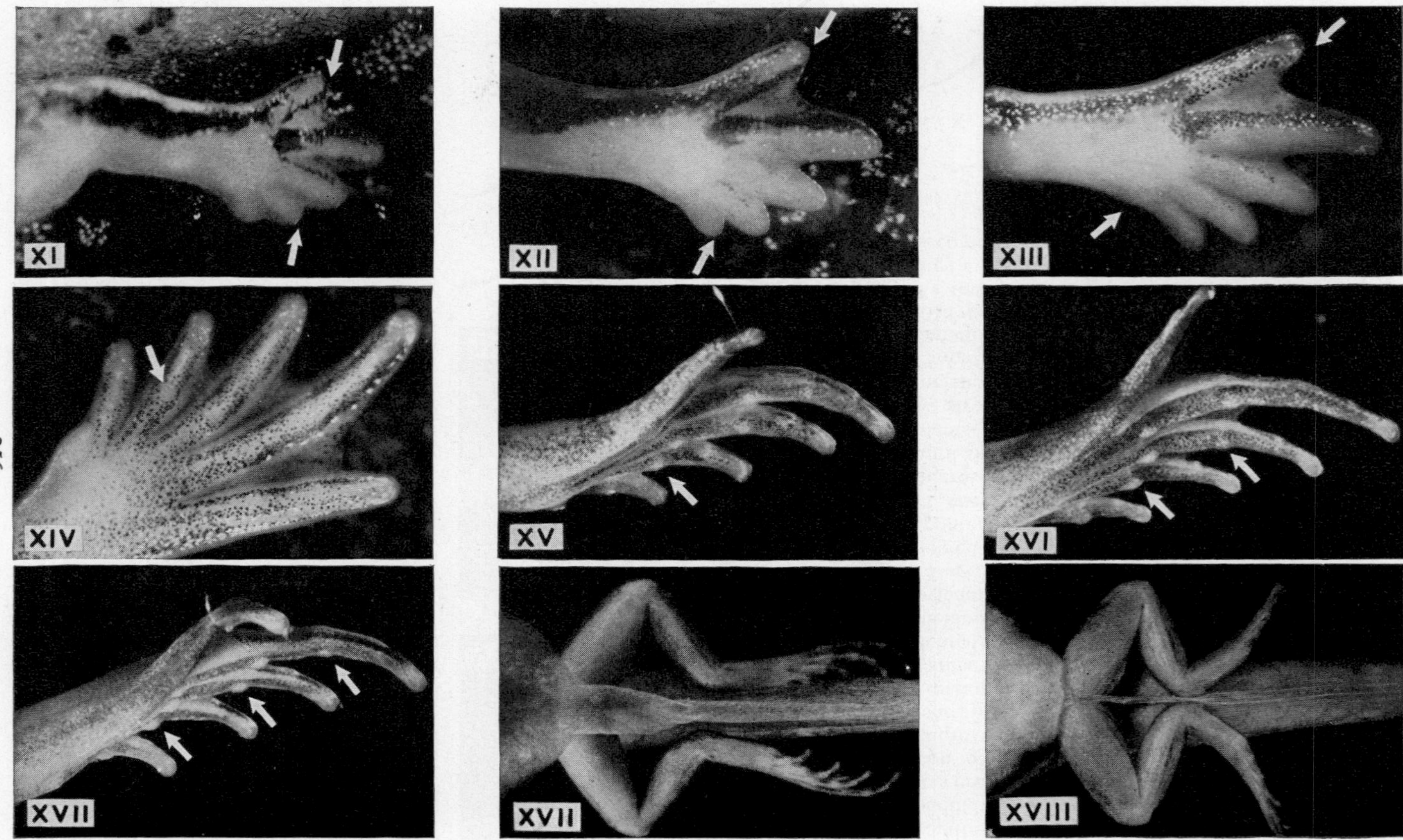

Stages in the metamorphosis of *Rana pipiens*—(*Continued*). (*Stage XI*) The margin of the fifth toe web is directed toward the tip of the second toe. The third toe usually has a melanophore streak. (*Stage XII*) The margin of the fifth toe web is directed toward the tip of the first toe. Melanophores often appear on the second toe. (*Stage XIII*) The margin of the fifth toe web is directed toward the prehallux. (*Stage XIV*) Pigment-free patches appear at the metatarsophalangeal joints, where the proximal toe pads will later develop. About this time the brow-spot appears as a light spot in the mid-line slightly anterior to the level of the eyes. The nasolacrimal duct, developing as a cord of cells between the nostril and eye, is visible through the skin as a light line. (*Stage XV*) The proximal toe pads appear. These are wart-like elevations which develop on the ventral surface of the toes at the metatarsophalangeal joint. (*Stage XVI*) The middle toe pads appear. This is the second row of toe pads which form at the first interphalangeal joint on toes 3, 4, and 5. (*Stage XVII*) The distal toe pad appears at the second interphalangeal joint on toe 4. The cloacal tail piece is unreduced. Reflex withdrawal of the eyeball often can be elicited at this stage. (*Stage XVIII*) The cloacal tail piece has disappeared. (*Stage XIX*) The skin window becomes cleared. The wall of the gill chamber at the point where the forelegs will later protrude becomes thin and transparent. (*Stage XX*) One or both forelegs have protruded. The labial fringes are complete and the horny beak is still present. (*Stage XXI*) The angle of the mouth has reached a point midway between the nostril and the anterior margin of the eye. Rapid changes in the mouth, pharynx, and tail occur. A remnant of the labial fringe persists as a tuft at each corner of the mouth. The gills and operculum begin to be resorbed. The tail becomes darker and less transparent. The dorsal and ventral fins are shrunken and the length of the tail is reduced, but is still longer than the hindlimb. (*Stage XXII*) The angle of the mouth has reached the level of the middle of the eye. Tail tissue is darker and the dorsal and ventral (*Continued on next page.*)

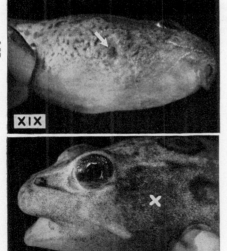

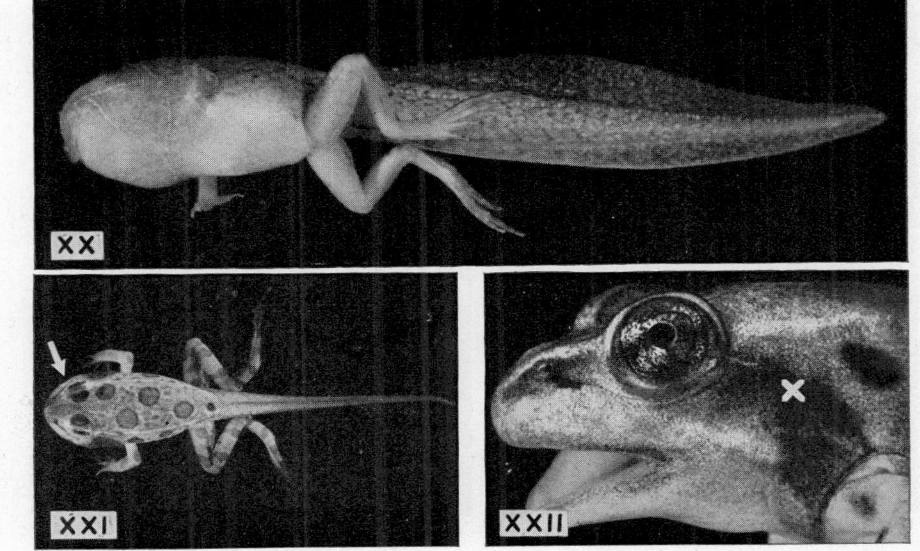

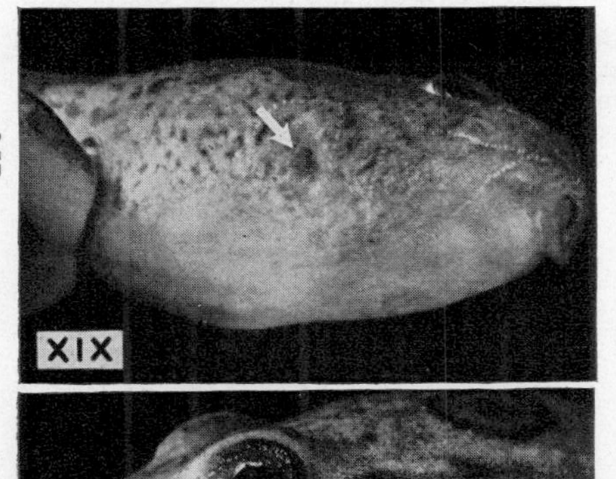

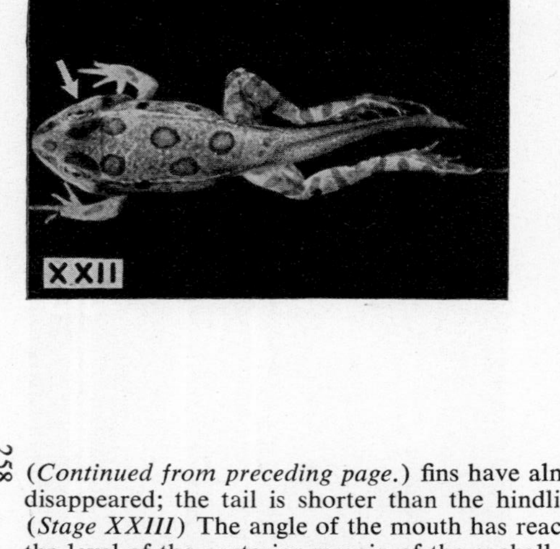

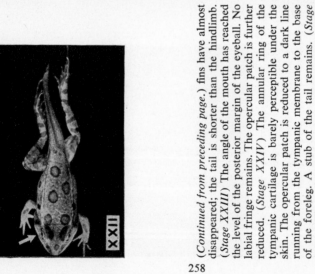

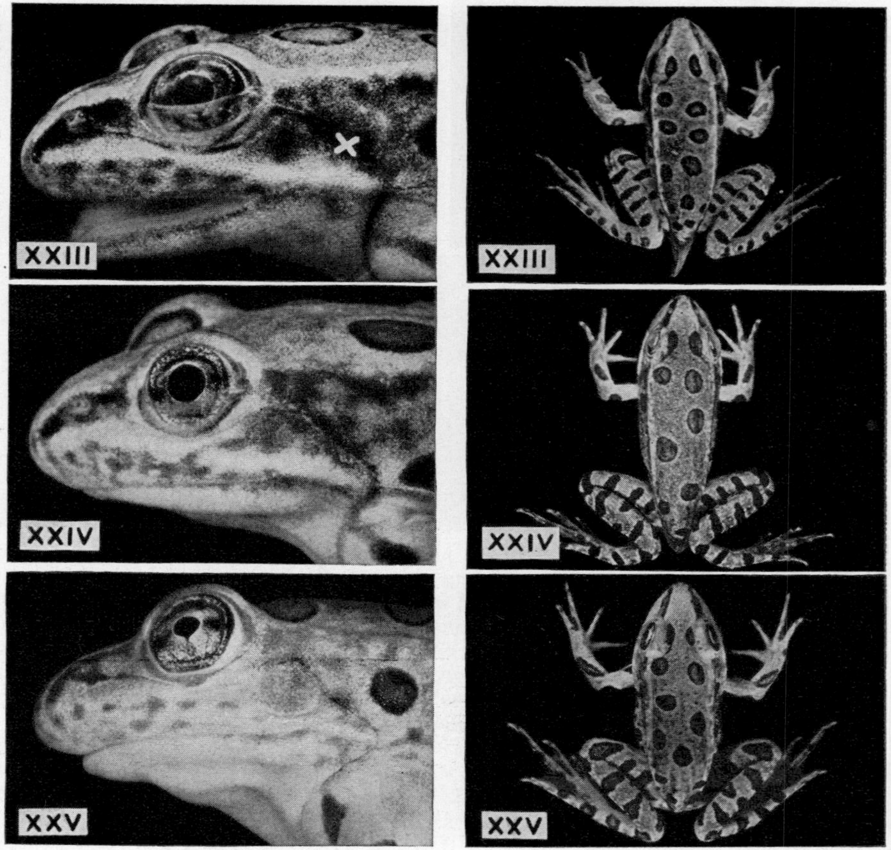

(*Continued from preceding page.*) fins have almost disappeared; the tail is shorter than the hindlimb. (*Stage XXIII*) The angle of the mouth has reached the level of the posterior margin of the eyeball. No labial fringe remains. The opercular patch is further reduced. (*Stage XXIV*) The annular ring of the tympanic cartilage is barely perceptible under the skin. The opercular patch is reduced to a dark line running from the tympanic membrane to the base of the foreleg. A stub of the tail remains. (*Stage XXV*) The tail is completely gone, as well as the operculum. (Courtesy, Taylor and Kollros, 1946.)

Stage 23: 9 mm. total body length.

Mouth developing with embryonic teeth, opercular fold begins backward growth, tongue anlage appears, carotid glands develop from ventral wall of first branchial pouch, epithelioid bodies from wall of second and third branchial pouches, oesophageal plug disappears, pancreas anlage is formed, pharyngeal arteries as well as subclavians grow from dorsal aorta, mesenteric and lumbar arteries appear, parachordal plate develops in floor of cranium, brain develops anterior choroid plexus, optic lobes, and cerebellum, cranial nerves (except abducens) well developed including all parts of trigeminal.

Stage 24: 10 mm. total body length.

Atrophy of mucous glands, mouth with horny jaws and cornified lips takes in vegetable diet, intestine long and looped, operculum closed on right side, thyroid bifurcates and separates from pharynx, spleen anlage appears, two or three branchial clefts break through, mesonephros developing, utricle separated from saccule by oblique partition, all semi-circular canals indicated, optic lobes formed, median cardinal vein appears, and posterior vena cava begins to develop.

Stage 25: 11 mm. total body length.

Cilia lost except on tail, operculum completed, cornification of horny rasping papillae of jaws and lips, oesophagus differentiated from stomach, lung buds invested with mesenchyme, pronephros large and conspicuous, retina develops rods and cones, olfactory apparatus develops lateral appendix, internal choanae open, olfactory nerve is derived from olfactory lobe neuroblasts, and abducens is formed from neuroblasts of medulla.

12 mm. total body length stage:

Olfactory tube develops complete lumen from external nares to internal choanae, thymus separates from dorsal part of first branchial pouch and comes to lie posterior to tympanic membrane near mandibular muscles, maximum development of the pronephros which degenerates by 20 mm. stage, cortical (interrenal) adrenal arises from peritoneum in vicinity of cardinal veins, paired gonad primordia prominent.

15 mm. total body length stage:

Notochordal cartilage sheath develops, vertebrae begin to appear, saccule gives rise to lagena (cochlea) and to a basilar chamber, sensory patches appear in ear epithelium, lateral line organ fully devel oped, mesonephric tubules associated with median cardinal vein.

Metamorphosis at 75 to 90 days:

Loss of horny jaws, widening of mouth, shortening of gut and changing of its histology to conform with a change from vegetable diet to an omnivorous diet, loss of tail with its 32 pairs of spinal nerves and development of two pairs of legs, shedding of larval skin, disappearance of lateral line system as frog leaves aquatic environment, loss of caudal veins, full development of tongue, active functioning of endocrine glands (particularly thyroid and pituitary), and appearance of differentiated gonads containing maturing gametes.

The finished product of normal frog embryology. (Copyright by General Biological Supply House, Chicago.)

Glossary of Embryological Terms*

Acidophil—oxyphil: cell constituents which stain with acid dyes, often used to designate an entire cell type. (See *Basophil.*)

Acrosome—apical organ at tip of mature spermatozoon, derived from spermatosphere (idiosome or centrosome) and presumably functional in aiding penetration of egg cortex by spermatozoon during fertilization. (Syn., perforatorium.)

Activation—process of initiating development in egg, normally achieved by spermatozoon of same species but also accomplished artificially (parthenogenesis); term also used to refer to stimulation of spermatozoon to accelerated activity by chemical (fertilizin) means.

Adnexa—extra-embryonic structures (e.g., yolk sac) discarded before adult condition is attained.

Aestivation—reduced activity of some animals during heat of summer. Opposed to hibernation.

Agglutination—cluster formation; a spontaneously reversible reaction of spermatozoa to certain chemical situations (e.g., egg water).

Aggregation—coming together of cells, such as spermatozoa, without sticking; a non-reversible response comparable to chemotropism.

Albuginea of Testis—stroma of primitive testis which forms a layer between germinal epithelium and seminiferous tubules.

Albumen—protein substance secreted by walls of oviducts around egg of reptiles and birds.

Albumen Sac—2-layered ectodermal sac enclosing albumen of chick egg during early development of embryo, separated for a time from yolk by vitelline membrane; later to release some of its contents into amniotic cavity through ruptured sero-amniotic connection.

Amitosis—direct nuclear division without chromosomal rearrangements; generally thought to be a sign of decadence or of high specialization, if it occurs at all.

*A supplementary list of some 350 specialized terms may be found in the author's "Experimental Embryology, a Manual of Techniques and Procedures," Minneapolis, Minn., Burgess Publishing Co., 1948.

Amphiblastula—double-structured blastula as in Porifera (sponges).

Amphimixis—mixing of germinal substances accomplished during fertilization.

Amphitene—one end of chromosome is thick, one end is thin, moving toward full pachytene during maturation.

Amplexus—sexual embrace of female amphibian by male, a process which may (frogs and toads) or may not (urodeles) occur at time of oviposition.

Anal Plate—thickening and invagination of mid-ventral ectoderm which meets evaginating endoderm of hindgut, later to be perforated as proctodeum (anus). (Syn., cloacal membrane.)

Analogy—similarity of parts in respect to function rather than to structure.

Anamniota—forms which never develop an amnion, e.g., cyclostomes, fishes, amphibia.

Anaphase—phase of mitosis when paired chromosomes are separating at equatorial plate and begin to move toward ends of spindle.

Anastomosis—joining together, as of blood vessels and nerves, generally forming a network.

Androgen—hormonal secretion of interstitial tissue of testis.

Androgenesis—development of an egg with paternal (sperm) chromosomes only, accomplished by removing or destroying egg nucleus before syngamy.

Angioblast—migratory mesenchyme cell associated with formation of vascular endothelium.

Animal Pole—region of egg where polar bodies are formed; region of telolecithal egg containing nucleus and bulk of cytoplasm; gives rise largely to ectodermal derivatives. (Syn., apical pole or hemispheres.)

Anlage—rudiment; group of cells which indicate a prospective development into a part or an organ. (Syn., ebauché or primordium.)

Anterior—toward head; head end. (Syn., cephalic, cranial, rostral.)

Anura—tailless amphibia (e.g., frogs and toads). (Syn., Salientia.)

Aortic Arch—blood vessel which connects dorsal and ventral aortae by way of visceral arch.

Aqueduct of Sylvius—ventricle of mesencephalon (mesocoel) becomes aqueduct of Sylvius, connecting with cavities of optic lobes. (Syn., iter.)

Aqueous Humor—fluid which fills anterior and posterior chambers of eye between lens, probably derived from mesoderm.

Archencephalon—pre-chordal brain, e.g., forebrain. Brain anterior to anterior end of notochord.

Archenteric Pouch—See *Enterocoel.*

Archenteron—primitive gut found in gastrula and communicating with outside by blastopore; precursor of embryonic gut. (Syn., gastrocoel, enteron.)

Arcualia—small blocks of sclerotomal connective tissue involved in formation of vertebrae.

Asexual Reproduction—reproduction without union of gametes; generally with no maturation divisions.

Aster—"star-shaped structure" surrounding centrosome (Fol, 1877); lines radiating in all directions from centrosome during mitosis.

Astral Rays—lines which make up aster.

Astrocytes—stellate-shaped cells arising from spongioblasts of mantle layer, classified under the more general term of neuroglia.

Atrium—two upper chambers of frog's embryonic heart, later to be known as auricles.

Attachment Point—point of chromosome to which spindle fiber is attached and therefore portion of chromosome nearest centrosome in anaphase. (Syn., centrosome, chromocenter, kinetochore.)

Attraction Sphere—See *Centrosphere.*

Auricles—two upper chambers of adult frog's heart, derived from embryonic atria.

Autogamy—self-fertilization.

Autosome—any chromosome except so-called sex (X or Y) chromosomes.

Auxocyte—pre-meiotic germ cell. (Syn., primary cyte, meiocyte.)

Axial Filament—central fiber in tail of a spermatozoon.

Axial Mesoderm—that portion of epimeric mesoderm nearest notochord. (Syn., vertebral plate.)

Axis—imaginary central or median line, generally correlated with a gradient.

Axis of the Cell—imaginary line passing through centrosome and nucleus of a cell, generally also through geometrical center of cell. In an egg such an axis generally is also gradient axis of materials such as cytoplasm, yolk, pigment, etc.

Axis of the Embryo—imaginary line representing antero-posterior axis of the future embryo.

Balancers—cylindrical and paired projections of ectoderm with mesenchymatous cores, used as adhesive organs in place of (anuran) suckers by many urodele amphibia.

Balfour's Law—"The velocity of segmentation in any part of the ovum is, roughly speaking, proportional to the concentration of the protoplasm there; and the size of the segments is inversely proportional to the concentration of the protoplasm." The intervals between cleavages increase in proportion to the amount of yolk which a cell contains in its protoplasm.

Basal Plate—ventro-lateral wall of myelencephalon, separated from dorsolateral alar plate by sulcus limitans.

Basophil—cell constituents having an affinity for basic dyes, often used as an adjective for an entire cell. (See *Acidophil.*)

Bidder's Organ—anterior portion of anuran pro-gonad, somewhat ovarian in character, developing from part of gonad rudiment consisting wholly of cortex; its development indicates failure of medullary substance to diffuse to anterior extremity of gonad rudiment.

Biogenetic Law—embryos of higher species tend to resemble embryos of lower species in certain respects but are never like adults of lower species. Embryonic development is a gradual deviation from the more general (phylogenetic) to the more specific characters of the individual species. Not to be confused with recapitulation theory.

Blastema—indifferent group of cells about to be organized into definite tissue; newly formed cells covering a cut surface, functional in regeneration of tissues.

Blastocoel—cavity of blastula. (Syn., segmentation or subgerminal cavity.)

Blastoderm—living portion of egg from which both embryo and all of its membranes are derived. The cellular blastodiscs. "Because the embryo chooses this as its seat and its domicile, contributing much to its configuration out of its own substance, therefore, in the future we shall call it blastoderm" (Pander, 1817).

Blastomere—cellular unit of developing egg or early embryo, prior to time of gastrulation. Smaller blastomeres are micromeres; intermediate ones are mesomeres; larger ones are macromeres, where there is great disparity in size.

Blastopore—opening of archenteron (gastrocoel) to exterior, occluded by yolk plug in amphibian embryos; consisting of a slit-like space between elevated margin of blastoderm and underlying yolk of chick egg; represented in amniota as primitive streak.

Blastopore, Dorsal Lip of—region of first involution of cells in amphibian gastrula; general area of the "organizer"; original gray crescent area; cells which turn in beneath potential central nervous system (Amphioxus) and form roof of archenteron. (Syn., germ ring or marginal zone.)

Blastopore, Ventral Lip of—region of blastopore opposite dorsal lip; region which gives rise to peristomial mesoderm of frog. (Syn., germ ring.)

Blastula—stage in embryonic development between appearance of distinct blastomeres and end of cleavage (i.e., beginning of gastrulation); a stage generally possessing a primary embryonic cavity or blastocoel; invariably monodermic. (See specific types under specific names.)

Blood Islands—pre-vascular groups of mesodermal cells found in splanchnopleure, from which will arise blood vessels and corpuscles.

Bowman's Capsule—double-walled glomerular cup associated with uriniferous tubule.

Branchial—having to do with respiration. (Syn., gill.)

Branchial Arch—visceral arches, beginning with third pair, which contain blood vessels which (phylogenetically) have respiratory function during embryonic development. Mesodermal components which support those blood vessels are branchial arches. (Syn., gill arch.) (See *Visceral Arches*.)

Branchial Artery—blood vessel which actually passes through gills (external or internal) of frog embryo. (Syn., gill artery.)

Branchial Chamber—closed chamber (except for a single spiracular opening on left side) which encloses internal gills of frog embryo. (Syn., opercular or gill chamber.)

Branchial Cleft—opening between branchial arches formed by invaginating head ectoderm and evaginating pharyngeal endoderm (pouch) through which water passes from pharynx to outside of frog. (Syn., gill cleft or slit, some visceral clefts.)

Branchial Groove—ectodermal invagination anterior or posterior to visceral arch, which joins branchial pouch to form branchial cleft, in most instances.

Branchiomery—type of serial metamerism involving respiratory structures exemplified by visceral arches.

Bud—undeveloped branch, generally an anlage of an appendage (e.g., limb or wing bud).

Budding—reproductive process by which a small secondary part is produced from parent organism, and which gradually grows to independence.

Bulbus Arteriosus—most anterior division of early, tubular, embryonic heart which leads from ventricle to truncus arteriosus.

Cardinal Veins—anterior, posterior, and sub-cardinal veins; anterior veins receive blood from head, including first three segmental veins; posterior veins receive blood from all pairs of trunk segmental veins and from veins of Wolffian bodies; paired cardinals enlarge and fuse, left half degenerates, and balance fuses with developing inferior (posterior) vena cava.

Cell—protoplasmic territory under control of a single nucleus, whether or not territory is bounded by a discrete membrane. By this definition a syncytium is made up of many cells with physiological rather than morphological boundaries.

Cell Lineage—study of origin and fate of specific blastomeres in embryonic development. (Syn., cytogeny.)

Cell Theory—body of any living organism is composed of structural and functional units, the primary agents of organization called cells. Each cell consists of a nucleus and its sphere of influence, including the cytoplasm, generally circumscribed by a membrane. "Omnis cellula e cellula" (Virchow).

Central Canal—See *Neurocoel.*

Centriole—granular core of centrosome.

Centrosome—granule (centriole) and surrounding sphere of rays (centrosphere) which function as kinetic centers in mitosis. Center of aster which does not disappear when astral rays disappear. Dynamic center of mitosis.

Centrosphere—rayed portion of centrosome; structure in spermatid which gives rise to acrosome. (Syn., spermatosphere, idiosome, attraction sphere.)

Cephalic Flexure—ventral bending of embryonic head at level of midbrain and hindbrain.

Chimera—compound embryo generally derived by grafting major portions of two embryos, usually of different species; may be derived by abnormal chromosome distribution in cleavage after normal fertilization.

Choana—openings of olfactory organ into pharynx, internal nares. Sometimes also used in connection with external olfactory opening.

Chondrification—process of forming cartilage, by secretion of a homogeneous matrix between the more primitive cells.

Chondrin—chemical substance in cartilage which makes it increasingly susceptible to basic stains.

Chondrocranium—that portion of skull which is originally cartilaginous.

Chorda Dorsalis—Syn., notochord.

Chorda Mesoderm—region of the late (amphibian) blastula, arising from gray crescent area, which will give rise to notochord and mesoderm and will, if transplanted, induce formation of secondary medullary folds.

Choroid Coat—mesenchymatous and sometimes pigmented coat within sclerotic coat but surrounding pigmented layer of eye in vertebrate embryos.

Choroid Fissure—inverted groove in optic stalk whose lips later close around blood vessels and nerves that enter eyeball.

Choroid Knot—thickened region of fused lips of choroid fissure, near pupil, from which arise cells of iris.

Chromatid—one of the parts of a tetrad (McClung, 1900); really a longitudinal half of a chromosome.

Chromatin—deeply staining substance of nuclear network and chromosomes, consisting of nuclein; gives Feulgen reaction and stains with basic dyes.

Chromatophore—pigment-bearing cell frequently capable of changing size, shape, and color; cells responsible for superficial color changes in animals; behavior under control of sympathetic nervous system or neurohumors.

Chromidia—granules within cytoplasm which stain like chromatin and which may actually be extruded chromatin granules.

Chromomere—unit of chromosome recognized as a chromatin granule.

Chromonema—slender thread of chromatin which is core of chromosome during mitosis.

Chromophil—cells which have an affinity for dyes.

Chromophobe—cells whose constituents are non-stainable; have no affinity for dyes.

Chromosome—chromatic or deeply staining bodies derived from nuclear network and containing a matrix and one or more chromonemata during process of mitosis; bodies found in all somatic cells of normal organism in a number characteristic of the species; bearers of gene.

Cleavage—mitotic division of egg resulting in blastomeres. (Syn., segmentation.)

Cleavage, Accessory—cleavage in peripheral or deeper portions of (chick) germinal disc caused by supernumerary sperm nuclei following (normal) polyspermy, sometimes occurring in urodeles.

Cleavage, Asymmetrical—extremely unequal divisions of egg as in Ctenophore.

Cleavage, Bilateral—cleavage in which egg substances are distributed symmetrically with respect to median plane of future embryo.

Cleavage, Determinate—cleavage in which certain parts of future embryo may be circumscribed in certain specific (early) blastomeres; cleavage which produces blastomeres that are not qualitatively equipotential, i.e., when such blastomeres are isolated they will not give rise to entire embryos. (Syn., mosaic development.)

Cleavage, Dexiotropic—cleavage resulting in a right-handed production of daughter blastomere(s), as in spiral cleavage.

Cleavage, Discoidal—See *Cleavage, Meroblastic.*

Cleavage, Equatorial—cleavage at right angles to egg axis, opposed to vertical or meridional; often the typical third cleavage plane. (Syn., latitudinal or horizontal cleavage.)

Cleavage, Holoblastic—complete division of egg into blastomeres, generally equal in size although not necessarily so (e.g., Amphioxus). (Syn., total cleavage.)

Cleavage, Horizontal—See *Cleavage, Equatorial.*

Cleavage, Indeterminate—cleavage resulting in qualitatively equipotential blastomeres in early stages of development. When such blastomeres are isolated from each other they give rise to complete embryos. Opposed to mosaic development. (Syn., regulatory development.)

Cleavage, Latitudinal—See *Cleavage, Equatorial.*

Cleavage Laws—See specific laws under names of Balfour, Hertwig, and Sachs.

Cleavage, Levotropic—cleavage resulting in left-handed or counterclockwise production of daughter blastomere(s) as in some cases of spiral cleavage.

Cleavage, Meridional—cleavage along egg axis, opposed to equatorial; generally the first two cleavages on any egg. (Syn., vertical cleavage.)

Cleavage, Meroblastic—cleavage restricted to peripherally located protoplasm, as in chick egg. (Syn., discoidal cleavage.)

Cleavage Nucleus—nucleus which controls cleavage. This may be syngamic nucleus of normal fertilization, egg nucleus of parthenogenetic or gynogenetic eggs, or sperm nucleus of androgenetic eggs.

Cleavage Path—path taken by syngamic nuclei to position awaiting first division.

Cleavage, Radial—holoblastic cleavage which results in tiers of cells.

Cleavage, Spiral—cleavage at an oblique angle with respect to egg axis so that resulting blastomeres (generally micromeres) lie in an interlocking fashion within furrows of original blastomeres, due to intrinsic genetic factors (e.g., Mollusca).

Cleavage, Superficial—cleavage around periphery of centrolecithal eggs. (Syn., peripheral cleavage.)

Cochlea—portion of original otic vesicle associated with sense of hearing; supplied by vestibular ganglion of eighth cranial nerve, having to do with equilibration.

Coeloblastula—spherical ball of blastomeres with a central cavity (e.g., Echinoderms).

Coelom—mesodermal cavity from walls of which gonads develop; cavity subdivided in higher forms into pericardial, pleural, and peritoneal cavities. (Syn., extra-embryonic body cavity and exocoel.)

Coitus—copulation of male and female, term generally used in connection with mammals. Comparable situation in amphibia is called amplexus.

Collecting Tubule—portion of nephric tubule system leading to nephric duct (Wolffian, etc.); term also used to refer to tubules which conduct spermatozoa from seminiferous tubule to vasa efferentia, within testis.

Colloid—dispersed substance whose particles are not smaller than 1 μ and not larger than 100 μ, approximately. Physical state of protoplasm.

Columella—bone in tubo-tympanic cavity of frog which aids in auditory sensations. (Syn., plectrum, malleus.)

Competence—ability of embryonic area to react to stimulus (e.g., evocator).

Concrescence—coming together of previously separate parts (cell areas) of embryo, generally resulting in a piling up of parts. One of the corollaries of gastrulation where a bottle-neck of cell movements occurs at lips of blastopore. Original meaning (His, 1874) referred to presumed preformed parts of fish germ ring. (See *Confluence*.)

Cone, Fertilization—conical projection of cytoplasm from surface of egg to meet spermatozoon which is to invade egg cortex. Cone makes contact and then draws sperm into egg. Not universally demonstrated or seen in frog, but seen in starfish (Chambers). (Syn., exudation cone.)

Cones of Growth—enlarged outgrowth of neuroblast forms axis cylinder or axon of nerve fiber and is termed cone of growth because growth processes by which axon increases in length are supposed to be located there.

Confluence—similar to concrescence except that this term refers specifically to "flow" of cells (or areas) together, whether or not they are piled up.

Constriction—gradual closure of blastopore (diametrical reduction of germ ring) over yolk toward vegetal pole. May be due to stretching of marginal zone, to pull or tension of dorsal lip, or even to narrowing of marginal zone. (Syn., convergence [Jordan] or Konzentrisches Urmundschluss [Vogt].)

Convergence, Dorsal—material of marginal zone moves toward dorsal mid-line as it involutes during gastrulation, resulting in a compensatory ventral divergence. (Syn., confluence [Smith] or dorsal Reffung [Vogt].)

Copulation Path—second portion of sperm migration path through egg toward egg nucleus, when there is any deviation from entrance or penetration path; path of spermatozoon which results in syngamy.

Cords, Medullary—structures which give rise to urogenital connections and take part in formation of seminiferous tubules, and are derived from blastema of mesonephric cords.

Cords, Sex—strands of somatic cells and primordial germ cells growing from cortex toward medulla of gonad primordium. Best seen in early stages of testes development.

Cornea—transparent head ectoderm plus underlying mesenchyme form a layer directly over eye of vertebrates, known as cornea.

Corticin—sex-differentiating substances which spread in some amphibia by blood stream and in other forms by diffusion and act as a hormone. (See *Medullarin.*)

Cranial—relative to head; "craniad" means toward head. (Syn., rostral, cephalad.)

Cranial Flexure—bending of forebrain forward with angle of bend occurring transversely at level of midbrain. (See *Cephalic Flexure.*)

Crescent, Gray—crescentic area between original animal and vegetal pole regions on surface of frog's egg, gray in color because of migration of pigment away from area and toward sperm entrance point (Roux, 1888); region of presumptive chorda-mesoderm, future blastopore, and anus.

Crest, Neural—paired cell masses derived from ectoderm cells along edge of former neural plate, and wedged into space between dorso-lateral wall of closed neural tube and integument. Gives rise to spinal ganglia, sympathetic ganglia, and chromatophores.

Crest Segment—original neural crest becomes divided into segments from which develop spinal and possibly cranial ganglia.

Cross-Fertilization—union of gametes produced by different individuals which, if they are of different species, may produce hybrids.

Crossing Over—mutual exchange of portions of allelomorphic pairs of chromosomes during process of synapsis in maturation.

Cyclopia—failure of eyes to separate; median fusion of eyes which may be due to suppression of rostral block of tissue which ordinarily separates eyes; exaggeration of vegetativization tendencies.

Cyst—tubular portions of testis within which aggregations of germ cells mature, often (e.g., Rhomaleum) containing cells all in same stage of maturation.

Cystic Duct—narrow, proximal portion of embryonic bile duct leading from gallbladder to common bile duct.

Cytasters—asters arising apart from nucleus in cytoplasm.

Cyte—suffix meaning cell (e.g., osteocyte for bone cell, oöcyte for egg cell). (See specific definitions.)

Cytology—study of cells.

Cytolysis—breakdown of cell indicated by dispersal of formed components.

Cytoplasm—material of cell exclusive of nucleus; protoplasm apart from nucleoplasm.

Delamination—separation (of cell layers) by splitting, a process in mesoderm formation.

Dermal Bones—bony plates which originate in dermis and cover cartilaginous skull.

Dermatome—outer unthickened wall of somite which gives rise to dermis. (Syn., cutis plate.)

Dermis—deeper layers of skin entirely derived from mesoderm (dermatome).

Dermocranium—portion of skull which does not go through an intermediate cartilaginous stage in development. (Syn., membranocranium.)

Determination—process of development indicated when a tissue, whether treated as an isolated unit or as a transplant, still develops in the originally predicted manner.

Determination of Sex—mechanism by which realization of sex differences is achieved, generally thought to be associated with chromosomal relations.

Deutencephalon—caudal region of brain which later forms mesencephalon and rhombencephalon.

Deutoplasm—yolk or secondary food substances of egg; non-living.

Development—gradual transformation of dependent differentiation into self-differentiation; transformation of invisible multiplicity into a visible mosaic elaboration of components in successive spatial hierarchies.

Development, Mosaic—"all the single primordia stand side by side, separate from each other like the stones of a mosaic work, and develop independently although in perfect harmony with each other, into the finished organism" (Spemann, 1938). Some believe there is prelocalization of embryonic potencies within egg, test for which would be self-differentiation.

Development, Regulative—type of development requiring organizer or inductor influences since each of the early blastomeres could develop into whole embryos. Structures are progressively determined through action of evocators.

Diencephalon—portion of forebrain posterior to telencephalon, including second and third neuromeres.

Differentiation—acquisition of specialized features which distinguish areas from each other; progressive increase in complexity and organization, visible and invisible; elaboration of diversity through determination leading to histogenesis; production of morphogenetic heterogeneity; process of change from a simple to a complex organism. (Syn., differenzierung.)

Differentiation, Axial—variations in density of chemical and often indefinable inclusion in direction of one diameter of the egg, called egg axis.

Differentiation, Dependent—all differentiation that is not self-differentiation; development of parts of organism under mutual influences, such influences being activating, limiting, or inhibiting. Inability of parts of organism to develop independently of other parts.

Differentiation, Self- —perseverance in a definite course of development of a part of an embryo, regardless of its altered surroundings (Roux, 1912).

Diocoel—cavity of diencephalon, ultimate third ventricle.

Diploid—normal complement of chromosomes in somatic and primordial germ cells, twice the haploid number characteristic of mature gametes.

Diplotene—stage in maturation following pachytene when chromosomes again appear double and do not converge toward centrosome. Sometimes refers to split individual chromosomes.

Discoblastula—disc-shaped blastula found in cases of discoidal (meroblastic) cleavage (e.g., Cephalopoda and chick).

Distal—farther from any point of reference, away from main body mass.

Divergence, Ventral—divergence of material from mid-ventral line, compensatory to process of dorsal convergence in gastrulation (Vogt).

Diverticulum—blind outpocketing of a tubular structure (e.g., liver or thyroid anlage).

Dominance—parts of a system which have greater growth momentum and also which gather strength from the rest, such as dorsal lip of blastopore.

Dorsal Mesentery—membrane formed by doubling of peritoneum from mid-dorsal line of body cavity, which supports intestine.

Dorsal Root Ganglion—aggregation of neuroblasts which are derived from neural crests and which send their processes into dorsal horns of spinal cord.

Dorsal Thickening—roof of mesencephalon which gives rise to optic lobes.

Duct. See ducts under specific names.

Ductus Arteriosus—See *Ductus Botalli.*

Ductus Botalli—dorsal portion of sixth pair of aortic arches which normally becomes occluded after birth, remainder of arch giving rise to pulmonary arteries. (Syn., ductus arteriosus.)

Ductus Cuvieri—union of all somatic veins which empty directly into heart, specifically the vein which unites common cardinals and sinus venosus. Sometimes regarded as synonymous with common cardinal.

Ductus Endolymphaticus—dorsal portion of original otic vesicle which has lost all connections with epidermis, and which is partially constricted from region which will form semi-circular canals.

Duodenum—portion of embryonic gut associated with outgrowths of pancreas and liver (bile) ducts.

Dyads—aggregations of chromosomes consisting of two rather than four (tetrad) parts, term used to describe condition during maturation process.

Ecdysis—process of molting a cuticular layer, shedding of epithelium.

Ectoblast—See *Epiblast.*

Ectoderm—outermost layer of didermic gastrula. (Syn., epiblast.)

Ectoplasm—external layer of protoplasm of egg cell; layer immediately beneath cell membrane. (Syn., egg cortex.)

Edema—condition in which tissues hold an excess of water, common in parthenogenetic tadpoles. (Older spelling: oedema.)

Egg, Alecithal—eggs with little or no yolk. Literally means "without yolk."

Egg, Cleidoic—eggs, such as those of reptiles, birds, and oviparous mammals, which are covered by a protective shell.

Egg, Ectolecithal—egg having yolk around formative protoplasm. Opposed to centrolecithal.

Egg Envelope—material enveloping egg but not necessarily a part of the egg, such as vitelline membrane, chorion, jelly, albumen.

Egg, Giant—abnormal polyploid condition where chromosome complexes are multiplied, resulting in giant cells and embryos.

Egg, Homolecithal—egg (e.g., mammal) in which but little yolk is scattered throughout cytoplasm.

Egg, Isolecithal—eggs with homogeneous distribution of yolk; may be isolecithal, alecithal, or homolecithal.

Egg Jelly—mucin covering deposited on amphibian egg as it passes through oviduct.

Egg, Macrolecithal—egg with large amount of yolk, generally telolecithal.

Egg Membranes—include all egg coverings such as vitelline membrane, chorion, and tertiary membranes.

Egg, Microlecithal—egg with small amount of yolk. (Syn., meiolecithal egg, oligolecithal egg.)

Egg Receptor—part of Lillie's scheme picturing parts that go into the fertilization reaction involving fertilizin. Egg receptor plus amboceptor plus sperm receptor gives fertilization.

Egg, Telolecithal—egg with large amount of yolk concentrated at one pole.

Egg Water—watery extract of materials diffusing from living eggs, presumably the "fertilizin" of Lillie. (Syn., egg water extract.)

Ejaculation—forcible emission of mature spermatozoa from body of male.

Ejaculatory Duct—short portion of mesonephric duct (mammal) between seminal vesicles and urethra.

Emboîtement—preformationist theory of Bonnet and others based on idea that ovary of first female (Eve?) contained the miniatures of all subsequently existing human beings. (Syn., encasement theory.)

Embryo—any stage in ontogeny of fertilized egg, generally limited to period prior to independent food-getting. Stage between second week and second month of human embryo.

Endocardium—delicate endothelial tissue forming lining of heart.

Endochondral Bone—bone preformed in cartilage. (Syn., cartilage bone.)

Endoderm—innermost layer of didermic gastrula. (Syn., entoderm.)

Endolymphatic Duct—See *Ductus Endolymphaticus.*

Endolymphatic Sac—See *Saccus Endolymphaticus.*

Endoplasm—inner medullary substance of (egg) cell which is generally granular, soft, watery, and less refractive than ectoplasm.

Entelchy—Driesch's theory of an (intangible) agent controlling development. (Syn., élan vital.)

Enterocoel—cavity or pouch within mesoderm just formed by evagination of gut (enteron) endoderm as in Amphioxus. (Syn., gut pouch, coelomic pouch, archenteric pouch.)

Enteron—definitive gut of embryo, always lined with endoderm.

Ento-mesoderm—refers to portion of invaginating blastoporal lips which will induce formation of medullary fields in amphibian embryo.

Entrance Cone—temporary depression on surface of egg following entrance of spermatozoon.

Entrance Path—See *Path, penetration.*

Ependymal Cells—narrow zone of non-nervous and ciliated cells which surround central canal (neurocoel), from outer ends of which branching processes extend to periphery, such processes forming a framework for other cellular elements in spinal cord and brain.

Epiblast—outermost layer of early embryo from which the various germ layers may be derived.

Epiboly—growing, spreading, or flowing over; process by which rapidly dividing animal pole cells or micromeres grow over and enclose vegetal pole material. Increase in areal extent of ectoderm.

Epibranchial Placode—placode (thickening) external to gills related to lateral line organs and tenth cranial nerves. (Syn., suprabranchial placode.)

Epidermis—ectodermal portion of skin including cutaneous glands, hair, feathers, nails, hoofs, and some types of horns and scales.

Epigenesis—development of systems starting with primitive, homogeneous, lowly organized condition and achieving great diversification.

Epimere—most dorsal mesoderm, that lying on either side of nerve and notochord, which gives rise to somites. (Syn., axial mesoderm.)

Epiphysis—evagination of anterior diencephalon of vertebrates which becomes separated from brain as pineal (endocrine) gland of adult.

Epithelioid Bodies—endodermal masses arising from second and third visceral pouches of amphibia.

Epithelium—thin covering layer of cells; may be ectodermal, endodermal, or mesodermal.

Equational Maturation Division—maturational divisions in which there is no (qualitative) reduction in chromosomal complex, similar in results to mitosis.

Equatorial Plate—lateral view of chromosomes, lined up on mitotic spindle, prior to any anaphase movement.

Eustachian Tube—vestige of endodermal portion of hyomandibular pouch connecting middle ear and pharyngeal cavities and lined with endoderm.

Evagination—growth from any surface outward.

"Ex Ovo Omnia"—all life comes from the egg (Harvey, 1657).

Exogastrula—gastrulation modified experimentally by abnormal conditions so that invagination is partially or totally hindered and there remains some mesendoderm not enclosed by ectoderm.

Experimental Method—concerted, organized, and scientific analysis of the causes, forces, and factors operating in any (embryological) system.

External Gills—outgrowths of (amphibian) branchial arches which function as temporary (anura) or permanent neotonic (urodela) respiratory organs.

Extra-Embryonic—refers to structures apart from embryonic body, such as membranes.

Fate Map—map of blastula or early gastrula stage which indicates prospective significance of various surface areas, based upon previously established studies of normal development aided by means of vital dye markings.

Fate, Prospective—destination toward which we know, from previous experience, that a given part would develop under normal conditions; lineage of each part of egg through its cell descendants into a definite region or portion of adult organism.

Fertilization—activation of egg by sperm and syngamy of pronuclei; union of male and female gamete nuclei.

Fertilization, Anti- —"eggs contain within their interior a substance capable of combining with the agglutinating group of the fertilizin, but which is separate from it as long as the egg is inactive" (Lillie).

Feulgen Reaction—chemical test for thymo-nucleic acid, used as a specific staining test for chromatin.

Field—mosaic of spatio-temporal activities within developing organism.

Field, Morphogenetic—embryonic field out of which will normally develop certain specific structures.

Flexure—refers to a bending such as cranial, cervical, and pontine flexures. Also dorsal and lumbo-sacral flexures of the pig.

Follicle—cellular sac within which egg generally goes through early maturation stages.

Forebrain—most anterior of first three primary brain vesicles, associated with lateral opticoels. (Syn., prosencephalon.)

Foregut—more anterior portion of enteric canal, first to appear, aided by development of pharyngeal derivatives.

Fovea Germinativa—pigment-free spot of animal hemisphere where amphibian germinal vesicle gives off its polar bodies.

Frontal—plane at right angles to both transverse and sagittal, dividing dorsal from ventral. (Syn., coronal.)

Gamete—differentiated (matured) germ cell, capable of functioning in fertilization (e.g., sperm or egg cell, germ cell).

Gametogenesis—process of developing and maturing germ cells.

Ganglion—aggregation of neurons, generally derived from a neural crest (e.g., cranial and spinal ganglia).

Ganglion, Acoustic—eighth cranial ganglion from which fibers of eighth cranial nerve arise, purely sensory.

Ganglion, Acustico-facialis—early undifferentiated association of seventh and eighth cranial ganglia.

Ganglion, Gasserian—fifth cranial ganglion, carrying both sensory and motor fibers. (Syn., trigeminal ganglion, semilunar ganglion.)

Ganglion, Geniculate—ganglion at root of facial (VII) cranial nerve, carrying both sensory and motor fibers.

Ganglion, Nodosal—ganglion associated with vagus (X) cranial nerve which carries afferent fibers to pharynx, larynx, trachea, oesophagus, and thoracic and abdominal viscera.

Ganglion, Petrosal—ganglion associated with glossopharyngeal (IX) cranial nerve, more peripheral than superior ganglion carrying sensory fibers from pharynx and root of tongue.

Ganglion, Superior—ganglion associated with glossopharyngeal (X) cranial nerve, mesial to petrosal ganglion.

Gasserian Ganglion—fifth cranial or trigeminal ganglion, derived from midbrain.

Gastraea Theory—theory of Haeckel that since all higher forms have gastrula stages there may have existed a common ancestor built on the plan of a permanent gastrula, as are the recent Coeloenterata.

Gastral Mesoderm—mesoderm derived from dorso-lateral bands (enterocoelic) in Amphioxus or from dorsal lip in frog. Opposed to peristomial mesoderm.

Gastrocoel—cavity formed during process of gastrulation. (Syn., archenteron.)

Gastrula—didermic embryo, possessing a newly formed cavity, gastrocoel or archenteron. The two layers are ectoderm and endoderm.

Gastrular Cleavage—separation of ectoderm and endoderm, during gastrulation, by a slit-like crevice, actually compressed blastocoel.

Gastrulation—dynamic process involving cell movements which change embryo from a monodermic to either a di- or tridermic form. Generally involves inward movement of cells to form enteric endoderm. Description includes epiboly, concrescence, confluence, involution, invagination, extension, and convergence.

Genital—refers to reproductive organs or processes, or both.

Genital Ducts—any ducts which convey gametes from their point of origin to region of insemination (e.g., collecting tubules, vas deferens, vas efferens, seminal vesicle, oviduct, uterus, etc.).

Genital Ridge—initial elevation or thickening for development of external genitalia.

Germ—egg throughout its development, or at any stage.

Germ Cell—cell capable of sharing in reproductive process, in contrast with a somatic cell (e.g., sperm or egg cell). (Syn., gamete.)

Germ Layer—more or less artificial spatial and histogenic distinction of cell groups beginning in gastrula stage, consisting of ectodermal, endodermal, and mesodermal layers. No permanent and clear-cut distinction, as shown by transplantation experiments.

Germ Plasm—hereditary material, generally referring specifically to the genotype. Opposed to somatoplasm.

Germ Ring—ring of cells showing accelerated mitotic activity, generally a synonym for lips of blastopore. The rapidly advancing cells in epiboly.

Germinal Epithelium—peritoneal epithelium out of which reproductive cells of both male and female presumably develop. (Syn., germinal ridges, gonadal ridges.)

Germinal Localization—every area of blastoderm or of unfertilized egg, corresponds to some future organ. Unequal growth produces differentiation of parts (His, 1874). This concept led to Mosaic Theory of Roux (see Fate Map, p. 101).

Germinal Spot—nucleolus of ovum.

Germinal Vesicle—pre-maturation nucleus of egg.

Gestalten—system of configuration consisting of a ladder of levels; electrons, atom, molecule, cell tissue, organ, and organism, each one of which exhibits specifically new modes of action that cannot be understood as mere additive phenomena of the previous levels. With each higher level new concepts become necessary. The parts of the cell cannot exist independently, hence the cell is more than a mere aggregation of its parts—it is a patterned whole. A coherent unit reaching a final configuration in space (W. Kohler). Gestaltung means formation.

Gill—See *Branchial Arch, Branchial Chamber, Branchial Cleft.*

Gill Plate—elevated and thickened areas of ectoderm posterior to sense plate of embryo where visceral grooves will subsequently form.

Gill Rakers—ectodermal, finger-like obstructions which sift water as it passes from oral cavity to gill chambers of frog tadpole.

Glia Cells—small rounded supporting cells of spinal cord, derived from germinal cells of neural ectoderm.

Glomerulus—aggregation of capillaries associated with branches of dorsal aorta but lying within substance of functional kidney; function is excretory.

Glomus—vascular aggregations within head kidney or pronephros, never to become a glomerulus.

Glottis—opening between pharynx and larynx.

Gonad—organ within which germ cells are produced and generally matured (e.g., ovary or testis). (Syn., sex or germ gland.)

Gonadromorph—condition in which part of an animal may be male and another part female; not to be confused with hermaphroditism.

Gonium—suffix referring to a stage in maturation of a germ cell prior to any maturation division (e.g., spermatogonium, or oögonium).

Gonoduct—See *Genital Ducts.*

Gradient—gradual variation of developmental forces along an axis; scaled regions of preference. (See *Axis.*)

Gray Crescent—See *Crescent, Gray.*

Growth—developmental increase in total mass of protoplasm at expense of raw materials; an embryonic process, generally differentiation; cell proliferation.

Gynogenesis—development of sperm activated egg but without benefit of sperm nucleus.

Haploid—having a single set of chromosomes not appearing in allelomorphic pairs, as in mature gametes. Opposed to diploid, or the condition in somatic cells.

Harmonious-Equipotential System—embryonic system in which all parts are equally ready to respond to organism as a whole. Isolated blastomeres of such a system may give rise to complete embryos.

Hatching—beginning of larval life of amphibian, accomplished by temporarily secreted hatching enzymes which aid embryo to escape from its gelatinous capsule.

Hepatic Sinusoids—maze of dilated and irregular capillaries between loosely packed framework of hepatic tubules.

Hepatic Veins—veins from liver to heart, originating as anterior portions of vitelline veins of amphibia.

Hepatic Veins, Portal—remnants of posterior portions of left vitelline vein.

Hermaphrodite—individual capable of producing both spermatozoa and ova.

Hermaphrodite, Protandrous—male elements mature prior to female elements in hermaphrodite.

Hermaphrodite, Protogynous—female elements mature prior to male elements in hermaphrodite.

Hertwig's Law—nucleus tends to place itself in center of its sphere of activity; longitudinal axis of mitotic spindle tends to lie in longitudinal axis of yolk-free cytoplasm of cell.

Heteroagglutinin—agglutinin (fertilizin) of eggs which acts on sperm of different species, substance extractable from egg water which causes irreversible agglutination of foreign species.

Heterozygous—condition in which zygote is composed of gametes bearing allelomorphic genes. Opposed to homozygous.

Hibernation—spending the cold (winter) period in a state of reduced activity.

Hindbrain—most posterior of the three original brain divisions. (Syn., rhombencephalon.)

Hindgut—portion of amphibian embryonic gut just anterior to neurenteric canal. Level of origin of rectum, cloaca, post-anal gut, and caudal portions of urogenital systems.

Histogenesis—development of tissues.

Homoiothermal—pertaining to a condition in which temperature of body of organism is under control of an internal mechanism; body temperature regulated. Opposed to poikilothermal.

Homology—similarity in structure based upon similar embryonic origin.

Homoplastic—pertaining to a graft to an organism of same species, or even to another position on the same individual. (Syn., autoplastic.)

Homozygous—condition in which zygote is composed of gametes bearing identical rather than allelomorphic genes.

Horizontal—unsatisfactory term sometimes used synonymously with frontal, longitudinal, and even sagittal plane or section. Actually means across the lines of gravitational forces.

Hormone—secretion of a ductless (endocrine) gland which can stimulate or inhibit activity of distant parts of biological system already formed.

Hyaloplasm—viscid liquid regarded as essential living protoplasm.

Hybrid—successful cross between different species (e.g., horse and ass give a mule, which is sterile).

Hyoid Arch—mesodermal mass between hyomandibular and first branchial clefts, or between first and second visceral pouches or clefts which give rise to columella and parts of hyoid apparatus. (Syn., second visceral arch.)

Hyomandibular—pertaining to pouch, cleft, or slit between mandibular and hyoid arches.

Hyperplasia—overgrowth; abnormal or unusual increase in elements composing a part.

Hypertrophy—increase in size due to increase in demands upon part concerned.

Hypochordal Rod—transitory string of cells constricted off between dorsal wall of midgut and notochord of amphibian embryo, between level of pancreas and tail, and disappearing before hatching time. (Syn., sub-notochordal rod.)

Hypomere—most ventral segment of mesoderm out of which develop somatopleure, splanchnopleure, and coelom. (Syn., lateral plate mesoderm.)

Hypophysis—ectodermally derived solid structure arising anterior to stomodeum and growing inwardly toward infundibulum to give rise to anterior and intermediate parts of pituitary gland.

Hypoplasia—undergrowth or deficiency in elements composing a part.

Hypothesis—complemental supposition; presumption based on fragmentary but suggestive data offered to bridge a gap in incomplete knowledge of the facts. May be offered as an explanation of facts unproved, until subjected to verification or disproof.

Idiosome—material out of which acrosome is formed during metamorphosis of spermatid to spermatozoon. (Syn., spermatosphere, centrosphere.)

Induction—successive and purposeful influences which bring about morphogenetic changes within embryo.

Inductor—a loose word which includes both organizer and evocator (Needham). Generally means a piece of living tissue which brings about differentiation within otherwise indifferent tissue.

Infundibulum of the Brain—funnel-like evagination of floor of diencephalon which, along with hypophysis, will give rise to pituitary gland of adult.

Infundibulum of the Oviduct—See *Ostium Abdominale Tubae*.

Ingression—inward movement of yolk endoderm of amphibian blastula (Nicholas, 1945).

Insemination—process of impregnation; fertilization.

Interauricular Septum—longitudinal sheet of mesodermal tissue which grows ventrally from roof of atrial chamber to divide it into right and left halves.

Interkinesis—resting stage between mitotic divisions.

Intermediate Cell Mass—narrow strip of mesoderm which, for a time, joins dorsal epimere with ventral hypomere, being made up of a dorsal portion continuous with dorsal wall of somite and somatic mesoderm and a ventral portion continuous with ventral wall of somite and splanchnic mesoderm. Source of origin of excretory system. (Syn., nephrotome or middle plate.)

Internal Gills—filamentous outgrowths on posterior side of first three pairs of branchial arches and a single row on anterior side of fourth pair of branchial arches of frog tadpole, which have a respiratory function concurrent with and following absorption of external gills.

Internal Limiting Membrane—membrane which develops on innermost surface of inner wall of optic cup during fourth day of chick development.

Intersex—individual without typical sexual differentiation.

Interstitial Cells—specialized cells between seminiferous tubules of testis which produce hormones.

Interstitial Tissue of Testis—cell aggregations between seminiferous tubules of testis which elaborate a male sex hormone.

Invagination—folding or inpushing of a layer of cells into a preformed cavity, as in one of the processes of gastrulation. Opposed to involution.

Involution—rolling inward or turning in of cells over a rim, as in gastrulation of chick embryo.

Iris—narrow zone bounding pupil of eye in which two layers of optic cup become blended so that pigment from outer layer invades material of inner layer, giving eye a specific color by variable reflection.

Isogamy—similar gametes, without differentiations into spermatozoa and ova.

Isolation Culture—removal of a part of an organism and its maintenance in a suitable medium in living condition.

Isthmus of the Brain—depression in dorsal wall of embryonic brain which partially separates mesencephalon from metencephalon.

Isthmus of the Oviduct—short, tubular, posterior end of oviduct (e.g., chick) in which fluid albumen and shell membranes are applied to egg.

Iter—See *Aqueduct of Sylvius.*

Jacobson's Organ—ventro-medial evaginations from olfactory pits (amphibia and reptilia) which later become glandular and sensitive olfactory epithelia.

Jelly—mucin covering of amphibian egg derived from oviduct and applied outside vitelline membrane.

Jugular Veins—veins which bring blood from head, superior or internal jugular being anterior cardinal veins and inferior jugular veins growing toward lower jaw and mouth from base of each ductus Cuvieri.

Karyoplasm—protoplasm within confines of nucleus.

Kern-Plasma Relation—ratio of amount of nuclear and of cytoplasmic materials present in the cell. It seems to be a function of cleavage to restore kern-plasma relation from unbalanced condition of ovum with its excessive yolk and cytoplasm to new ratio of gastrula or somatic cell.

Lamina Terminalis—point of suture of anterior neural folds (i.e., anterior neuropore) where they are finally separated from head ectoderm; it consists of a median ventral thickening at anterior limit of telencephalon (from anterior side of optic recess to beginning of velum transversum) and includes anterior commissure of torus transversus.

Larva—stage in development when organism has emerged from its membranes and is able to lead an independent existence, but may not have completed its development. Generally (except in cases of neoteny or paedogenesis) larvae cannot reproduce.

Larynx—anterior part of original laryngo-tracheal groove which becomes a tube opening into pharynx by way of glottis.

Lateral—either right (dextral) or left (sinistral) side; laterad means toward the side.

Lateral Line Organs (or System)—line of sensory structures along side of body of fishes and amphibia, generally embedded in skin and innervated by a branch from vagus ganglion, presumably concerned with recognition of low vibrations in water. Appears first at about 4 mm. stage in frog embryo. (Syn., ramus lateralis.)

Lateral Mesocardium—septum posterior to heart extending from base of each vitelline vein obliquely upward to dorso-lateral body wall, representing one of the three parts of septum transversum.

Lateral Mesoderm—See *Lateral Plate Mesoderm.*

Lateral Neural Folds—See *Neural Fold.*

Lateral Plates or Lateral Plate Mesoderm—lateral mesoblast within which body cavity (coelom and exocoel) arises. (Syn., lateral mesoderm.)

Lateral Ventricles of the Brain—thick-walled and laterally compressed cavities of prosencephalon which open into third ventricle by way of foramen of Monro; walls will become cerebral hemispheres.

Lecithin—fat from an animal organism which is phosphorized in form of phosphatides.

Lens—thickening in head ectoderm opposite optic cup at about time of hatching in frog embryo; it becomes a placode, invaginates to acquire a vesicle, and then pinches off into space of optic cup as a lens. Inner surface convex; substance fibrous.

Lens Placode—early thickened ectodermal primordium of lens.

Leptotene—stage in maturation which follows last -gonial division and prior to synaptene stage, structurally similar to resting cell stage. The chromatin material in form of a spireme. Term means thin, diffuse.

Lipids—fats and fatty substances such as oil and yolk (lecithin) found in eggs (e.g., cholesterol, ergosterol).

Lips of the Blastopore—See *Blastopore, Lips of*.

Localization—cytological separation of parts of the mosaic egg, each of which has a known specific subsequent differentiation. There is often a substratum associated with these areas, made up of pigmented granules, but it is cytoplasm rather than pigmented elements in which localization occurs.

Macromere—larger of the blastomeres where there is a conspicuous size difference.

Malpighian Body—unit of functional kidney including Bowman's capsule and glomerulus. (Syn., renal corpuscle, Malpighian corpuscle.)

Mandibular Arch—rudiment of lower jaw, mesodermal, and anterior to first or hyomandibular pouch.

Mantle Fibers—those fibers of mitotic spindle which attach chromosomes to centrosomes.

Mantle Layer of the Cord—zone of developing spinal cord with densely packed nuclei slightly peripheral to germinal cells from which they are derived. Includes elongated cells of ependyma.

Maturation—process of transformation of a primordial germ cell (spermatogonium or oögonium) into a functionally mature germ cell, the process involving two special divisions, one of which is always meiotic. Divisions known as equational and reductional.

Mechanism—assumption that biological processes do not violate physical and chemical laws but that they are more than the mere functioning of a machine because material taken into the organism becomes an integral part of the organism, through chemical changes. (Syn., the scientific attitude.) (See *Vitalism.*)

Meckel's Cartilage—core of lower jaw derived from ventral part of cartilaginous mandibular arch.

Median plane—"middle" plane, as of an embryo. May be median sagittal or median frontal.

Medulla Oblongata—that portion of adult brain derived from rhombencephalon.

Medullarin—sex differentiating substance spread in some amphibia by blood stream as a hormone and in other forms by diffusion. (See *Corticin.*)

Medullary—See terms under *Neural,* such as canal, fold, groove, plate, tube.

Medullary Cords—that portion of suprarenal glands derived from sympathetic nervous system; central cords. Also that portion of embryonic gonad presumably derived from pre-migratory germ cells upon reaching genital ridge.

Meiosis—process of nuclear division found in maturation of germ cells, involving a separation of members of pairs of chromosomes. (Syn., reductional division.)

Melanophore—well with black or brown pigment (melanin), derived from neural crests and migrating throughout body.

Membrane Bone—bone developed in regions occupied by connective tissue, not cartilage.

Membrane, Vitelline—See *Vitelline Membrane.*

Membranes—See *Egg Membranes.*

Meroblastic Cleavage or Ova—See under *Cleavage* or *Egg.*

Mesencephalon—section of primary brain between posterior level of prosencephalon and an imaginary line drawn from tuberculum posterius to a point just posterior to dorsal thickening. Gives rise to optic lobes, crura cerebri, and aqueduct of Sylvius. (Syn., midbrain.)

Mesenchyme—form of embryonic mesoderm or mesoblast in which migrating cells unite secondarily to form a syncitium or network having nuclei in thickened nodes between intercellular spaces filled with fluid; often derived from mesothelium.

Mesendoderm—newly formed layer of (urodele) gastrula before there has been any separation of endoderm and mesoderm. (Syn., mesentoderm, mesentoblast, ento-mesoblast.)

Mesentery—sheet of (mesodermal) tissue generally supporting organ systems (e.g., mesorchium, mesocardium).

Mesial—median, medial, middle.

Mesoblast, Gastral—See *Gastral Mesoderm.*

Mesoblast, Peristomial—involuted, ventral lip mesoderm, continuous with gastral mesoderm from dorsal lip.

Mesocardium—mesentery of heart; may be dorsal, ventral, or lateral. (See under *Lateral Mesocardium.*)

Mesoderm—the third primary germ layer developed in point of time, may be derived from endoderm in some forms and from ectoderm in others. (See other terms such as *Mesoblast, Mesenchyme, Lateral Plate Mesoderm, Epimere, Mesomere, Hypomere, Gastral Mesoderm, Peristomial Mesoderm, Axial Mesoderm,* etc.)

Mesomere—cell of intermediate size where there are conspicuous size differences in an early embryo; also refers to intermediate cell mass: intermediate mesoderm.

Mesonephric Duct—duct which grows posteriorly from mesonephros to cloaca and functions also as vas deferens in male. (Syn., Wolffian duct.)

Mesonephric Tubules—primary, secondary, and sometimes tertiary tubules developing in Wolffian body, functioning in adult amphibia.

Mesonephros—Wolffian body, or intermediate kidney, functional as kidney in adult fish and amphibian.

Mesorchium—mesentery (mesodermal) which surrounds and supports testis to body wall.

Mesothelium—epithelial layers or membranes of mesodermal origin.

Mesovarium—mesentery (mesodermal) which suspends ovary from dorsal body wall.

Metamerism—serial segmentation, as seen in nervous, muscular, and circulatory systems.

Metamorphosis—end of larval period of amphibia when growth is suspended temporarily. There is autolysis and resorption of old tissues and organs such as gills, and development of new structures such as eyelids and limbs; changes in structure correlated with changes in habitat from one that is aquatic to one that is terrestrial; change in structure without retention of original form, as in change from spermatid to spermatozoon.

Metaphase—stage in mitosis when paired chromosomes are lined up on equatorial plate midway between amphiasters, supported by mitotic spindle, prior to any anaphase movement.

Micromere—smaller of cells when there is a conspicuous difference in size, characteristic of Annelids and Molluscs.

Micropyle—aperture in egg covering through which spermatozoa may enter; in such eggs the only possible point of insemination (e.g., many fish eggs).

Midbrain—See *Mesencephalon.*

Midgut—that portion of archenteron which will give rise to intestines.

Milieu—Term used to include all of the physico-chemical and biological factors surrounding a living system (e.g., external or internal milieu).

Mitochondria—small, permanent, cytoplasmic granules which stain with Janus green B and Janus red; granules which have powers of growth and division; probably lipoid.

Mitosis—cytoplasmic division involving a nucleus and spindle apparatus.

Mitotic Index—proportion in any tissue and at any specified time of the dividing cells; percentage of actively dividing cells.

Monospermy—fertilization accomplished by only one sperm. Opposed to polyspermy.

Monro, Foramina of—tubular connections between single third and paired lateral ventricles of forebrain.

Morphogenesis—all of the topogenetic processes which result in structure formation; origin of characteristic structure (form) in an organ or in an organism compounded of organs.

Morphogenetic Movements—cell or cell area movements concerned with formation of germ layers (e.g., during gastrulation) or of organ primordia.

Morula—spherical mass of cells, as yet without segmentation cavity.

Mosaic—type of egg or development in which fate of all parts is fixed at an early stage, possibly even at time of fertilization. Local injury or excisions generally result in loss of specific organs in developing embryo. Opposed to regulative development.

Müllerian Duct—See *Oviducts.*

Muscle Plate—See *Myotome.*

Myeloblasts—muscle-forming (embryonic) cells.

Myoblasts—formative cells within myotome or muscle plate which will give rise to true striated muscles of adult.

Myocardium—muscular part of heart arising from splanchnic mesoblast.

Myocoel—cavity within which ovaries of Amphioxus develop; temporary cavities within myotomes which may have been connected with coelom.

Myotome—thickened primordium of muscle found in each somite. (Syn., muscle plate.)

Nares, External—external openings of tubes which are connected with olfactory vesicles.

Nares, Internal—openings of tubular organ from olfactory placodes into anterior part of pharynx of 12 mm. frog tadpole. (Syn., choanae.)

Nasal Choanae—openings of olfactory chambers into mouth.

Nasal Pit—See *Olfactory Pit.*

Nebenkern—cytological structure near nucleus of early spermatid.

Neoteny—condition of many urodeles and of experimentally produced (thyroidless) anuran embryos in which larval period is extended or retained, i.e., larvae fail to go through normal metamorphosis. Sexual maturity in larval stage (e.g., axolotl, Necturus).

Nephrocoel—cavity, found in nephrotome or intermediate cell mass, which temporarily joins myocoel and coelom.

Nephrogenic Cord—continuous band of intermediate mesoderm (mesomere) without apparent segmentation, prior to budding off of mesonephric tubules.

Nephrogenic Tissue—intermediate cell mass, mesomere, or nephrotome which will give rise to excretory system.

Nephrostome—funnel-shaped opening of kidney tubules into coelom; outer tubules of amphibian mesonephric kidney acquire ciliated nephrostomal openings from coelom and shift their connections to renal portal sinus.

Nephrotome—intermediate cell mass.

Nephrotomic Plate—intermediate mesoderm, mesomere.

Nerve, Abducens—sixth (VI) cranial nerve arising from basal plate of rhombencephalon which controls external rectus muscles of eye.

Nerve, Auditory—eighth (VIII) cranial nerve, purely sensory, arising from acoustic ganglion and associated with geniculate ganglion of seventh nerve.

Nerve, Facial—seventh (VII) cranial nerve, both sensory and motor, related to taste buds and facial muscles.

Nerve, Glossopharyngeal—ninth (IX) cranial nerve, mixed, associated with superior and petrosal ganglia.

Nerve, Oculomotor—third (III) cranial nerve which arises from neuroblasts in ventral zone of midbrain near median line just before hatching in frog tadpole.

Nerve, Vagus—tenth (X) cranial nerve, mixed, arising from rhombencephalon and associated with jugular ganglion.

Nervous Layer—innermost of two layers found in roof of segmentation cavity of amphibian blastula, from which bulk of central nervous system is developed.

Neural Arch—ossified cartilages which extend dorsally from centrum around nerve cord.

Neural Canal—See *Neurocoel* and *Neural Tube*.

Neural Crest—continuous cord of ectodermally derived cells lying on each side in angle between neural tube and body ectoderm, separated from ectoderm at time of closure of neural tube and extending from extreme anterior to posterior end of embryo; material out of which spinal and possibly some cranial ganglia develop, and related to development of sympathetic ganglia by cell migration.

Neural Fold—elevation of ectoderm on either side of thickened and depressing medullary plate; folds which close dorsally to form neural tube. (Syn., medullary folds.)

Neural Groove—depression caused by sinking in of center of medullary plate to form a longitudinal groove, later to be incorporated within neural tube (spinal cord). (Syn., medullary groove.)

Neural Plate—thickened broad strip of ectoderm along future dorsal side of all vertebrate embryos, later to give rise to central nervous system. (Syn., medullary plate.)

Neural Tube—tube formed by dorsal fusion of neural folds, rudiment of nerve or spinal cord.

Neurenteric Canal—posterior neurocoel where it is connected with closing blastopore and posterior enteron of amphibian; the large common nervous and enteric chamber of Amphioxus; the Kupffer's vesicle of fish embryo; possibly the primitive pit of chick embryo. (Syn., notochordal canal, primitive pit.)

Neuroblasts—primitive or formative nerve cells, probably derived (along with epithelial and glia cells) from germinal cells of embryonic neural tube.

Neurocoel—cavity of neural tube, formed simultaneously with closure of neural folds. (Syn., central canal, neural canal.)

Neurocranium—dorsal portion of skull associated with brain and sense organs.

Neuroglia—see *Glia Cells.*

Neuropore—temporary opening into neural canal due to a lag in fusion of neural folds at anterior extremity; permanent in Amphioxus and in vicinity of epiphysis of higher vertebrates.

Neurula—stage in embryonic development which follows gastrulation and during which neural axis is formed and histogenesis proceeds rapidly. Notochord and neural plate are already differentiated, and basic vertebrate pattern is indicated.

Notochord—rod of vacuolated cells representing axis of all vertebrates, found beneath neural tube and dorsal to archenteron. Thought to be derived from or simultaneously with endoderm.

Notochordal Sheath—double mesodermal sheath around notochord consisting of an outer elastic sheath developed from superficial chorda cells and an inner secondary or fibrous sheath from chorda epithelium.

Nucleolus—the body generally within the nucleus which has no affinity for chromatin dyes, but stains with acid or cytoplasmic dyes. Function unknown. (Syn., plasmosome.)

Oesophagus—elongated portion of foregut between future glottis and opening of bile duct of frog embryo; temporarily occluded just behind glottis but opens again.

Olfactory Lobes—anterior extremities of telencephalic cerebral lobes, partially constricted, associated with first pair of cranial nerves.

Olfactory Pit—depressions within olfactory placodes of 6 mm. frog embryo which will become olfactory organs (external nares).

Olfactory Placode—thickened ectoderm lateral to stomodeal region found in 5 mm. frog embryo, primordia of olfactory pits.

"Omne Vivum e Vivo"—all life is derived from preëxisting life (Pasteur).

Omnipotent—term used in connection with a cell which could, under various conditions, assume every cytological differentiation known to the species or which, by division, could give rise to such varied differentiations.

"Omnis Cellula e Cellula"—all cells from preëxisting cells (Virchow).

Ontogeny—developmental history of an organism; sequence of stages in early development.

Oöcyte—presumptive egg cell after initiation of growth phase of maturation. (Syn., ovocyte.)

Oögenesis—process of maturation of ovum; transformation of oögonium to mature ovum. (Syn., ovogenesis.)

Oögonia—multiplication (mitotic) stage prior to maturation of presumptive egg cell (ovum), found most frequently in peripheral germinal epithelium.

Oöplasm—cytoplasmic substances connected with building rather than reserve materials utilized in developmental processes.

Opercular Chamber—See *Branchial Chamber.*

Operculum—integumentary growth posteriorly from each of the hyoid arches of frog embryo, which covers and encloses gills.

Optic Chiasma—thickening in forebrain ventral to infundibulum, found as a bunch of optic nerve fibers in future diencephalon.

Optic Cup—invagination of outer wall of primary optic vesicle to form a secondary optic vesicle made up of two layers; a thick internal or retinal layer continuous at pupil and choroid fissure, and a thin external layer which is pigmented. Cavity of cup becomes future posterior chamber of eye.

Optic Lobes—thickened, evaginated, dorso-lateral walls of mesencephalon.

Optic Recess—depression in forebrain anterior to optic chiasma which leads to optic stalks.

Optic Stalk—attachment of optic vesicle to forebrain, at first a tubular connection between optic vesicle and diencephalon. Lumen is later obliterated by development of optic nerve fibers.

Optic Vesicle—evagination of forebrain ectoderm to form primary optic vesicles which in turn invaginate to form secondary optic vesicles or optic cups of eyes.

Opticoel—cavity of primary optic cup.

Oral Plate—stomodeal ectoderm and pharyngeal endoderm fused to form oral membrane. Breaks through to form mouth. (Syn., pharyngeal membrane, oral membrane, stomodeal plate.)

Oral Suckers—elongated, pigmented depressions at antero-ventral ends of mandibular arches of frog embryo which give rise to mucous glands; with adhesive function.

Organization—indicated by interdependence of parts and the whole. "When elements of a certain degree of complexity become organized into an entity belonging to a higher level of organization," says Waddington, "we must suppose that the coherence of the higher level depends on properties which the isolated elements indeed possessed but which could not be entered into certain relations with one another." See *Gestalten.*

Organizer—chorda-mesodermal field of amphibian embryo; a tissue area which has power of organizing indifferent tissue into a neural axis; possibly comparable to Henson's node of chick embryo.

Osteoblasts—mesenchymal cells which actively secrete a calcareous material in formation of bone; bone-forming cells.

Osteoclasts—bone-destroying cells; cells which appear in and tend to destroy formed bone; constantly active, even in embryo.

Ostium Abdominale Tubae—most anterior, fimbriated end of oviduct in female vertebrates; point of entrance of ovulated egg into oviduct; double in amphibia. (Syn., infundibulum of oviduct, tubal ridge.)

Otic Vesicle—auditory vesicle, otocyst.

Otocyst—original auditory vesicle appearing at level of rhombencephalon in amphibian embryo just before hatching, forming first as a placode. (Syn., auditory vesicle.)

Oviducal Membranes of Ovum—tertiary membranes applied over egg as it passes through oviduct.

Oviducts—paired Müllerian ducts in both males and females, which generally persist in males.

Ovigerous Cords—columns or strands of tissue which divide germinal epithelium of primordium of ovary, carrying primordial germ cells with them and later breaking up into nests of cells, each of which contains an oögonium. (Syn., egg tubes or cords of Pflüger [mammal].)

Oviposition—process of laying eggs.

Ovocyte—See *Oöcyte.*

Ovogenesis—See *Oögenesis.*

Ovogonia—See *Oögonia.*

Ovulation—release of egg from ovary, not necessarily from body.

Ovum—Latin for egg.

Pachytene—stage in maturation when allelomorphic pairs of chromosomes are fused (telosynapsis or parasynapsis) so as to appear haploid, during which process crossing over may occur; stage just prior to diplotene. Term means thick or condensed. (Syn., diplonema.)

Paedogenesis—reproduction during larval stage; precocious sex development.

Pancreas—digestive and endocrine glands arising as single posterior and single anterior primordia in vicinity of liver.

Parthenogenesis—development of an egg without benefit of spermatozoon.

Parthenogenesis, Artificial—initiation of development of an egg by artificial means.

Parthenogenesis, Natural—maturation of eggs of some forms leads directly to development without aid of spermatozoa.

Parthenogenetic Cleavage—fragmentation of protoplasm of old and unfertilized chick eggs, originally thought to be true cleavage.

Path, Copulation—See *Copulation Path.*

Path, Penetration—initial direction of sperm entrance into egg, often shifting toward egg nucleus along a new copulation path. (Syn., entrance path.)

Perforatorium—See *Acrosome.*

Pericardial Cavity—cavity or membrane sac which encloses heart, representing a cephalic portion of coelom within embryonic body. (Syn., parietal cavity.)

Pericardium—thin mesodermal membrane which encloses pericardial cavity and heart.

Perichondrium—mesenchymal layer immediately around forming cartilage.

Perichordal Sheath—thin, mesodermal (sclerotomal), continuous sheet of tissue immediately around notochord.

Periosteum—mesenchymal layer, often originally perichondrium, which will be found immediately around forming bone.

Peristomial Mesoderm—mesoderm of amphibian gastrula derived from (ventral) lips of blastopore. Opposed to gastral mesoderm.

Peritoneal cavity—body cavity (coelom).

Peritoneum—coelomic mesothelium of abdominal region reinforced by connective tissue.

Perivitelline Membrane—See *Vitelline Membrane.*

Perivitelline Space—space between vitelline (fertilization) membrane and contained egg, generally filled with a fluid.

Pflüger's Law—dividing nucleus elongates in direction of least resistance.

Phenotype—outward appearance of an organism regardless of its genetic make-up. Opposed to genotype.

Pigment Layer of Optic Cup—thin outer wall of primary optic cup, posterior to retina, which never fuses with rods and cones of retina.

Pineal—See *Epiphysis.*

Pituitary—See *Hypophysis.*

Placode—Plate-like thickening of ectoderm from which arise sensory or nervous structures (e.g., olfactory placode).

Plane—imaginary two-dimensional surface; may be frontal, sagittal, transverse, median, or lateral.

Plasmosome—a true nucleolus. (See *Nucleolus.*)

Plectrum—See *Columella.*

Plexus Choroid—Vascular folds in roof of prosencephalon, diencephalon, and rhombencephalon.

Poikilothermal—cold-blooded; animals whose body temperatures are subject to environmental changes because they lack regulating mechanisms. Opposed to homoiothermal.

Polar—pertaining, in most cases, to animal pole, although may refer to vegetal pole, or both.

Polar Body—relatively minute, discarded nucleus of maturing oöcyte (generally three). (Syn., polocytes.)

Polarity—axial distribution of component parts; animal and vegetal poles; stratification.

Pole, Animal—region of egg where polar bodies are eliminated; ectoderm forming portion of pre-cleaved egg. (Syn., apical or animal hemisphere.)

Pole, Vegetal—region of egg opposite animal pole; region of lowest metabolic rate; pole with greater density of yolk in telolecithal eggs; generally endoderm-forming region of egg.

Polyembryony—production of several separate individuals from one egg by an early separation of its blastomeres; possible origin of some identical twins.

Polyploid—possessing a multiple number of chromosomes, such as triploid (three times the haploid number), tetraploid (four times the haploid number), etc. Alwavs more than the normal diploid of the typical zygote.

Polyspermy—insemination of an egg with more than a single sperm, occurring generally in chick egg, although but a single sperm nucleus is functional, in syngamy.

Post-Anal Gut—posteriorly projecting blind pocket of hindgut, that portion of hindgut posterior to anal plate or proctodeal plate. (Syn., post-cloacal gut.)

Post-Reduction—maturation in which equational and reductional divisions occur in that order.

Posterior Tubercle—See *Tuberculum posterius.*

Potency, Prospective—sum total of developmental possibilities, the full range of developmental performance of which a given area (or germ) is capable. Not to be confused with competence.

Preformation—theory that adult is represented in miniature within egg or sperm and that development is simply enlargement.

Pre-migratory Germ Cell—yolk-laden cells of splanchnopleuric origin which migrate by way of blood vessels to gonad primordia. Believed by some to be precursors of gonad stroma or functional germ cells.

Pre-Reduction—maturation in which reductional and equational divisions occur in that order.

Presumptive—expected or predicted outcome of development of a given area (e.g., fate of a part in question) based on previous fate map studies.

Primary Oöcyte—termination of growth phase in maturation of ovum from oögonial stage, prior to any maturational divisions.

Primary Spermatocyte—stage in spermatogenesis in which division results in secondary spermatocytes; stage beginning with growth of spermatogonia.

Primitive Groove—groove through center of primitive streak, bounded by primitive folds and terminated anteriorly by primitive pit and posteriorly by primitive plate.

Primordial Germ Cells—diploid cells which are destined to become germ cells (e.g., oögonia and spermatogonia). (Syn., primitive germ cells.)

Primordium—See *Anlage.*

Proctodeum—ectodermal pit in region of future cloaca which invaginates to fuse with hindgut endoderm to form anal or proctodeal plate, later to rupture and form anus.

Pronephric Capsule—mesodermal connective tissue covering of pronephric masses derived from adjacent myotomes and somatic mesoderm.

Pronephric Chamber—portion of amphibian coelomic cavity open anteriorly and posteriorly but closed ventrally by development of lungs.

Pronephric Duct—outer portion of pronephric nephrotomes which develops a lumen connected posteriorly with mesonephric or Wolffian duct. (Syn., segmental duct.)

Pronephric Tubules—lateral outgrowths of the most anterior nephrotomal masses which acquire cavities in amphibia, connected with pronephric duct. Possibly become infundibulum of oviduct.

Pronephros—embryonic kidney of all vertebrates, extending from second to fourth somites of frog embryo and consisting of as many primitive tubules as somites concerned; completely lost in all adult vertebrates except a few bony fish. (Syn., head kidney.)

Pronucleus—egg nucleus after polar body formation and sperm nucleus after entrance of spermatozoon into egg.

Prophase—first stage in mitotic cycle when spireme is broken up into definite chromosomes, prior to lining up on metaphase (equatorial) plate.

Prosencephalon—See *Forebrain.*

Prosocoel—cavity of prosencephalon.

Proximal—nearer the point of reference, toward main body mass.

Pupil—opening into secondary optic vesicle, occluded in part by lens, and regulated in diameter by ciliary muscles of iris.

Ramus Communicans—connection between sympathetic ganglion and spinal nerve, as numerous as ganglia in any vertebrate; probably originating from crest cells. Ramus means branch.

plate giving rise to mucous glands (oral suckers) of amphibia and to parts of olfactory organs, lens of eye, and possibly to part of inner ear.

Septum—partition.

Serial Sections—thin (often of microscopic dimensions) sections of embryos which are mounted on slides in order of their removal from the embryo, so that a study in sequence will provide an understanding of all organ systems from one region of embryo to the other.

Sertoli Cell—derivative of sexual cords of testis, found within seminiferous tubule and functionally similar to follicle cell in ovary in that it is the nutritive, supporting, or nurse cell of the maturing spermatozoa. The heads of adult spermatozoa may be seen embedded in the cytoplasm of Sertoli cells.

Sex Cell Cord—division of sex cell ridge or gonad primordium, not to be confused with sexual (rete) cords.

Sex Determination—See *Determination of Sex.*

Sexual Cords—derivatives of germinal epithelium from which they become separated and give rise to bulk of gonads of both sexes.

Sexual Cords of the Ovary—sex cords of the originally indifferent gonad primordium which form only cords of ovary, the functional follicles coming from germinal epithelium.

Sexual Cords of the Testis—sex cords of the originally indifferent gonad primordium which give rise to seminiferous tubules of testis, forming a rather solid mesenchymatous reticulum when cavities begin to appear lined with spermatogonia (from primordial germ cells) and Sertoli cells, the whole constituting seminiferous tubules.

Sheath, Myelin—myelin covering of axons in so-called white matter of spinal cord.

Sinus Venosus—point of fusion of vitelline veins of amphibian embryo bilaterally symmetrical and related to ducts of Cuvieri and ductus venosus.

Skeletogenous Sheath—sclerotomal cells which first form a continuous layer around both notochord and nerve cord.

Skin—See *Dermis* and *Epidermis*. (Syn., integument.)

Somatic—relating to body in contrast to germinal cells; or relating to outer body in contrast to inner splanchnic mesoderm.

Somatoblast—blastomeres with specific germ layer predisposition, i.e., ectodermal somatoblasts.

Somatopleure—layer of somatic mesoderm and closely associated ectoderm, extension of which (from body wall) gives rise to both amnion and chorion.

Somite—blocks of paraxial mesoblast, metamerically separated by transverse clefts, derived from enterocoelic or gastral mesoderm and giving rise to dermatome, myotome, and sclerotome.

Spawning—act of expelling eggs from uteri of anamniota (e.g., amphibia).

Sperm—germ cell characteristically produced by the male. (Syn., spermatozoon, sperm cell, male gamete, spermatosome.)

Spermatid—products of the second maturation division in spermatogenesis, the spermatids having certain cytological characteristics and being invariably haploid; cells which go through a metamorphosis into functionally mature spermatozoa.

Spermatocyte—stages in spermatogenesis between the time the primordial germ cell (spermatogonium) begins to grow, without division, until after the division which results in spermatids. (See *Primary Spermatocyte, Secondary Spermatocyte.*)

Spermatogenesis—entire process which results in maturation of spermatozoon.

Spermatogonium—primordial germ cell of male gonad, indistinguishable from somatic cells, both of which are diploid; stage prior to maturation when the presumptive spermatozoon undergoes rapid multiplication by mitosis.

Spermatophore—sperm-bearing bundle, such as that which is shed by male urodele, the bundles later to be picked up by cloacal lips of female.

Spermatosphere—See *Idiosome.*

Spermatozoon—functionally mature male gamete. (Syn., sperm.)

Spina Bifida—split tail, generally involving spine, in developing embryo caused by a variety of environmental conditions, most of which act through interference with normal gastrulation and neurulation.

Spinal Cord—that portion of central nervous system, excluding brain, which is derived from epithelial and neural ectoderm of original blastula, consisting of ependyma, glia, neuroblasts and their derivatives, and connecting cells.

Spindle—group of fibers between centrosomes during mitosis, to which chromosomes are attached and by means of which (mantle fiber portion) chromosomes are drawn to their respective poles.

Spinous Process—prolongation of neural processes fused dorsally to neural canal; becomes dorsal spine of vertebra.

Spiracle—short funnel between body wall and operculum on left side of head of frog tadpole, the only exit for water passing through gill chambers to exterior.

Spireme—continuous chromatin thread characteristic of so-called resting cell nucleus. Existence questioned by current cytologists.

Splanchnic—refers to viscera, opposed to somatic or body.

Splanchnic Mesoderm—visceral mesoderm, or that nearest embryonic axis in lateral plate.

Splanchnocoel—that portion of enterocoel (of Amphioxus) which lies between somatic and splanchnic mesoderm within body. (Syn., coelom.)

Splanchnocranium—that portion of skull which is preformed in cartilage and which arises from the first three pairs of visceral arches. Opposed to neurocranium.

Splanchnopleure—layer of endoderm and inner (splanchnic) mesoderm within which develop the numerous blood vessels of area vasculosa and later yolk sac septa; layers within the body which give rise to lining and to musculature of alimentary canal.

Spongioblasts—cells of mantle layer of developing spinal cord destined to form merely supporting tissue.

Stereoblastula—solid blastula as found in Crepidula.

Stomodeum—ectodermal invagination (pit) which fuses with pharyngeal endoderm to form oral plate, which later ruptures to form margins of mouth cavity. Stomodeal portion of mouth lining is therefore ectodermal.

Stroma—mesodermally derived, medullary, supporting tissues of an organ.

Sub-Germinal Cavity—See *Blastocoel, Segmentation Cavity.*

Sub-Notochordal Rod or Bar—hypochordal rod of amphibian embryo, found dorsal to midgut. Transitory.

Sucker—adhesive, connecting organ of oral region (larval stage).

Sustentacular Cell—cell which provides nourishment for another, such as Sertoli or follicle cells of gonads.

Sylvius, Aqueduct of—See *Aqueduct of Sylvius.*

Sympathetic System—originating either from mesenchymal element arising in situ or, more probably, from ectodermal elements emanating from neural crests, to organize as a chain of ganglia near dorsal aorta and controlling involuntary (visceral) musculature.

Synapsis—union, such as the lateral (parasynapsis) or terminal (telosynapsis) union of embryos; or pairing of homologous chromosomes.

Synaptene Stage—stage in maturation between leptotene and synizesis (contraction) stage wherein chromatin is in form of long threads, intertwined in homologous pairs. (Syn., zygotene, amphitene.)

Syncytium—nuclei and cytoplasm without cellular boundaries; multinucleate protoplasm without cell boundaries.

Syngamy—specifically the fusion of the gamete pronuclei, but also the union of gametes at fertilization. (Syn., zygotogenesis, fertilization.)

Synizesis—stage in maturation between synaptene and pachytene when chromatin threads are short and thick and ends away from centrosome are tangled.

Telencephalon—portion of forebrain (ventricle) anterior to a plane which includes posterior side of choroid plexus and anterior side of optic recess of 5 mm. frog embryo. Gives rise to torus transversus (anterior commissure), cerebral hemispheres, corpora striata, anterior choroid plexus, olfactory lobes, lateral ventricles, and part of foramina of Monro.

Telobiosis—fusion of embryos end-to-end. (Syn., parabiosis.)

Telocoel—cavity of telencephalon.

Telolecithal—See *Egg, telolecithal.*

Telophase—last phase in mitosis when respective chromosome groups have reached their respective astral centers and are beginning to re-form a resting cell nucleus; stage often accompanied by beginning of cytoplasmic division.

Telosynapsis—end-to-end fusion of chromosomes. (Syn., parasynapsis.)

Teratology—study of causes of monster formation.

Tetrads—paired (homologous) chromosomes which have become duplicated longitudinally in anticipation of the meiotic (reductional) division. When viewed from end will appear as a group of four chromosomes, hence a tetrad.

Thalamus—dorso-lateral wall of diencephalon which becomes thickened by development of fibers passing from cord to more posterior parts of cerebral hemispheres.

Theca externa—outermost of coverings of ovarian follicle, rather loose connective tissue with abundant blood supply. Continuous with peritoneum.

Theca interna—layer of connective tissue consisting of closely packed fibers, possibly some of smooth muscle, immediately external to egg. Consists of cyst wall.

Thymus—derivatives of first pair of branchial pouches of frog embryo which separate from pouches (12 mm.) and migrate to a position posterior to auditory capsules near surface of the head. Endocrine functions.

Thyroid (Body or Gland)—originates as an endodermal thickening in floor of pharynx between second pair of visceral arches; evaginates to form a vesicle temporarily connected with gut by a duct; separates from gut; becomes divided; and migrates to position near hyoglossus muscle. Somewhat similar history in all vertebrate embryos. Endocrine function.

Tissue Culture—in vitro culturing of isolated tissues; excision of tissues or organs and their maintenance in an artificial medium, generally consisting in part of embryonic extracts or blood plasma.

Tongue—solid mesodermal mass, covered with endoderm, derived by cell proliferation from floor of pharynx beginning in the 9 mm. frog tadpole.

Tonsils—lymphatic structures derived from endoderm and mesoderm of second pair of visceral pouches.

Torus Transversus—thickening in median ventro-anterior wall of lamina terminalis of telencephalon, just exterior to optic recess, representing rudiment of anterior commissure.

Totipotency—related to theory that isolated blastomere is capable of producing a complete embryo.

Trachea—that portion of respiratory tract between larynx and lung buds, lined with endoderm, probably derived from posterior portion of original laryngotracheal groove.

Tracheal Groove—Syn., laryngotracheal groove.

Transplant—an embryonic area (cell, tissue, or organ) removed to a different environment.

Transverse—a plane (or sections) which divides antero-posterior axis at right angles, separating more anterior from more posterior. (Syn., cross section, but this synonym is not generally satisfactory.)

Transverse Neural Fold—continuation of lateral neural folds (ridge) of early frog embryo around anterior neuropore. (Syn., transverse medullary fold or ridge.)

Trigeminal Ganglion—cranial (V) ganglia which consist of motor and sensory portions and arise from segments of the most anterior crest in conjunction with cells from inner (ganglionic) portion of corresponding placode. Give rise to ophthalmic, mandibular, and maxillary branches, associated with rhombencephalon at level of greatest width of fourth ventricle.

Trochlearis Nerves—cranial (IV) motor nerves which arise from dorsal surface of brain near isthmus, coming from medullary neuroblasts and innervating superior oblique muscles of eye.

Truncus Arteriosus—anterior continuation of bulbus arteriosus beneath foregut, divided in antero-posterior direction by a septum which is continuous through bulbus to ventricle; gives off external carotids to mandibular arches and second, third, and fourth aortic arches which join dorsal aorta. (Syn., ventral aorta.)

Tuberculum Posterius—a thickening in floor of brain at region of anterior end of notochord, representing posterior margin of diencephalon.

Tubo-tympanic Cavity—remnants of dorsal parts of first pair of visceral (hyomandibular) pouches and lateral walls of pharynx, connecting pharynx and middle ear, represented by Eustachian tube of adult bird or mammal.

Tubules—See under specific names such as *Collecting, Mesonephric, Pronephric, Seminiferous.*

Tunica Albuginea—See *Albuginea of Testis.*

Tympanic Cavity—cavity of middle ear, a vestige of hyomandibular pouch. (See *Tubo-tympanic Cavity.*)

Tympanic Membrane—membrane made up of ectoderm, mesenchyme, and endoderm which separates tympanic cavity from exterior. (Syn., ear drum.)

Urinary Bladder—endodermally lined vesicle derived from hindgut, homologous to allantois of chick. Connected with mesonephric (excretory) ducts of frog only through cloaca.

Uriniferous Tubule—functional kidney tubule of mesonephros.

Urodele—tailed amphibia (e.g., salamanders). (Syn., caudata.)

Urogenital Duct—ducts which open into cloaca of male amphibia and convey both excretory and genital products, derived from mesonephric (Wolffian) ducts.

Urogenital System—entire excretory and reproductive systems, some embryonic parts of which degenerate before hatching. Shows various degrees of common origin and ultimate function. (See specific excretory and reproductive components.)

Urostyle—fused skeletogenous elements of the last two somites in frog embryo which surround end of notochord as cartilage and finally ossify.

Utricle—a vesicle, generally referring to superior portion of otocyst which gives rise to the various semi-circular canals of the ear, and into which these canals open. Lined with ectoderm.

Vasa Deferentia—mesonephric or Wolffian ducts of frog, which persist as male gonoducts of bird and mammal, connecting with testes through vasa efferentia and epididymis and functioning as sperm ducts after degeneration of embryonic mesonephros and development of gonads. (Sing., vas deferens.)

Vasa Efferentia—ducts which convey frog sperm from collecting tubules through mesorchium to Malpighian corpuscles of mesonephric kidney; derived from rete cords and connected with mesonephric tubules of anterior (sexual) half of the mesonephric or Wolffian body.

Vegetal Pole—pole of a telolecithal egg where there is greatest concentration of yolk, usually opposite animal pole and location of germinal vesicle. (Syn., vegetal or vegetative hemisphere; abapical or antipolar hemisphere.) (See *Animal Pole.*)

Vein—See under specific names.

Velar Plate—folds or flaps developing anterior and posterior to branchial regions of frog (anuran) embryo derived from pharyngeal wall and serving as a gross sifting organ between pharynx and gill (branchial) chamber.

Velum Transversum—depressed roof of telencephalon just anterior to lamina terminalis, which later becomes much folded and vascular as anterior roof of third ventricle.

Vena Cava Anterior—junction of inferior jugular (anterior cardinal) and subclavian and vertebral veins which empty into ductus Cuvieri, and later the right auricle. (Syn., superior vena cava, superior caval veins.)

Vena Cava Posterior—single median ventral vein which represents remnant of anterior right cardinal and which later receives hepatic vein prior to joining ductus Cuvieri, and later joins right auricle directly.

Ventral—belly surface. Ventrad means toward belly surface.

Ventral Mesentery—double layer of mesoblast which connects alimentary canal with splanchnopleure in embryo.

Ventricle III—main cavity (diocoel) of forebrain, related to paired lateral ventricles or telocoels, by way of foramina of Monro.

Ventricle IV—main cavity of hindbrain (rhombencephalon) connected anteriorly with aqueduct of Sylvius and posteriorly with neural canal, having as a roof the vascular posterior choroid plexus.

Ventricle, Lateral—See *Lateral Ventricles of the Brain.*

Ventricle of the Heart—chamber of the heart, single in frog and very muscular, developing from anterior myocardium and provided with valves; connected with bulbus arteriosus anteriorly.

Vertebra—derivatives of sclerotome which surround nerve cord and notochord, and finally incorporate notochord by chondrification and ossification (centrum).

Vertebral Arch—See *Neural Arch.*

Vertebral Plate—See *Axial Mesoderm.* (Syn., segmental plate.)

Vesicle, Germinal—nucleus of egg while it is a distinct entity and before elimination of either of the polar bodies.

Visceral—pertaining to viscera.

Visceral Arches—mesodermal masses (usually six pairs) between visceral pouches and lateral to pharynx of all vertebrate embryos, including mandibular, hyoid, and four branchial arches. Each arch is bounded by endoderm on pharyngeal side and ectoderm on outside. (Syn., visceral arches III to VI are also called branchial arches I to IV, respectively; pharyngeal arch.)

Visceral Clefts—slit-like openings between pharynx and outside, found in vertebrate embryos on either side of visceral arches II to V, or less, consisting of peripheral lining of ectoderm and mesial lining of endoderm. (Syn., pharyngeal, and some may be called gill or branchial clefts.)

Visceral Furrow—ectodermal invaginations which may meet endodermal pharyngeal evaginations to form visceral clefts. (Syn., visceral groove.)

Visceral Groove—See *Visceral Furrow.*

Visceral Mesoderm—See *Splanchnic Mesoderm, Splanchnopleure.*

Visceral Plexus—aggregation of sympathetic neurons which control viscera, having migrated posteriorly from tenth (vagus) cranial ganglia.

Visceral Pouch—endodermal evagination of pharynx which, if it meets corresponding visceral furrow, often breaks through to form visceral cleft. (Syn., pharyngeal pouch.)

Vital Stain—localized staining of living embryonic areas with vital, non-toxic dyes.

Vitalism—a philosophical approach to biological phenomena which bases its proof on present inability of scientists to explain all phenomena of development. Idea that biological activities are directed by forces neither physical nor chemical but which must be supra-scientific or supernatural. Effective guidance in development by some non-material agency. (See *Mechanism.*)

Vitelline—pertains to yolk (e.g., vitelline vein brings blood from yolk; vitelline membrane is that which covers yolked egg).

Vitelline Artery—paired off shoots of dorsal aorta which take blood to belly yolk of early embryo, later to become coeliac and mesenteric arteries.

Vitelline Membrane—delicate, outer, non-living egg covering derived while egg is still within ovary, probably by joint action of egg and its follicle cells; probably same membrane that is elevated as the fertilization membrane after successful insemination. (Syn., fertilization membrane.)

Vitelline Substance—yolk.

Vitelline Vein—paired veins, first to be formed in embryo, found in ventrolateral splanchnopleure, carrying nutritious blood from yolk region to their junction with sinus venosus prior to the full development and function of heart.

Vitreous Humor—the rather viscous fluid of eye chamber posterior to lens, formed by cells budded from retinal wall and from inner side of lens, hence ectodermal and probably also mesenchymal in origin. (See *Aqueous Humor.*)

Wolffian Body—See *Mesonephros.*

Wolffian Duct—See *Mesonephric Duct, Urogenital Duct, Vasa Deferentia.*

Yolk—highly nutritious food (metaplasm) consisting of non-nucleated spheres and globules of fatty material found in all except alecithal eggs.

Yolk Nuclei—darkly staining chromatin-like substances within cytoplasm of young (immature) eggs around which yolk is accumulated during growth phase of oögenesis. May be derived from nucleoli which escape from nucleus.

Yolk Plug—a plug formed by large yolk cells which are too large to be incorporated immediately in floor of archenteron of amphibian embryo, hence are found protruding slightly from blastopore. Size of plug is often used to determine approximate stage of gastrulation.

Zone, Marginal—presumptive chorda-mesodermal complex at junction of roof and floor of early gastrula. (Syn., germ ring.)

Bibliography for Frog Embryology

Contributions to this book on Frog Embryology have been made from many of the following references. It is therefore quite a complete bibliography on normal frog development. Those interested in more detailed references to specific subjects should consult the author's "Experimental Embryology."

Books

Allen, B. M., **1930,** "The Early Development of Organ Anlagen in Amphibia," California, Stanford University Press, Contributions to Marine Biology, 204–212.

Anglas, J., **1904,** "Observations sur les metamorphoses internes des batraciens anoures," Grenoble, Assoc. Franç. p. l. Avanc. d. Sciences, 33 Sess., p. 855.

Arey, L. B., **1946,** "Developmental Anatomy," 5th ed., Philadelphia, W. B. Saunders Co.

Barth, L. G., **1949,** "Embryology," New York, The Dryden Press, Inc.

Brachet, A., **1935,** "Traité d'embryologie des Vertébrés," Paris, Masson et Cie.

Brachet, Jean, **1947,** "Embryologie Chimique," Paris, Masson et Cie.

Bütschli, O., **1915,** "Bemerkung zur mechanischen Erklärung der Gastrula-Invagination," Sitz. ber. Heidelberg Akad. Wiss., vol. 6, Part II, pp. 1–13.

Celestino da Costa, A., **1938,** "Elements d'Embryologie," Paris, Masson et Cie.

Dalcq, A., **1938,** "Form and Causality in Early Development," London, Cambridge University Press.

———, **1935,** "L'Organisation de l'oeuf chez les chordes. Etude d'embryologie causale," Paris, Gauthier-Villars.

DeBeer, G. R., **1926,** "The Comparative Anatomy, Histology, and Development of the Pituitary Body," London, Oliver & Boyd.

Dickerson, M. C., **1906,** "The Frog Book," New York, Doubleday & Company, Inc.

Ecker, A., **1889,** "Anatomy of the Frog," Oxford, Clarendon Press.

Furbinger, M., **1877,** "Zur Entwicklungs der Amphibienniere," Heidelberg.

Gaupp, E., **1904,** "Anatomie des Frosches," Braunschweig, Vieweg & Sohn.

Goette, A., **1875,** "Die Entwicklungsgeschichte der Unke (*Bombinator igneus*)," Leipzig, Leopold Voss.

Goodrich, E. S., **1930,** "Studies on the Structure and Development of Vertebrates," New York, The Macmillan Co.

Held, H., **1909,** "Entwicklung des Nervengewebe bei den Wirbeltiere," Leipzig.

Hertwig, O., **1909,** "Handbuch der vergleichenden und experimentellen Entwicklungslehre der Wirbeltiere," 6 vols., Jena, Fischer.

Hinsberg, B., **1901,** "Die Entwicklung der Nasenhohle und experimentellen Entwicklungslehre der Wirbeltiere," Jena.

His, Wilhelm, **1874,** "Unsere Körperform und des physiologische Problem ihrer Entstehung," Leipzig, Vogel.

Holmes, S. J., **1927,** "Biology of the Frog," 4th ed., rev., New York, The Macmillan Co.

Huettner, A. F., **1949,** "Fundamentals of Comparative Embryology of the Vertebrates," New York, The Macmillan Co.

Jordan, H. E., and J. E. Kindred, **1948,** "A Textbook of Embryology," New York, D. Appleton-Century Co.

Kellicott, W. E., **1913,** "Outlines of Chordate Development," New York, Henry Holt & Company, Inc.

———, **1913,** "A Textbook of General Embryology," New York, Henry Holt & Company, Inc.

Kingsley, J. S., **1907,** "The Frog, An Anurous Amphibian," New York, Henry Holt & Company, Inc.

Marshall, A. M., **1893,** "Vertebrate Embryology," London, Putnam & Co., Ltd.

———, **1885,** "The Frog: An Introduction to Anatomy, Histology, and Embryology," New York, The Macmillan Co.

Marshall, F. H. A., **1922,** "Physiology of Reproduction," 2d ed., rev., New York, Longmans, Green & Company.

McEwen, R. F., **1949,** "Vertebrate Embryology," New York, Henry Holt & Company, Inc.

Minot, C. S., **1910,** "A Laboratory Text-book of Embryology," Philadelphia, The Blakiston Company.

Morgan, T. H., **1897,** "Development of the Frog's Egg: Introduction to Experimental Embryology," New York, The Macmillan Co.

Needham, J., **1942,** "Biochemistry and Morphogenesis," 6th ed., London, Cambridge University Press.

Noble, G. K., **1931,** "The Biology of the Amphibia," New York, The McGraw-Hill Book Company, Inc.

Pasteels, Jean, **1939,** "Sur l'origine du materiel caudal des Urodeles," Bruxelles, Palais des Academies.

Pope, C. H., **1944,** "Amphibians and Reptiles of the Chicago Area," Chicago, Chicago Natural History Museum.

Reese, A. M., **1947,** "The Lamina Terminalis and the Preoptic Recess in Amphibia," Washington, D. C., Smithsonian Miscellaneous Collection, vol. 106.

Richards, Aute, **1931,** "Outline of Comparative Embryology," New York, John Wiley & Sons, Inc.

Rugh, Roberts, **1949,** "A Laboratory Manual of Vertebrate Embryology," Minneapolis, Burgess Publishing Company.

———, **1948,** "Experimental Embryology; A Manual of Techniques and Procedures," Minneapolis, Burgess Publishing Company.

Shumway, W., **1935,** "Introduction to Vertebrate Embryology," 3d ed., rev., New York, John Wiley & Sons, Inc.

Thompson, D'Arcy W., **1942,** "On Growth and Form," London, Cambridge University Press.

Waddington, C. H., **1940,** "Organizers and Genes," New York, The Macmillan Co.

Waterman, A. J., **1948,** "A Laboratory Manual of Comparative Vertebrate Embryology," New York, Henry Holt & Company, Inc.

Weiss, Paul, **1939,** "Principles of Development; A Text in Experimental Embryology," New York, Henry Holt & Company, Inc.

Wieman, H. L., **1949,** "An Introduction to Vertebrate Embryology," New York, The McGraw-Hill Book Company, Inc.

Wright, A. A., and A. H. Wright, **1949,** "Handbook of Frogs and Toads of the United States and Canada," 3d ed., Ithaca, N. Y., Comstock Publishing Co., 1949.

Articles

Adelmann, H. B., **1936,** The problem of cyclopia, *Quart. Rev. Biol.,* Part I, **11:**161; Part II, **11:**284.

Alderman, A. L., **1935,** The determination of the eye in the anuran, *Hyla regilla, J. Exper. Zoöl.,* **70:**205.

Allen, B. M., **1919,** The development of the thyreoid glands of *Bufo* and their normal relation to metamorphosis, *J. Morphol.,* **32:**489.

———, **1907,** An important period in the history of the sex-cells of *Rana pipiens, Anat. Anz.,* **31:**339.

Assheton, R., **1905,** On growth centres in vertebrate embryos, *Anat. Anz.,* **27:**125; 156.

Atlas, Meyer, **1938,** The rate of oxygen consumption of frogs during embryonic development and growth, *Physiol. Zool.,* **11:**278.

———, **1935,** The effect of temperature on the development of *Rana pipiens, Physiol. Zool.,* **8:**290.

Atwell, W. J., **1919,** The development of the hypophysis of the Anura, *Anat. Rec.,* **15:**73.

Bataillon, E., **1910,** L'embryogenèse, complète provoquèes chez les Amphibiens par piqûre de l'oeuf vierge, larves parthénogénésiques de *Rana fusca, Comp. rend. Acad. de sc.,* **150:**996.

———, **1891,** Recherches anatomiques et expérimentales sur la métamorphose des amphibiens anoures, *Ann. d. l. Univers. de Lyon,* **2:**1.

Beneden, V., and V. Bambeke, **1927,** Extrait des Archives de Biologie, *J. Anat.,* p. 486

Bialaszewicz, K., **1909,** Beiträge zur Kenntnis der Wachstumsvorgänge bei Amphibienembryonen, *Bull. Acad. Sci. Cracovie* (review in *Arch. f. Entwcklngsmechn. d. Organ.,* **28:**160).

Born, G., **1884,** Ueber den Einfluss der Schwere auf des Froschei, *Bresl. ärztl. Ztschr.,* **15:**185.

Bouin, M., **1901,** Histogenèse de la glande génitale femelle chez *Rana temporaria, Arch. de biol., Paris,* **17:**201.

Boyd, E. M., **1938,** Lipoid substances of the ovary during ova production in *Rana pipiens, J. Physiol.,* **91:**394.

Brachet, A., **1911,** Etudes sur les localisations germinales et leur potentialité réelle dans l'oeuf parthénogénétique de *Rana fusca, Arch. de biol., Paris,* **26:**337.

———, **1905,** Gastrulation et formation de l'embryon chez les Chordés, *Anat. Anz.,* **27:**212; 239.

Braem, F. von, **1898,** Epiphysis und Hypophysis von *Rana, Ztschr. wiss. Zool.,* **63:**433.

Broman, I., **1907,** Über Bau und Entwicklung der Spermien von *Rana fusca, Arch. mikr. Anat.,* **70:**330.

Brown, M. E., **1946,** The histology of the tadpole tail during metamorphosis, with special reference to the nervous system, *Am. J. Anat.,* **78:**79.

Burns, R. K., Jr., **1934,** The effect of the removal of the pronephros and duct upon development, *Anat. Rec.,* **58:** suppl. 7.

Cameron, J. A., **1941,** Primitive blood-cell generations in Amblystoma, *J. Morphol.,* **68:**231.

Carnoy, J. B., and H. Lebrun, **1900,** La vésicule germinative et les globules polaires chez les batraciens, *Cellule,* **17:**199.

Cooper, Ruth Snyder, **1943,** An experimental study of the development of the larval olfactory organ of *Rana pipiens* Schreber, *J. Exper. Zoöl.*, **93:**415.

Corning, H. K. von, **1899,** Über einige Entwicklungsvorgänge am Kopf der Anuren, *Morphol. Jahrb.*, **27:**173.

Dalcq, A. M., **1940,** Contributions à l'étude du Potentiel Morphogénétique chez les Anoures: I. Expériences sur la zone marginale dorsale et le plancher du blastocoele, *Arch. de biol., Paris,* **51:**387.

———, **1933,** La détermination de la vésicule auditive chez le discoglosse, *Arch. d'anat. micr.*, **29:**389.

D'Angelo, S. A., **1941,** An analysis of the morphology of the pituitary and thyroid glands in amphibian metamorphosis, *Am. J. Anat.*, **69:**407.

———, and H. A. Charipper, **1939,** The morphology of the thyroid gland in the metamorphosing *Rana pipiens, J. Morphol.*, **64:**355.

Delpino, Itala, **1932,** Ricerche sperimentali sullo sviluppo degli organi adesivi in *Rana esculenta, Arch. zool. ital.*, **17:**401.

Desclin, Léon, **1927,** Etude de la localisation des ébauches ganglionnaires craniennes dans le germe de *Rana fusca, Arch. de biol., Paris,* **37:**485.

Durham, H. E., **1886,** Note on the presence of the neurenteric canal in *Rana, Quart. J. Micr. Sci.*, **26:**509.

Du Shane, G. P., **1938,** Neural fold derivatives in the Amphibia: Pigment cells, spinal ganglia and Rohon-Beard cells, *J. Exper. Zoöl.*, **78.**

Dustin, A. P., **1908,** Recherches sur l'origine des gonocytes chez les Amphibiens, *Arch. de biol., Paris,* **23:**411.

Elliott, A. I. M., **1907,** Some facts in the later development of the frog, *Rana temporaria:* I. The segments of the occipital region of the skull, *Quart. J. Micr. Sci.*, **51:**647.

Erlanger, R. von, **1890,** Ueber den Blastoporus der anuran Amphibien, sein Schicksal und seine Beziehungen zum bleidenden After, *Zool. Jahrb.*, **4:**239.

Etkin, W., **1936,** The phenomena of anuran metamorphosis: III. The development of the thyroid gland, *J. Morphol.,* **59:**69.

Farrington, O. C., **1892,** The nephrostomes of *Rana*, *Tr. Conn. Acad.*, **8:**309.

Federow, V., **1910,** Über die Entwickelung der Lungenvene, *Anat. Heft.*, **40:**529.

Field, H. H., **1891,** Contributions from the Zoological Laboratory. XXVII: The development of the pronephros and segmental duct in Amphibia, *Bull. Mus. Comp. Zool. Harvard,* **21:**201.

Filatow, D. P., **1904,** Zur Entwickelungsgeschichte des Exkretionssystems der Amphibien, *Anat. Anz.*, **25:**33.

Foxon, G. E. H., **1947,** Circulation in the frog, *Nature,* **159:**236.

Giannelli, L., **1903,** Sulle prime fasi di sviluppo del pancreas negli Anfibii anuri (*Rana esculenta*), *Monit. zool. ital.,* **14:**33.

Göppert, E., **1891,** "Die Entwicklung und das spätere Verhalten des Pankreas der Amphibien, *Morphol. Jahrb.,* **17:**100.

Greil, A., **1905,** Über die Anlage der Lungen, sowie der ultimobranchialen (postbranchialen, supraperikardialen) Körper bei anuren Amphibien, *Anat. Heft.,* **29:**445.

Hall, R. W., **1904,** Contributions from the Zoölogical Laboratory, No. 150, The development of the mesonephros and the Müllerian ducts in Amphibia, *Bull. Mus. Comp. Zool. Harvard,* **45,** No. 2.

Harrison, R. G., **1904,** Experimentelle Untersuchungen über die Entwicklung der Sinnesorgane der Seitenlinie bei den Amphibien, *Arch. mikr. Anat.,* **63:**35.

Hegre, E. S., **1946,** The developmental relationship between the nervous and epithelial components of the hypophysis, *J. Exper. Zoöl.,* **101:**65.

Helff, O. M., **1930,** Studies in amphibian metamorphosis: VIII. The rôle of the urostyle in the atrophy of the tail, *Anat. Rec.,* **47:**177.

Hempstead, M., **1901**, Development of the lungs in the frogs *Rana catesbiana, R. sylvatica,* and *R. virescens, Science,* **12.**

Holtfreter, J., **1943, 1944,** A study of the mechanics of gastrulation, *J. Exper. Zoöl.,* Part I, **94:**261; Part II, **95:**171.

———, **1944,** Experimental studies on the development of the Pronephros, *Rev. canadienne de biol.,* **3:**220.

Hoskins, E. R., and M. M. Hoskins, **1920,** The inter-relation of the thyreoid and hypophysis in the growth and development of frog larvae, *Endocrinology,* **4:**1.

Howland, R. B., **1926,** Regeneration of the segmental duct and experimental acceleration of growth of the mesonephros in *Amblystoma punctatum, J. Exper. Zoöl.,* **44:**327.

Hoyer, H., **1905,** Ueber das Lymphgefässystem der Froschlarven, *Verhandl. d. anat. Gesellsch.,* **19:**50.

Janes, R. G., **1938,** Studies on the amphibian digestive system: III. The origin and development of pancreatic islands in certain species of Anura, *J. Morphol.,* **62:**375.

Jenkinson, J. W., **1909,** On the relation between the symmetry of the egg, the symmetry of segmentation, and the symmetry of the embryo in the frog, *Biometrika,* **7:**148.

Kindahl, M., **1938,** Zur Entwicklung der Exkretionsorgane von Dipnoern und Amphibien, *Acta. zool. org.,* **19:**H-1.

King, H. D., **1905,** Experimental studies on the eye of the frog embryo, *Arch. f. Entwcklngsmechn. d. Organ.,* **19:**85.

Knouff, R. A., **1935,** The developmental pattern of ectodermal placodes in *Rana pipiens, J. Comp. Neurol.,* **62:**17.

———, **1927,** The origin of the cranial ganglia of *Rana, J. Comp. Neurol.,* **44:**259.

Knower, H. McE., **1908,** The origin and development of the anterior lymph hearts and the subcutaneous sacs in the frog, *Anat. Rec.,* **2:**59.

Kopsch, Fr., **1895,** Beitrage zur Gastrulation beim Axolotl- und Froschei, *Verhandl. d. anat. Gesellsch.,* **9:**181.

Lams, H., **1907,** Contribution à l'etude de la genèse du vitellus dans l'ovule des Amphibiens (*Rana temporaria*), *Arch. d'anat. micr.,* **9:**607.

Lebrun, H., **1902,** La vèsicule germinative et les globules polaires chez les Anoures, *Cellule,* **19:**315.

Lewis, W. H., **1904,** Experimental studies on the development of the eye in amphibia: I. On the origin of the lens, *Am. J. Anat.,* **3:**505.

Lindeman, V. F., **1929,** Integumentary pigmentation in the frog, *Rana pipiens,* during metamorphosis, with especial reference to tail-skin histolysis, *Physiol. Zool.,* **2:**225.

Marcelin, R. H., **1903,** Histogènése de l'Epithélium intestinal chez la Grenouille (*Rana esculenta*), *Rev. Suisse zool.,* **11:**269.

Marx, A., **1925,** Experimentelle Untersuchungen zur Frage der Determination der Medullarplatte, *Arch. mikr. Anat.,* **55.**

Maurer, F. von, **1890,** Die erste Anlage der Milz und das erste Auftreten von lymphatischen Zellen bei Amphibien, *Morphol. Jahrb.,* **16:**203.

———, **1888,** Die Kiemen und ihre Gefässe bei anuren und urodelen Amphibien, und die Umbildungen der beiden ersten Arterienbogen bei Teleostiern, *Morphol. Jahrb.,* **14:**175.

———, **1887,** Schilddrüse, Thymus und Kiemenreste der Amphibien, *Morphol. Jahrb.,* **13:**296.

Maximow, A., **1910,** Ueber embryonale Entwickelung der Blutzellen bei Selachiern und Amphibien, *Verhandl. d. anat. Gesellsch.,* **24:**64.

Merwin, R., **1945,** Some group effects on the rate of cleavage and early development of frog eggs (*Rana pipiens*), *Physiol. Zool.,* **18:**16.

———, and W. C. Allee, **1943,** The effect of low concentrations of carbon dioxide on the cleavage rate in frog's eggs, *Ecology,* **24:**61.

Miller, R. A., and S. R. Detwiler, **1936,** Comparative studies upon the origin and development of the brachial plexus, *Anat. Rec.,* **65:**273.

Morgan, T. H., **1906,** The origin of the organ-forming materials in the frog's embryo, *Biol. Bull.,* **11:**124.

Nicholas, J. S., **1945,** Blastulation, its role in pregastrula organization in *Amblystoma punctatum, J. Exper. Zoöl.,* **100:**265.

Nishibe, M., **1928,** On the cultivation of kidney tissue from the adult toad, *Arch. f. exper. Zellforsch.,* **7:**87–97.

Nussbaum, M. von, **1895,** Zur Mechanik du Eiablage bei *Rana fusca, Arch. mikr. Anat.,* **46:**479.

O'Conner, R. J., **1940,** The evolutionary significance of the embryology of the amphibian nephric system, *J. Anat.,* **75:** 95.

Pasteels, Jean, **1943,** Fermeture du blastopore, anus et intestin caudal chez les Amphibiens Anoures, *Acta Neerland. morphol.,* **5:**11.

———, **1943,** Proliférations et croissance dans la gastrulation de la queue des Vertébrés, *Arch. de biol., Paris,* **54:**2.

———, **1942,** New observations concerning the maps of presumptive areas of young amphibian gastrula (Amblystoma and Discoglossus), *J. Exper. Zoöl.,* **89:**255.

Pezard, A., and R. M. May, **1937,** Les terminaisons nerveuses du muscle conturier de la Grenouille et la question de sa partie aneurale, *Ann. de physiol.,* **13:**460.

Pollister, A. W., and J. A. Moore, **1937,** Tables for the normal development of *Rana sylvatica, Anat. Rec.,* **68:**489.

Porter, K. R., **1939,** Androgenetic development of the egg of *Rana pipiens, Biol. Bull.,* **77:**233.

Reed, Margaret, **1905,** The formation of the interior cells of the segmentation of the frog's egg, *Biol. Bull.,* **8:**189.

Roux, W. von, **1893,** Ueber die ersten Teilungen des Froscheies und ihre Beziehungen zur der Organbildung des Embryo, *Anat. Anz.,* **8:**605.

Schechtman, A. M., **1939,** Experiments on anus formation in a frog egg, *Proc. Soc. Exper. Biol. & Med.,* **41:**48.

Schechtman, A. M., **1942,** "The Mechanism of Amphibian Gastrulation: I. Gastrulation-promoting Interactions Between Various Regions of an Anuran Egg (*Hyla regilla*)," University of California Publications—Zoology, vol. 51, pp. 1–39.

Schmalhausen, J. J., **1908,** Die Entwickelung des Skelettes der hinteren Extremität der anuren Amphibien, *Anat. Anz.,* **33:**337.

Schultz, O. von, **1900,** Ueber das erste Auftreten der bilateralen Symmetrie im Verlauf der Entwicklung, *Arch. mikr. Anat.,* **55:**171.

———, **1887,** Untersuchungen über die Reifung und Befruchtung des Amphibieneies, *Ztschr. wiss. Zool.,* **45:**177.

Schwind, J. L., **1933,** Tissue specificity at the time of metamorphosis of the frog larvae, *J. Exper. Zoöl.,* **66:**1.

Schwink, von, **1891,** Untersuchungen über die Entwicklung des Endothels und der Blutkörperchen der Amphibien, *Morphol. Jahrb.,* **17:**288.

Shore, T. W., **1902,** The development of the renal-portals and fate of the posterior cardinal veins in the frog, *J. Anat. & Physiol.,* **36:**20.

Shumway, W., **1940, 1942,** Stages in the normal development of *Rana* *pipiens:* I. External form, *Anat. Rec.,* **78:**139; II. Identification of the stages from sectioned material, *Anat. Rec.,* **83:**309.

Silver, M. L., **1942,** The motoneurons of the spinal cord of the frog, *J. Comp. Neurol.,* **77:**1.

Spek, J., **1919,** Studien über den Mechanismus des Gastrulainvagination, *Biol. Zentralbl.,* **39:**13.

Spemann, H., **1898,** Ueber die erste Entwicklung der Tuba Eustachii und des Kopfskelets von *Rana temporaria, Zool. Jahrb.,* **11:** 389.

Stenger, A., and H. A. Charipper, **1946,** A study of adrenal cortical tissue in *Rana pipiens* with special reference to metamorphosis, *J. Morphol.,* **78:**27.

Stewart, S. G., **1927,** The morphology of the frog's kidney, *Anat. Rec.,* **36:**259.

Stöhr, Ph. von, **1895,** Über die Entwicklung der Hypochorda und des dorsalen Pankreas bei *Rana temporaria, Morphol. Jahrb.,* **23:**123.

Suntzowa, W., **1931,** Analyse der Gewebe beim Wachstum der Froschniere in vitro, *Arch. f. exper. Zellforsch.,* **10:**178.

Swingle, W. W., **1926,** The germ cells of Anurans: II. An embryological study of sex differentiation in *Rana catesbeana, J. Morphol. & Physiol.,* **41:**441.

Taylor, A. C., **1944,** Selectivity of nerve fibers from the dorsal and ventral roots in the development of the frog limb, *J. Exper. Zoöl.,* **96:**189.

———, and J. J. Kollros, **1946,** Stages in the normal development of *Rana pipiens* larvae, *Anat. Rec.,* **94:**7.

Taylor, S. J., and E. H. Craigie, **1938,** The vascularity of the hypophysis of the frog (*Rana pipiens*), *Anat. Rec.,* **71:**277.

Tretjakoff, D., **1906,** Die vordere Augenhölfte des Frosches, *Ztschr. wiss. Zool.,* **80:**327.

Tsui, C. L., **1931,** Seasonal changes in the kidney of the frog, *Contr. Biol. Lab. Sci. Soc. China,* **7:**239.

Ussoff, S. A. von, **1910,** Stomodaeum-Ektochorda (das vordere Ende der Chorda). Vergleichend-embryologische Studien des axialen Skelettes, *Anat. Anz.,* **35:**168.

Villy, F., **1890,** The development of the ear and accessory organs in the common frog, *Quart. J. Micr. Sci.,* **30:**523.

Vintemberger, P., **1938,** Sur les Résultats de la Transplantation d'Organinsateurs d'étendues différentes, chez *Rana fusca,* dans la Région Blastoporale ventrale, *Comp. rend. Soc. de biol.,* **127:**433; Sur les Résultats de la Transplantation d'Organinsateurs d'étendues différentes, chez *Rana fusca,* dans la Région ventrale, de la voûte blastuléene, *Comp. rend. Soc. de biol.,* **127:**436.

Vogt, W., **1929,** Gestaltungsanalyse am Amphibienkeim mit örtlicher Vitalfärbung: II. Teil gastrulation und Mesodermbildung bei Urodelen und Anuren, *Arch. f. Entwcklngsmechn. d. Organ.,* **116:**384.

Weber, A., **1908,** Etude de la torsion de l'ébauche cardiaque chez *Rana esculenta, Bibliog. Anatomique,* **18:**136.

Wetzel, G., **1908,** Der Wassergeholt des fertigen Froscheies und der Mechanismus der Bildung seiner Hülle im Eileiter, *Arch. f. Entwcklngsmechn. d. Organ.,* **26:**651.

Williams, S. C., **1930,** Regeneration of peripheral nerves in Amphibia studied with the aid of a vital stain, *J. Exper. Zoöl.,* **57:**145.

Wilson, C. B., **1896,** The wrinkling of frog's eggs during segmentation, *Am. Naturalist,* **30:**761.

Wilson, H. V., **1902,** Closure of the blastopore in the normally placed frog egg, *Anat. Anz.,* **20:**123.

Witschi, E., **1929,** Studies on sex differentiation and sex determination in amphibians: I. Development and sexual differentiation of the gonads of *Rana sylvatica, J. Exper. Zoöl.,* **52:**235.

Zwilling, E., **1941,** The determination of the otic vesicle in *Rana pipiens, J. Exper. Zoöl.,* **86:**333.

———, **1940,** An experimental analysis of the development of the anuran olfactory organ, *J. Exper. Zoöl.,* **84:**291.

Index

Page numbers set in *italics* refer to illustrations in the text. Also consult the Glossary for specialized terms.

D

N

O

P

W

X

Y

Z